ALCHEMY,
MEDICINE,
RELIGION
in the China of A.D. 320

ALCHEMY, MEDICINE, RELIGION

in the China of A.D. 320:

The Nei P'ien of Ko Hung
(Pao-p'u tzu)

translated by
James R. Ware

THE M.I.T. PRESS
Massachusetts Institute of Technology
Cambridge, Massachusetts, and London, England

In Memoriam

MARCEL GRANET

Directeur d'Études à l'École des Hautes Études
Professeur à l'École des Langues Orientales
Administrateur de l'Institut des Hautes Études Chinoises de Paris

and

TENNEY L. DAVIS

Professor of Organic Chemistry
Massachusetts Institute of Technology

Foreword

THE BASIC CHINESE TEXT for Ko Hung's *Nei p'ien* is available in the 1885 edition of Sun Hsing-yen's *P'ing-chin-kuan ts'ung-shu*. Throughout this text, references to this original text are indicated in the margins, giving the chapter, page number, side [recto (*a*) or verso (*b*)], and column (e.g., 2.4*b*8 signifies chapter 2, page 4, verso, column 8). References to Ko Hung's autobiography, which forms part of the Introduction, are preceded by the letter A.

In references to China's Dynastic Histories, I have used the T'u-shu-chi-ch'eng yin-shu-chü edition. For the Philosophers I have used The Twenty-two published by Chechiang shu-chü in 1901 and, when necessary, The Hundred published in 1927 by Sao-yeh-shan fang. For *The Analects of Confucius*, *Mencius*, and *Chuang Chou*, the references are to my own translations.[1] The publications of the late Professor H. Maspero (*Journal Asiatique*, Vol. 229 [1937] and *Le Taoisme*, Paris, 1950) and TT 900 (Synonyms for Minerals and Medicines) were indispensable, and the notes of Y. Ishijima (Tokyo, 1942) and Father E. Feifel (*Monumenta Serica* Vol. 6 [1941] *et seq.*) have been helpful. The late Professor T. L. Davis also worked with this text (*Proceedings of the American Academy of Arts and Sciences* Vol. 70 [1935] *et seq.*) out of his interest in the history of alchemy. The terms for

[1] New American Library, New York, 1955, 1960, and 1963.

vii

minerals and plants can only be, for the present translator, the definitions found in available dictionaries and vocabularies.

An asterisk in the text signifies that the work referred to is listed in Ko Hung's *Nei p'ien* 19.

Chinese words are transliterated according to the long-established Wade–Giles system, now used by writers in most western languages except French. Any consonant or group of consonants followed by an apostrophe (in origin, the Greek rough breathing) is to be pronounced approximately as in English; the apostrophe is merely indicative of this fact. The other consonants roughly approximate these English sounds: *ch* is approximately *j*, *t* is *d*, *p* is *b*, *k* is *g*, *ts* is *dz*, and *j* and *-ih* are approximately *r*.

In Chinese personal names the surname or family name is given first; thus Ko Hung is Mr. Ko, and Shen-t'u P'an is Mr. Shen-t'u. The rest of the name corresponds to our first name.

The translator is grateful to the Administrative Committee of the Harvard Foundation for a grant from the Joseph H. Clark Fund subventioning preparation of the typescript. For actual publication of this translation, his first deep bow of gratitude must be to Professor Nathan Sivin.

Cambridge, Massachusetts
March 31, 1966   JAMES R. WARE

Abbreviations

A: Ko Hung's autobiography = ch. 50 of his *Wai p'ien*.

Ana: Analects of Confucius.

ChanKT: *Chan kuo ts'e*, pre-Han historical romance (1869 Hu-pei ch'ung-wen shu-chü ed.).

Chen kao: T'ao Hung-ching's (A.D. 500) poem on Taoist arcana (1915 Chin-ling ts'ung-shu, pt. 2).

Ch'u tz'u: China's first collection of belles-lettres (tr. D. Hawkes, Oxford 1959).

Chuang: The Sayings of Chuang Chou.

Ch'üanHHW: from 1894 ed. of miscellaneous Pre-T'ang prose collected by the Manchu Dynasty scholar Yen K'o-chün.

CS: History of Chin.

CTS: Old T'ang History.

HanF: Philosophical writings of Han Fei (250 B.C.).

HHS: History of Second Han.

HNT: *Huai-nan tzu*, Liu An's (100 B.C.) Taoist compendium.

HS: History of First Han.

KshihC: *Kao shih chuan*, Huang-fu Mi's (A.D. 260) Biographies of Eminent Processors (1592 Kuang Han Wei ts'ung-shu ed.).

KTCY: *K'ung tzu chia yü* (1925 Commercial Press's Han Wei ts'ung shu ed.).

ix

Kuo yü: Pre-Han discourses of the Feudal States of Chinese antiquity (1869 Hu-pei ch'ung-wen shu-chü ed.).

LHC: *Lieh hsien chuan,* Liu Hsiang's (20 B.C.) Biographies of Illustrious Genii (1931 Chih-hai ts'ung-shu ed.).

Li ki: Book of Rites (Father S. Couvreur's 1913 French translation), No. 4 in The Thirteen Classics.

Lieh: Lieh Yü-k'ou's (?Late Chou) Taoist booklet (Kambun-taikei ed. 1912).

LiehNC: *Lieh nü chuan,* Huang-fu Mi's (A.D. 260) Biographies of Illustrious Women (1931 Chih-hai ts'ung-shu ed.).

LSCC: *Lü shih ch'un ch'iu,* Lü Pu-wei's (240 B.C.) Miscellany.

LunH: *Lun heng,* Wang Ch'ung's (A.D. 80) philosophical writings (1925 Commercial Press's Han Wei ts'ung-shu ed.).

M: Mencius.

Mo Ti: the 400 B.C. philosopher.

P: preface to Ko Hung's *Nei p'ien.*

SC: Ssu-ma Ch'ien's Memoirs (*Shih chi*), the first of China's great histories (100 B.C.).

ShanHC: *Shan hai ching,* an early Han work on geography and mythology.

SHC: *Shen hsien chuan,* Ko Hung's Biographies of Gods and Genii (Kuang Han Wei ts'ung-shu, 1592).

Shu i chi: ?Jen Fang's (A.D. 500) Mirabilia (in The Hundred Philosophers).

Shui ching chu: Li Tao-yüan's (A.D. 500) famous re-edition of a work on China's streams (Chang Shou-jung's 1880 ed.).

SKC: History of the Three Kingdoms.

Sou shen chi: Kan Pao's (A.D. 350) Mirabilia (The Hundred).

SS: History of Sui.

T: Tao te ching.

Tso: The Annals of Chinese antiquity = No. 5 in The Thirteen Classics; French translation by Father S. Couvreur, 1914.

TT: Commercial Press's photographic edition of Taoist Canon of A.D. 1450 (Weng Tu-chien's numberings).

WuYCC: Chao Yeh's (A.D. 50) Ancient Annals of South China and Vietnam (1917 Lung-hsi-ching-she ts'ung-shu ed.).

Y: *Yün chi ch'i ch'ien* (Ssu-pu ts'ung-k'an ed.): a Taoist encyclopedia of A.D. 1019.

Yüeh chüeh shu: Yüan K'ang's (A.D. 40) History of Vietnam (1917 Lung-hsi-ching-she ts'ung-shu ed.).

Contents

ALCHEMY,
MEDICINE,
RELIGION
in the China of A.D. 320

Introduction

IN TWO CHINESE texts dating from around 300 B.C., *Tao Te Ching* and *Chuang tzu*, we meet the thought, and sporadically the practices, of men who rejected the normal human and materialistic descriptions of God. Impressed by the evanescence of the material universe and yearning for permanency, they were impelled to postulate, through intuition, that the phantasmagoria was reducible to Unity. *Tao Te Ching*, verse 25 (Duyvendak's text[1]), puts it most succinctly and explicitly:

> *A Something, chaotic in formation, was begotten before nature.*
> *Quiet and uncommitted, It exists of Itself, never changing.*
> *Since It never tires of moving everywhere, we may well think of It as*
>   *the world's mother.*
> *Its rightful name I do not know, but I give It the sobriquet Tao (=God).*
> *If a rightful name is insisted upon, I would call It Maximal.*

Then, upon noticing that *Tao Te Ching*, verse 34, is willing to call the Something "Minimal," every schoolman would have understood that the Chinese author was talking about God, for only in God do contraries become identical!

Accordingly, the present translator will always render this use of the term Tao by *God*. In doing so, he keeps always in

[1] J. J. L. Duyvendak, *Le Livre de la Voie et de la Vertu* (Paris 1953, Librairie d'Amérique et d'Orient).

I

mind as the one and only definition the equation establish-
able from *Exod.* 3:13–15 and *Mark* 12:26–27, to mention
only two very clear statements. It will be recalled that in the
first God says, "My name is I AM, I LIVE, I EXIST," while
the second reads, "God is not of the dead but of the living."
Therefore, God = Life or Being.

Widespread revolution and pressure from nomads, which
had begun in A.D. 180, characterized the social climate that
favored preparation by the Confucianist Ko (*ca.* A.D. 320) of
the compendium translated here. His autobiography, in-
corporated into this introduction, refers intimately to the
disorders and turmoil in the China of his day. Most naturally, then, did he seek a resolution of his woes, and he found
it in the conception of God preached six centuries earlier by
Lao Tan and Chuang Chou, although, despite his first chapter, he finds these authors too abstruse (8.5*a*2; 14.9*b*11). He
was Confucianist enough to insist upon doing something
(the two Ancients seem to have been satisfied with the mere
conception) to achieve personally a share in God's permanency. To this end, he undertook to establish that "Fullness
of Life" (the Christian speaks of "eternal life") can be
achieved only by feeding upon God. With this as the goal,
he shows interest in augmenting and preserving breath
(5.5*b*2) and sperm. Methods are devised for preparing and
taking gold, the most indestructible of metals, and use is
made of other metals and such spontaneous growths as mushrooms and lichens. In all this he lays no claim to originality;
he says in his book that he is merely transmitting things
learned from his teacher who also did not originate them
(4.2*a*2).

Thanks to its redness and permanency gold is the one ideal
available material that seems to embody Life or God. Since
man becomes what he eats, man would become Life by
feeding upon gold. At this juncture, however, a great difficulty looms: Those in possession of sufficient gold are either
atheists or — and faith is of the essence — they simply do

not believe in the doctrine. The ardent believer, being too poor to afford gold (4.15*a*10; 16.5*a*1), is forced to fabricate his own. Ko has no interest in gold as a medium of exchange (16.4*b*9), but only as a medicine or food that will endow him with a Fullness of Life comparable with God. Thrown upon his own resources he evolves compounds and mixtures that can only be called alchemical. He would use gold (*chin*) if he had it, but circumstances compel him to prepare Potable Gold (*chin-i*), using blood-red cinnabar and other reagents to make what may or may not have been dilute gold solutions. At any rate, he did produce mixtures and oxidations from cinnabar, realgar, malachite, sulphur, mica, salt, saltpeter, and orpiment. As preliminary and ancillary procedures, our author recommends calisthenics, breathing exercises, a pharmacopoeia of herbs and minerals for the treatment of illnesses, and correct sexual procedures where an ultimate goal is the development of the sperm and its retention within the originator's body to repair his brain. The successful practitioner of the art will achieve *ch'ang sheng*, which I translate literally as Fullness of Life. A synonym occurs at 2.2*b*7 and 8.7*a*6 in the form of *ch'ang ts'un*, and *ch'ang ts'ai* at 8.1*a*6 is possibly an equivalent. I take these terms to be analogous with the *ch'ang ch'ien* that is contrasted with *tuan pai* at 6.5*b*5: the string of cash containing a full count of 100 as opposed to the string that does not hold a full count but wishes to be accepted as such. Behind all this there seems to hover the concept that the universe will ultimately end (3.7*a*4) and will then be recreated by God, the waxing and waning being an eternal process.

It is clear that the word *tao* appears frequently in this text not as a designation of God but of the process by which God is to be approximated or attained. In such cases I shall translate it as "the divine process." In instances where either this or "God" would be appropriate, a translator is obliged to be arbitrary. The term *tao shih* is rendered "processor"; *hsien* is translated "genie" rather than "immortal." Since

Taoism recognizes God as ineffable (5.1*a*6), wide use is made of epithets as designations (9.1*a*—). In such cases the translation will normally be "God," and the literal epithet will be noted in parentheses. *Chen* (true) being a common epithet for God, the term *chen jen* has been rendered "God's Man."[2]

With Ko Hung, as with Chuang Chou, much can be understood only in the light of accepted anatomical concepts and current medical practice. Breath (*ch'i*), that sure sign of vitality, was classified into ten sorts, three of them subtle (*hun*) and seven coarse (*p'o*) (2.10*a*6). Anatomically the body fell into the three divisions of top, bottom, and median (5.2*a*8), in each of which there were a governing bureau and branch offices operated by inhabiting divinities. Late sources claim that these numbered 36,000. It was the function of the physician to know which of these might be causing illness. A correct knowledge of their names and uniforms was indispensable if they were to be controlled.

Two episodes in *Tso chuan*, one of the Confucian classics of Chinese antiquity, bear eloquent witness to Chinese medical theory, and with the mention of Doctors Ho and Huan in 5.3*a*10 these are the stories evoked by Ko Hung for his readers:

Ch'eng 10.5: The patient dreamed that his illness was two lackeys, one of whom remarked, "The physician whom Ch'in is sending is first class. I'm afraid that he will harm us. Where shall we run to?" The other replied, "Let's go and stay above the diaphragm and below the heart, then he will be unable to do anything about us." After examining his patient the physician said, "Nothing can be done about this illness, because it lies above the diaphragm and below the heart where we cannot reach it. Medicines are ineffective when they do not reach the illness."

---

[2] Since Taoism is by no means nihilistic in outlook, its cardinal dynamism can be stressed by using positives to translate some other technical terms which, literally, are overtly or implicitly negative because they deny the popular assumption that empiric existences constitute reality. *Yu* designates these empirical existences with their bound and discreet forms. *Wu* is the antithesis of *yu*, and to underscore its lack of bonds, "perfect freedom" is used for its translation. *Hsü*, to all essential purposes, is a synonym of *wu*, but to preserve the verbal distinction it will be translated "uncommitted." *Ch'ing* (pure) is best rendered "unprejudiced."

Chao 1.8: The physician said, "Nothing can be done about this man's illness; this shows that he has spent too much time with his wives. Illness is comparable to a gnawing worm or insect; it is not caused by ghosts or diet. In the present case, delusion has ruined the will. This meritorious minister of yours is on the point of death; his predetermined destiny is of no help (cf. 3.8*b*9)." — "Do you mean that our wives should not be approached?" — "Discipline that activity. The kings of old disciplined everything through music. That is why there are five musical chords, and when the tempo, the melody, and the overtones are in agreement, perfect sounds will form the chord. After five chords the strings of the lute go untouched. When, however, excessive music from overplaying smothers our hearts and ears with its delights, steadying harmony is forgotten; and this, Great Man does not allow. Accepting this ideal, all creation rejects excess when it occurs; in this way no illness will be caused. Great Man uses the lute for self-discipline, not for pleasure.

"There are six breaths in nature, and they produce all savors, colors, and musical chords. Excess causes the illnesses. The six breaths are: *yin*, *yang*, wind, rain, darkness, and light. They are apportioned among the four seasons and arranged into the five musical chords. Excess on the part of any of the six breaths causes damage. Too much *yin*, there will be chills; too much *yang*, fever; too much wind, illness in the extremities; too much rain, digestive troubles; too much darkness, delusion; too much light, illness for the heart and mind.

"Though she experience estrus, woman is a season of darkness. Excessive contact with her produces internal fever and delusion. In the present instance, how could his lordship fail to attain his present condition, since he has been undisciplined and untimely. . . ." — "What do you mean by 'gnawing worm or insect'?" — "Worms or insects are the cause of excess, depravity, delusion, and confusion . . . .. *The Changes* uses the identical term to designate a female causing delusion in a male, or a wind tumbling a hill . . .."

In the preceding excerpt two untranslatable terms were encountered: *yin* and *yang*. They are a succinct product of Chinese culture which the rest of the world might well adopt in classifying its own observation and experience conveniently. *Yin* is dark and feminine; *yang* is light and masculine; thus these words denote the whole gamut of antagonistic, complementary pairs of which our universe is composed.

The Taoism represented by Ko Hung peopled the universe with gods, ghosts, and genii. What was merely "sky" in the old Chinese state cult had become by his day an organization and a vast country, populated and governed like China itself. This compels us to translate the *t'ien* of this text by "heaven." Further, the Chinese of the fourth century A.D. were accepting a detailed correlation between heaven, earth, and man, which was handled through equations using the sexagenary cycle (with its denary and duodenary cycles), the Five Agents (wood, fire, earth, water, metal), the seasons, the cardinal points, the colors, the musical notes, and the stars.

The author of the present book, Ko Hung, can be assigned only the approximate dates of A.D. 280–340, since sources other than *Chin shu* (Chin History) 72.7*a*4, which records for him the ideal Taoist age of 81, give his age as 60. He belonged to a family where education in the literary and philosophical traditions of the country was automatic. His bent was certainly stronger toward quiet living than toward government service, but he could not escape the latter completely. In his twenties (A.D. 302) he was pressed into service as a strict commander of troops in the field, for his education had naturally embraced the use of arrows, sword, spear, and staff.

To conclude this introduction, let Ko Hung now tell his own story, which falls into two sections, written about twenty years apart:

KO HUNG'S AUTOBIOGRAPHY
(*Pao-p'u tzu wai p'ien*, 50)

(Writing around A.D. 320:) My family name is Ko, my personal name Hung, my sobriquet Chih-ch'uan, and I am a man of Chü-jung in the metropolitan district of Tan-yang [near modern Nanking]. My first ancestor, T'ien of Ko, would seem to have been a king far back in antiquity, but later his territory became one of the states of ancient China, and his name came to be used as a surname. Another ancestor of mine was governor of Ching-chou [Hupei-Hunan], but when Wang Mang [A.D. 9–23] usurped power he blushed to serve a bandit. Quitting the governorship, he joined Chai Yi, Governor of Tung-chün [S. Hopei] in raising troops to punish Wang Mang, but they were defeated and subsequently pardoned. Thereupon, alleging illness, he withdrew from public life. Wang Mang, however, feeling that my ancestor was too influential and that he would ultimately lead a revolution, shifted him to Lang-yeh [in Shantung, west of Tsingtao]. This ancestor's son Lu [some say P'u-lu] raised troops and won a name for himself in helping to win the throne for Liu Hsiu [A.D. 23]. When the latter came to power, Ko Lu was made a member of his private mounted escort and later promoted to become honorary escort with the title of Commander-in-Chief. He was also made Marquis of T'ung in the metropolitan district of Hsia-p'ei [N. Kiangsu], where he enjoyed the income from five thousand households.

Before the Han dynasty was fully restored [A.D. 23], Ko Lu's younger brother Wen had been with him on his campaigns, often participating in fine victories. He was frequently praised in the despatches, but officialdom held the point of view that Ko Wen was with his elder brother in a private capacity and could be given no military credit. This forced Ko Lu to comment, "Wen braved arrows *1b* and stones along with me and was wounded over his whole body, losing his right eye, without ever receiving one speck of reward. I, on the other hand, have repeatedly been the recipient of money and honors. How can I reconcile myself to this?" Then he personally petitioned that his fief be transferred to his younger brother. Approval was recommended at the highest level, and the Han court granted special permission in order to acclaim such an unselfish proposal. Ko Wen first declined, but then, having no alternative, accepted the fief; for his brother, who retained the honorary title, he built a home in the village of Po-wang whose foundation stones exist to this day. He also divided his revenues to provide attendants sufficient for two lords. His brother, however, insisted that he refrain, and would accede to none of these plans. His remarks were, "This would create such hardship for your people that they could never accept the situation. They would move away to the protection of another lord."

Then Ko Lu moved south of the Yangtze and made his home at Chü-jung, his children personally doing the farming and diverting themselves with the classics. Ko Wen frequently sent for his elder brother to return, but he never did. Ko Wen also had people take care of the home in Po-wang in the hope that his brother would return there, but for generations nobody ever lived there.

My grandfather, Ko Hsi, was a profound student of everything. As a man of letters he was without peer in his day. Being a competent administrator, he served the state of Wu [A.D. 222–280] successively as governor of Hai-yen, Lin-an, and Shan-yin. Later, at the capital, he held the posts of Vice-Chairman in the Department of Civil Service, Member of the Privy Secretariat, Governor of Lu-ling, Chairman of the Department of Civil Service, Associate Tutor to the Heir Apparent, Imperial Secretary, Secretary for Foreign Affairs, Courtier, Secretary in the Imperial Household Department, and General-who-supported-Wu. He was enfeoffed Marquis of Wu-shou *hsien*.

My father, Ko T'i, was famous for filial piety and friendships. He was a model gentleman, for he had read fully all the important books out of antiquity. After serving Wu as Administrative Assistant, Governor of Chien-ch'eng and also of Nan-ch'ang, Secretary in the Imperial Secretariat, in the Department of Justice, and in the Ministry of War, he was named Governor of Kuei-chi. Before he could decline, however, the forces of Chin were winning allegiance and the frontier to the west was not defended. His wide acquaintance with the reports, literary style, a talent for military strategy, and reputation both in court circles and throughout the country at large combined to push my father forward. He was made commander-in-chief for the defense of five prefectures with provision for five thousand personal troops. He commanded the offensive force and garrisoned his frontiers, but man cannot shore up what heaven itself is destroying. The former sovereign of Wu respectfully submitted, and all China welcomed the new power (CS 3.8*b*10: A.D. 280). Owing to the posts he had held earlier, my father was appointed Imperial Attendant, and shortly later was promoted to Chamberlain. After that he was successively Chamberlain-in-chief and Governor of Fei-hsiang (S. Hopei), a district of 20,000 households.

Under the new dynasty of Chin all of China enjoyed perfect order, and the effects of its excellence were a wonder to behold. His Majesty being gracious toward all law-abiding men, his praises were sung throughout the land. All traces of depravity disappearing from the roads and the levies upon agriculture being suspended, even foreigners turned to China in droves. Not a single present was allowed entrance to official homes, and paper and brushes were provided at personal expense. With no need for punishments and prohibitions, the renewal proceeded without a word being uttered. There was some complaint, however, about the abandonment of government positions; therefore a command was issued to employ those who had been court officials or governors under the Wu, in order to rectify attitudes, punish violations, increase approval, abolish disapproval, promote morality, and denounce evil, that a country which had been at war might become serious and peaceful again (CS 3.3*a*1, 8*b*3—). My father was promoted to the governorship of Shao-ling [C. Hunan], and died in that office.

I was his third son and, being born late, was spoiled by my parents. I was not trained at an early age in the study of history. When I was thirteen [*ca.* A.D. 293] my father died, so that I lost his paternal counsel too soon. In the face of famine, cold, and destitution, I personally did the farming and harvesting, for one fated by the stars to walk on grass is not to concern himself in the slightest with any inheritance. Having frequently been caught in the midst of warfare, my father's library had become dispersed, leaving me no means for study during the moments of leisure from farming and obliging me to travel on foot, a little bundle of books on my back, and to borrow material. Whenever I happened upon any household that owned some complete texts, it cost me still more labor and time, for I had to cut and sell firewood to provide myself with the paper and brushes for making copies of them; it was in official barracks and paddocks that I did my copying by firelight. Owing to these conditions I could not concern myself with literature at a very early age. Since paper was generally scarce, I used both sides to make my copies, and they were hardly legible.

At the age of sixteen I began the study of *Filial Piety*, *The Analects*, *The Poems*, and *The Changes*, but in my poverty I lacked the means for searching afar for teachers and friends. I became a person of little learning, shallow understanding, and literal thoughts, the fuller content and significance largely escaping me. Yet I was eager to browse widely in everything written, and there was nothing whose essence I did not learn and acquire in an untutored way. I acquainted myself with everything from the orthodox classics, the histories, and the philosophers down to short, miscellaneous compositions — almost ten thousand scrolls in all. Since I was naturally stupid and apt to forget — my vocabulary was small and my purpose scattered — my knowledge remained very slight and steeped in doubts, yet in my writing I can draw upon this reading. Having never fully embraced Confucianism, I have never become a teacher in that tradition. After one look at their *Ho t'u*, *Lo shu*, and books of divination, I stopped and could pay them no further attention (7.5*a*4). Taking no pleasure in the astrological and numerological, I devoted no time at all to

3a

Sky's Nine Divisions, Three Marvels, Grand Unity, or "*Express*" *Amulets,* because such things can give a person much trouble and contain little that is attractive. Later I did study and got a rough acquaintance with the arts of divination by wind and weather, good and bad days, and the periodicity of the primary agents. I never went into them thoroughly, however, for I considered that all such activities were specific useful arts, practiced only by those thus personally inclined, and that there being no urgency requiring that we belabor ourselves with them, it was better to concentrate on the profitable things that the philosophers have to say. So I have neglected divination.

Altogether, *Ch'i lüeh pieh lu* and Chapter 30 of *Han shu* list 13,299 scrolls of books, and since the advent of the Wei dynasty [A.D. 220—] writing has mounted in floods twice as great as before. I am conscious, therefore, of how much I have never seen. Everywhere south of the Yangtze there was a universal shortage of written material; I therefore wished to go to teachers at the capital (7*b*11) in search of rarities, but I encountered a serious rebellion and retraced my steps when already halfway there. This makes me constantly sigh with regret. Today I am approaching forty, and my will for such searching has declined. I think only of "diminishing further what has already been diminished and carrying on in the action that is perfect freedom" (T 48); doing my part in tilling the paddies and fruitlessly continuing my existence. Thus the task of extending contacts meets with ever increasing hurdles every day.

I am an unsophisticated person; dull by nature, and a stammerer. My physical frame is unpleasant to look at; and I am not competent enough to boast of myself and gloss over the defects. My hat and shoes are dirty; my clothes sometimes the worse for wear or patched; but this does not always bother me. Styles in clothing change too quickly and too often: One moment they are broad at the neck, and the belt is wide; another moment they fit tight and have big sleeves; then again they become long and sweep the ground, or short and do not cover the feet. It has been my plan to preserve regularity and not to follow the whims of the world. My speech is frank and sincere; I engage in no banter. If I do not come upon the right person, I can spend the day in silence. That is the reason my neighbors call me Simplex (*Pao-p'u*), which name I have used as a sobriquet in my writings.

By nature I am weak and thin; these two qualities have combined to produce much illness. I am too poor to own either chair or horse, and I am unable to go afoot. In fact, I have a natural distaste for travel.

3b

4a

Also I shrink from the habits of the crowd, which bypasses all that is fundamental and pursues the petty, its social life being excessive. Accordingly, I cling to my brush and stay within a barred door. As I guard my peace behind a thorny entrance, no place is left for frequenters. As for the high and mighty, I live near them, but we are not close friends. I do not have sufficient clothing to keep out the cold, and the roof of my hut sometimes leaks. I eat very little, and it does not worry me that I am unknown outside my own home. Since I am too poor to have a servant boy, only a hedge bows to my decisions. Thorny bushes being thick in my courts, and weeds blocking the steps and gutters, I push aside bushes when leaving my gate and tread upon grass to enter a room (8.5*b*7). People say that I live differently from others because, my mind being on the abstruse, I neglect whatever is close at hand, but the real reason is that there is nobody to do the work.

Since I do not know how to visit, I have never been given to calls upon the heads of government offices. With a great effort of will which makes the necessity clear I do manage to go and express condolences at the loss of a parent or to visit those who are ill, but my own poor health lessens my perseverance, and I do not make as many such visits as I ought. Whenever I find myself criticized for this, I accept the blame, but I do not worry about it. My guess would be that when faced with persistent illness the heart and mind turn contrary and no longer feel shame; so how are they to be restored to normalcy by mistrust on the part of others? Only truly enlightened gentlemen accept my sincere embrace of simplicity, and understand that it is not with an eye to renown that I live as I do.

Most people cherish association with friends and reject the idea that any home should contain secrets. I, on the other hand, have never found it easy to be on close terms with others; the most renowned sages have also found this difficult. Idle argumentation is conducive to injuries to our inner gods; it is not beneficial; it causes loss. I may not be able to cut myself off as completely from friendships as Chu Mu did, but they must be of a kind inspired by the purest motives; to this I pay close attention. On this score many persons have experienced my unalterable dislike. All those pursuing idle successes and making themselves dependents of the powerful also complain that I differ from them; they find me reprehensible, saying that I am proud and disdainful of normal good manners. But I am a man who acts from sincerity; I disregard both praise and blame. It troubles me very much that some of my acquaintances accept their own strong points but disdain the shortcomings of others.

4b

I confess to being the most miserable of Confucianists. Whenever
I talk with another I always turn the conversation to things he knows;
I do not force him into subjects he does not know. Whenever discussing something for students to learn, I always confine myself to
the chief points. If they object to my terseness and find it difficult to
5a   understand what I have in mind, it is deliberately that I merely
express the approximate direction and the associations of my thought,
just enough to arouse their minds. I do not employ painful argumentation from which none of them can recover. Thus, their minds
remaining untroubled, they think about what I have said and generally come to feel that they have achieved the idea of themselves. Whenever I judge a student to be one of those with whom it is impossible
to talk, even though he may raise some questions, I always decline
on the grounds of ignorance in order not to be guilty of wasting my
words.

It is in my nature to dislike interfering with officials and leaders.
Throughout my life I have gone to the aid of friends who were not
receiving appointments and in spite of myself have spoken with those
in power, but my friends never realized the trouble this caused me.
It was merely a case of secretly planning something on their behalf
when I could no longer tolerate seeing them trapped in a senseless
situation. As for the rest, even including my closest relations if they
are men with power but with no sympathy for me, I do not become
in the least involved with them either by word or in writing.

When supplies of food are gone or an emergency has me preparing
infusions or medicines, I appeal to friends, and if I happen to receive
their help I do not decline it. Such gifts must, I feel, be repaid very
gradually over the long run so that my friends will not know that I
am doing it. I am very careful not to accept anything from those who
5b   are not close friends. Whenever I have a ten days' supply of food, I
share it with those who have nothing, but when there is not enough
for myself, I do not deprive myself. I do not practice any of the
contemptible, little moral acts; I refrain from performing small, ir-
reproachable upright deeds. Pious folk of the town sometimes visit
me with gifts of wine and food, and I do not reject them, even though
I do not know the donors well. Later, but not immediately, I ac-
knowledge their gifts. I once put it this way: Fan Jan's refusal of
support from the rest of his family and Hua Hsin's being so meticulously puritan toward the befriended guest who was overloading the
boat were probably sham acts in search of glory, not great deeds to
be long remembered at the ancestral temple.

It troubles me much when unprincipled men do not work hard at the basic occupations of farming and sericulture but cherish the venal profits of improprieties. When held in the high esteem of their towns they sell appointments to office in order to win the gratitude of others; when in authority they make recommendations for money. Sometimes bribes from wrong-doers bring injustice upon those who are in the right. Other times, serving as refuge for runaways, they feed those fleeing for their lives, or they take adults under their wing, thus interfering with the public corvée. They deliberately accumulate currency to make it dearer, or they corner markets to usurp profits belonging to the people. They cut off slices from people's farms and seize the patrimonies of orphans. They crowd about our government offices to ferret out the advantages of any exactions they might effect; then they boast about them to their wives and concubines and gain a reputation for themselves in the town. I do not associate with people of this type. For these reasons, ordinary folk dislike the complaints I levy against such unprincipled men, and, naturally enough, a distance is maintained between us. My street, therefore, bears no trace of carriages and horses, and my reception room contains no guests with goals other than my own. Bird traps can be set in my courtyard, and my tabourets and mats accumulate dust. *6a*

I am fully conscious of the fact that I am growing old. I do not mention the faults of others, nor do I discuss their private affairs. This goes without saying. If there is anything defective or shameful in my servants, I do not mock them for it. I never discuss the excellences or the defects of others. I find no pleasure in shouting about the virtues and vices of human society. Whenever my superiors insist upon questioning me, I decline, but when I can no longer hold out against them, I mention only the higher qualities in others and leave it at that. If a piece of writing is being discussed, I point out whatever excellence it may have, but I do not criticize its defects. Thus I avoid all resentment for criticism. Distinguished persons sometimes inquire how I would qualify officials or other people, and in such a case I always point out whatever is best in their moral character and their abilities. As for their avarices and any skeletons in their closets, my *6b* reply is that I do not happen to know any details. For all this I have been roundly criticized as being too solicitous and unable to distinguish the good from the bad and making too little difference between black and white, but I have never dared change.

Whenever I see my contemporaries engaged in discussing personalities, their conclusions of praise or blame are sometimes exaggerated because they did not first agree upon standards of comparison; thus the one praised will say that he certainly does not believe he can be as excellent as they say, and the one disapproved of becomes deeply angry with his critics, even to the point of a blood feud. I take this more and more as a warning and no longer talk about others. When the members of my own clan are to be evaluated, I assign the task to neighboring families in order not to undervalue them. Sometimes I am criticized for this, and then my reply is, "My own person being within myself, it ought to be easy for me to know what criterion is in question. Yet, if I were asked to compare myself with the Ancients or even my contemporaries and determine with whom I was to be classed, I would truly be unable to reach a conclusion. How then am I to criticize and classify a person other than myself?"

In the unfavorable social climate at the end of the Han (A.D. 220), coteries of friends were formed, and people like Hsü Shao issued verbal approvals and warnings. There were complaints and discussions, and various clans fell to feuding. Accordingly, the people of Ju-nan [SE. Honan] no longer enjoyed fixed assessments; they were being rated at the beginning of every month (HHS 98.4a10). Emperor Wu of the Wei [Ts'ao Ts'ao, died A.D. 220], complained bitterly of this situation; he merely wished to get Hsü to admit his error, but he had to flee hurriedly toward the sea and barely escaped being butchered. Let us learn from this example, which is not too distant in time.

The human being is so hard to know that even fathers and older brothers are not sure of understanding their own sons and younger brothers thoroughly. Those resembling ourselves receive immediate approval; those differing, immediate disapproval. Some start well but do not end so. Yao, the Duke of Chou, Confucius, and Chi Cha, on the other hand, all regretted that they were not completely successful when they could not get their contemporaries to believe their teachings. To pass easy judgment upon others while viewing them through a narrow tube or under the light of a taper is to forget completely the great sages and high-calibered men of yore!

(Writing around A.D. 335:) Long ago, in the T'ai-an period (A.D. 303–4), Shih Ping led a revolt resulting in serious disturbances throughout six states; lawful government was interfered with and hostile cliques were formed against the state. The Commander-in-Chief of the Loyalists (Ku Pi) ordered me to take a command, and I felt subjected to many pressures. Since my own native region feared the rebels, who were causing much damage and wide concern, and the Ancients considered action proper in emergencies, and, finally, being personally awed by martial law, I dared not yield to my own

7a

wishes. Drafting several hundred men, I advanced with the other units of the army. On that day we attacked and defeated a Vice-Commander of the rebels; money and silks were piled about like 7*b* mountains, jewels and trinkets covered the ground. When the commanders released their soldiers for the looting, which filled whole wagon trains, I was the only one to maintain discipline in his command, which was not permitted to break its ranks. I warned that I would behead any soldier who joined the looters, and from that point on nobody dared counter my authority. As was natural, however, several hundred rebels who had been concealed made a sally and inflicted wounds upon the rest of the army, all of which rose to the defense but without its usual organization into companies and squads. Men and horses had been burdened with booty and no longer had any fighting spirit. The result was fright and confusion, producing a welter of dead and wounded, which almost defied rescue. My company was the only one to maintain good order and arrange itself like a hub. Suffering no casualties, it was able to save the rest of the army from total defeat. My own strength was a factor in this, for later I fought a minor rebel commander and decapitated him (10*b*5). Many loricas and heads were taken, and the booty presented to headquarters. The commandant then gave me the title of Wave-Subduing General and awarded all those of my rank one hundred pieces of cloth. Most of the commanders packed theirs or sent them home, but I shared mine with my officers and men and gave some to the poorer of my friends. The remaining ten pieces I exchanged for meat and wine with which to feast my officers, thus winning for myself a day of glory.

When peace returned, I threw down my spear, removed my lorica, and immediately started for Lo-yang (see 3*b*2) to search extensively for writings that are out of the ordinary but certainly not to discuss my military merit, for I cherish the way Lu Chung-lien would not accept any reward from Liao-ch'eng and the way Shen Pao-hsü accepted no reward for preserving Ch'u. It is proper conduct to do 8*a* things without letting the mind dwell upon them (T 77). At that point rebellion broke out around the capital, cutting the roads to the north, while at the same time Ch'en Min began his revolt in Chiang-tung, so that my road back home was also blocked. It was at that moment [*ca.* A.D. 306] that an old friend, Chi Han of Ch'iao-kuo, was appointed governor of Kuang-chou [Canton area]. He requested me to become his military aide, and although this was not what I wanted, it did present a convenient way to escape south. I therefore hastened to accept the post, and was sent ahead to requisition arms.

After my departure Chi Han was murdered, but I remained in Kuang-chou, frequently invited by the commissioner to accept a post, but always declining.

Riches and honors can be gradually attained if one thinks long enough about them, but it is impossible to garner them quickly. Meanwhile, little things here and there often wear out a man; power and glory are like overnight guests. Since they are nothing permanent, their departure cannot be put off indefinitely. All flourishings come to an end, and moments of glory die. They are like the flowers of spring that suddenly succumb to frost. Let there then be no joy at their attainment, no grief at their loss! Since it is impossible to enumerate all the regrets they occasion and all the worry and fear they inspire, they are not worth our efforts.

I am aware that I am naturally lazy and possess only the slightest talent possible. With perfect laziness as my tool and a minute talent as my vehicle, even if I were to flex my shoulders and bend my knees to rush forward through wind and dust, I should most certainly never negotiate any great name or position for myself; meanwhile I should not be able to avoid all sorts of fears. It is therefore best that I follow in the footsteps of Ch'ih-sung tzu and Wang Ch'iao and depend solely upon myself, not upon others.

8b

I am going to retire into the famous mountains to regulate my diet and nurture my life, so that there can be no abandonment of the plan on my part. When a man's activities are not mutually helpful, how is he to cultivate God (the Dark and Tranquil) without quitting the world's normal activities? Further, this is so difficult to understand, that I cannot, with my lack of learning, discuss it with others. For this reason my carriage and horses have not been passing by the honored and powerful, nor have letters of mine been going to those in office. Although I cannot rise above the level of the state's gentlemen, I feel that my humble purpose is not to be resisted, nor are obstacles to be raised against my specializing. If you call to me that there are no roads in the mountains and forests, I must remind you that the ancient practitioners of the divine process were also obliged to enter the mountains and forests because they truly wished to avoid noise and keep their hearts and minds at peace. I am now about to pursue that which is my deepest wish: I shall quit my native district for Mount Sung in search of the path trod by Wang Yüan and Liang Mu.

Fortunately, the philosophical writings which I had started earlier, both the inner and the outer chapters, have already had my attention. It now only remains to rearrange them for posterity. The regular poetry, the free verse, and the miscellaneous compositions prepared

9a

when I was fifteen and sixteen seemed at that time to be ready for publication. However, at the age of twenty [*ca.* A.D. 300] I reexamined them and a great many no longer met my approval. I cannot suppose that my natural talents had enjoyed any definite increase; thus it was only after having acquired much wider experience and having come to feel the difference between beauty and ugliness that I rejected practically all of my enormous literary output, and retained less than one percent. Today, with the exception of my philosophical writings, only a few hundred miscellaneous scrolls still satisfy my demands. Since not all the deletions and additions have yet been made, I am ashamed of most of them, but there is no time to think again of improving them. When others finish a piece of writing they shout with glee, but I have really never been able to do that, my talent being dull and my thought sluggish. Whenever I change a word in composition, I become personally overwhelmed in turn. It is only out of fear of my own laziness and because of the abundance of my composition that it has been impossible to reexamine my work frequently.

In my twenties I planned to compose some little things in order not to waste my time, for it seemed best to create something that would constitute the sayings of one sole thinker. This is when I outlined my philosophical writing, but it was also the moment when I became involved in armed rebellion and found myself wandering and scattered even farther afield, some of my things getting lost. Although constantly on the move, I did not abandon my brush again for a dozen or so years, so that at the age of 37 or 38 [A.D. 317–18] I found my work completed.

In all, I have composed *Nei p'ien* in 20 scrolls, *Wai p'ien* in 50; inscriptions, lauds, regular and free poetry in 100; *Chün shu yao i* and *Chang piao chien chi* in 30. I also compiled a book on those who are not normally listed, which became the *Shen hsien chuan* in 10 scrolls; I did the same for those who out of idealism do not enter public office, which became the *Yin i chuan*, also in 10 scrolls. I further extracted from the Five Classics, the seven histories, and the philosophers all they had to say on military matters, recipes and arts, miscellanea, and extraordinary phenomena; this grew to 310 scrolls plus a table of contents. My *Nei p'ien*, telling of gods and genii, prescriptions and medicines, ghosts and marvels, transformations, maintenance of life, extension of years, exorcising evils, and banishing misfortune, belongs to the Taoist school. My *Wai p'ien*, giving an account of success and failure in human affairs and of good and evil in public affairs, belongs to the Confucian school (16.1*b*1).

9b

I have noticed that at the end of the author's postscript to the *Tien lun* (see 2.4*b*8) of Emperor Wen of the Wei, mention is made of crossbows, backgammon, lute-playing, and swordsmanship. The purpose was to speak more or less of what the author knew, and in fact no account was given of the things in which the author had little ability. One should not vaunt oneself idly. Today, therefore, I am going to give a complete account of what I can *not* do. I am dull of character and a jade in natural endowment; I have few amusements; I do up my hair like a child's. In throwing tiles and catching them with the hands I am inferior to boys and young lads. I have never engaged in cock or drake fighting, nor have I ever raced dogs or horses. When I notice that people are playing backgammon, I do not give them a glance. Sometimes I am taken to observe a game, but it never penetrates my mind, for I am like a man asleep during the day. The result is that to this very day I do not know how many rows there are on a backgammon board or what the names of the different throws of the dice are. I am indeed mindful that this sort of lowly art disturbs thought and wastes days and months. For those in authority it detracts from the conduct of public affairs. It causes Confucianists to abandon their studies, ordinary people to forget their crops, and merchants to neglect their businesses. Even before the winners and losers have been determined, wrangling occurs in the metropolitan market places. The players become heated within, and externally their faces show worry. They call this gambling a pleasure, but it is really torture. It destroys all sense of forthrightness and shame, and encourages quarrels. On the surface there is the gain of much wealth, but underneath resentment and feuds are formed. Already in ancient times, Duke Min of Sung and the heir apparent of Wu had their skulls cracked with gaming boards. Such activity has caused rebellions. It overturned the Seven Kingdoms. And very recently the government has issued a warning against gambling for all eternity. Let this serve as a lesson. Whenever I watch the players, they are flushing with anger at their associates; their hands and feet have contact with one another; they swear at each other; and frequently friendships are broken. It does not matter whether the resentment is big or little; it evokes too many regrets and it is not worth creating.

Confucius may have warned against sleeping during the day (Ana. 5.10); yet when I talk about myself I am not above admitting that I am no better than a day-dreamer. What is a day-dreamer? Merely somebody who contributes nothing but at least is never involved in resentment or quarrels. Considering how the Sage devoted himself to the study of a classic until the thongs holding his book together

10a

broke three times (20.4a5), how can present-day people with their ordinary talents successfully do more than one thing at a time? Since all these games put together are not worth the reading of one foot of writing, I find no pleasure whatever in them and do not play them. One might say that they are the things with which the lower classes are on familiar terms.

As a young man I studied a bit of archery, but my strength was too little for me to be able to draw a bow as strong as Yen Kao's. I believe that one learns archery because it is one of the six arts practiced by a gentleman and also because with it one may check bandits, drive away pillagers, or shoot down birds and animals. Long ago, when in the army, I once shot at pursuing horsemen. In response to my bowstring, two rebels and one horse toppled over dead; I thus escaped death myself (7b6).

I also had instruction in sword plus shield and in single sword plus double lance, all of which have abstruse instructions and significant tricks for use against adversaries. After acquiring these secret methods and becoming adept at them, it becomes possible to remain unscathed and win a victory all alone provided this procedure is used against an uninitiated person. No matter which way one advances there will be nothing to interfere.

Late in life I also studied the art of the seven-foot staff, which can be used against a bare blade or a long lance. But this also constitutes a nonvital study of the lowest order. This skill may be compared with the unicorn's horn or the phoenix's spur. Where is it needed? Beyond the things which I have just listed, there is probably nothing further that I have learned.

Already as a young man it had been my fixed purpose not to seek prominence for myself. Whenever I read the accounts of Hsü Yu, Tzu-chou Chih-fu, Pei-jen Wu-tse, and Shih-hu-chih-nung (all four in *Chuang*), the two Chiangs, the pair of Yüans, Fa-chen, and Shen-t'u P'an (all in HHS), I always forgot the book and advanced off my mat as I cherished the memory of the type of man they had been, and my thoughts turned to mastering the Five Classics in order to be able to compose a philosophical work of my own, so that later generations might know that I was a literary Confucianist and nothing more.

Later, various heads of local government and even a Commander-in-Chief offered me appointments, but I accepted none of them. My name was also recommended to the office of the premiership held by the Prince of Lang-yeh [= Ssu-ma Jui; sometime during A.D. 313–16], but since the mobilization of volunteers and the defeat of the rebels long ago (7a7—), I cultivated no fame whatever and avoided all government offices.

Those who had been judged meritorious because of their support of the Chin when it was compelled to yield northern China were for a long time without any hope of reward. When, however, the King of Chin (Ssu-ma Jui; CS 6.1b12) had been accepted by both heaven and men, rebellion had been checked and orthodoxy restored, the imperial order saved from imminent dissolution, and the abandoned offerings to the ancestral shrine reeastablished, it was recalled that there remained rewards due from previous rulers which had not yet been distributed for the encouragement of adherence; then, along with many others, I accepted an appointment. By the decree of A.D. 330 I was granted the fief title of Marquis of Kuan-chung with 200 households of Chü-jung for my income. I stated at the time that I had fought the rebels only to save my native town, and such labor did not merit high appointment which had never been my desire; my first wish had always been to cherish Lu Chung-lien of old (7b11) from afar and to devote myself for the present to farming. I presented a reply firmly declining the honor in order to pursue lesser aims, but I was confronted with a general order that no such requests would be honored. In olden days, Chung Yu had declined an offer that should have been accepted, and his efforts at dissuasion have been considered a virtue. But at this time the rebels had not yet been pacified, and the world was still in much trouble. The government therefore wished to make its rewards evident and its punishments certain in order to clarify the whole system of its laws. How could I in my fruitless fashion presume to maintain the innocence of a paltry wish and thereby interfere with an arrangement that was to be universal? Accordingly, I subdued my own desires and respectfully accepted the imperial order.

11b

When I had completed [the first half of] this autobiography, someone raised this objection: "Of old, in his sixties when his course had been run and his hopes were at an end, Wang Ch'ung, fearing that both his body and his name would disappear together, wrote an autobiography as a conclusion to his work (*Lun heng* 30). You, however, upon completing your thirties, happen to incur a shift to the better in your fortunes, and are about to be treated royally, as was Master Shen, and transported with reed-covered wheels like Master Mu. The position of overlord is a glorious one; high noon defies description. Why in your dislike of the serenity of the virtuous [administrative] life do you turn your energies to the tasks of oldsters?" My reply to this was: "*Yin* and *yang* are highly inscrutable, and man is only a temporary sojourner in them. With all the glorious prosperity of a short-lived mushroom, he tumbles to ruin within a day. With all the momentary glory of a spring flower, he succumbs to the frost within a week. Not even the winds blowing through high heaven or the sudden flash of lightning can move any faster. A century is to be likened to the smoke ridden by a meteor; whitening hair comes with all the speed of an arrow passing by a crack. Man appears like a perishing bamboo shoot before he has even sprouted; he meets his autumn and tumbles to pieces. That is why there was such a cry over the promise shown by Hsiang T'o before he died at the age of ten and the lament over Yang Wu's early demise."

When we consider the exalted gentlemen of olden days, we find *12a* that some pranced like dragons in the domain of literature; others were like crouching tigers in their military merit. Their high renown was published in the bureau of oaths; the tidings of their excellence resounded on pipes and strings. Their bodies may lie buried in the depths of the earth, but their fair renown is proclaimed for days on end, so that even after hundreds or thousands of years it is still cherished.

My lowly self has sat quietly out of sight, for I was not fitted to the times, and my work has been out of tune with the day. Whatever I said ran counter to popular belief; every step I took was against the direction of the masses. At home, I have lacked the resources of the rich; abroad, I have been without friends in officialdom. The road I have traveled may be broad and level, but my feet have not been those of the unicorn. The universe may be broad, but I have not had the wings of the great *p'eng* of which Chuang Chou speaks. I have not been able to have a military career or help govern our country, and I have lacked the means to glorify my parents and leave a name behind me. I cannot depend upon official historians to praise me, nor do bells and tripods record my name. This is why I take advantage of these fragments to write a chapter of autobiography. It may do nothing for my failure or success, but that will be for writers of the future to say (4.17*a*7–17*b*6).

The Nei P'ien of Ko Hung

Author's Preface

SINCE I HAVE no extraordinary talent but do happen to like the pursuit of action that constitutes perfect freedom, by deploying my wings I might well traverse the dark heavens, and by speeding my feet move over the landscape with the speed of wind. It has been my desire, however, to continue to stack my sinews and wings with low-flying flocks and store my poor doings with lame donkeys, especially since God (the Mass of Greatness) has provided me with ordinary short wings and creation has conferred upon me the poor shanks of a jade.

Those able to judge themselves are careful; where incompetent, they desist. One with only the strength of a greenhead does not expect to rise to high heaven; and he who rides a crippled tortoise does not follow in the tracks of the thoroughbred. Nobody as ugly as Mu-mu (Yellow Emperor's No. 4 wife) seeks to talk as charmingly as does a go-between, and the man with only sand or pebbles to offer does not expect thousands in gold at Pien Ho's shop. Petty talent only stumbles when, with its pygmy steps, it pretends to stride like seven-league boots. I am mindful that a man of Ch'in (SC 5.11*b*1) broke his very sinews when, although weak as Yao-li, he presumed to be strong enough to uphold one end of the pole by which a tripod was to be carried. *1b* Therefore, being without hope of traveling a path of glory, my will has found peace in a barren domain where greens taste as sweet as the eight rarest foods, and thatch gives as much pleasure as a ridgepole painted like sea grass. This scion of a powerful house has, therefore, declined even imperial commissions, although as one who understands God, he has been obliged to achieve the difficult and the distant.

I have examined not a few writings dealing with God (the Marvelous) and found that most of them use obscure language and are hard to understand thoroughly. Unless one is of the very best, it is impossible to examine these writings in depth; without true diligence it is impossible to read them all. Few processors have a profound, broad learning in their subject, while those engaging in personal opinions and making incoherent claims are legion. The occasional dilettante desirous of something to practice, not knowing whom to accept, finds himself in doubt and without any source of correct information.

In the present book I speak in general terms of the principles governing life in all its fullness, but the really marvelous part of it cannot be reduced to writing. One might say that my account is so rough and skeletal that I may reveal just one corner of the topic in the hope that those who are really concerned may examine it and infer of themselves the greater part. Since there is no need for me to be able to exhaust all minutiae and to clarify abstruse elements for ignoramuses, I have discussed the initial elements only.

The Confucianists of our day know only how to maintain faithfully the memory of the Duke of Chou and Confucius, both of whom died in the stocks. None of them believe in the gods and the genii; they consider such talk ill-omened or mad. When they see this book of mine, they will not only break into guffaws of laughter; they will also malign the truths and the correct statements it contains. I therefore do not join it to my other philosophical writings, but give it the title of *Nei p'ien*, twenty chapters in all, and will employ a numerical order separate from that of the *Wai p'ien*.

2a

Although this book is not worthy to be stored in the stone caves of famous mountains (as are the heaven-inspired Taoist writings), I do wish to secure it in a metal coffer, so that it may become known to connoisseurs. Let it not be seen by those with whom these matters may not be discussed! My purpose is that those of the future interested in the Fullness of Life may find a place where their doubts can be resolved. The confidence of nonbelievers is not sought. Respectfully submitted.

I

God (the Mystery) Defined

2b   GOD IS THE FIRST ancestor to nature, the grandsire of all the different empiricals (18.3*b*2). God's depth being such as to make us squint and see obscurely, the epithet *subtle* may be used. God's length being so great, we may well speak of marvelousness. God is so high that even the ninth heaven is topped; so broad that all space is encompassed. God is brighter than the sun or moon; speedier than lightning or the fleet steed. Sometimes God passes by as a flash of light; or blows and spouts in a show of stars. God is vaster and deeper than the deepest pool of pure water; and then again, God is the mist or snow, and the floating clouds. In the million various things, God is empirical existence; in the secret and the silent, God is perfect freedom. Plunged into the abyss "Big Obscure," God sinks to the bottom of the universe; rising to the celestial pole, God soars at its top. Metal and stone are no analogy for God's hardness; nor are the wet and the dew any comparison for God's softness. God is square, but no carpenter's square has been applied; God is round, but there has been no compass. Nobody sees whence God comes, and nobody follows where God goes. Through God heaven is lofty and earth low. Through God the clouds move and rain is dispensed.

God enwombed Primal Unity and cast in their mold the two symbols (the straight line, either whole or broken at the middle, = *yang* and *yin*). God breathed forth Grand Beginning and forged the thousands of genera. God turns the cycle of the 28 celestial mansions and fashions the beginnings of things. God is the reins and the whip for the whole complex of spiritual powers and blows the breaths characterizing the four seasons. God holds in subtle embrace all vast, silent space; enfolds in relaxed embrace all that is brilliant. Suppressing the turbid and promoting the clear, God distinguishes between the muddy Yellow River and its limpid affluent, the Wei. Additions do not make God overflow, nor do withdrawals exhaust God. What is given does not glorify God. Depredations do God no harm. Therefore, where God   *3a* is present, joy is inexhaustible; whomever God abandons finds his body declining and his inner gods departing.

Distinguishing of the five notes, the eight instruments, and the various musical modes wears away our hearing. Ornamentation with all its variety and beauty with its brilliance harm our eyesight. Festive gatherings, leisure, indulgence, and drinking throw our very natures into disorder. Lovely faces, fair skins artfully painted, erode our very lives. It is only with the Mystery that is God that there can be permanance. For those who do not grasp this Mystery, a mere glance may become the potent instrument of life or death; lips can become the key to rise or fall.

Our pavilions of catalpa loom like the Milky Way; our decorated rooms are as beautiful as Orion and Scorpio. Sheathings are woven as light as mists; coverings, fluffy as clouds. Beauties like Hsi-shih and Mao Ch'iang are displayed in our living rooms. Our metal goblets are adorned with intertwined, prancing steeds. The strings of our lutes reverberate clearly to the songs of Ch'i; Cheng dancers twist and turn in profusion. Flutes sound mournfully to high heaven; feather canopies float and ripple in the breezes. We pluck fragrant blossoms from gardens abounding in fragrances; toy with a red flower in pools of pearl. We scale cliffs to gaze into the distance and forget our worries; search the valley depths for things that will allay our morning hunger. At home, banquets are served in resplendent abodes of a thousand doors; abroad, we race vehicles elegant with their *3b* red wheels.

When joy has attained culmination, however, grief ensues; perfect fullness is bound to be followed by deficiency. When the song is ended, sighs are heard; when the feasting is over, hearts turn sad. Truly the evocations of logical situations are as closely knitted to their sources as shadows and echoes. Being artifice and unreal, all these activities, when ended, leave a void. The Mystery that is God is attained within, but lost through externals. God's users become veritable gods; God's forgettors, instrumentalities. Thus I feel that God has been put to you succinctly.

God's possessor will be honored even without the prestige of the gilt ax as badge of office. Who embodies God is rich; he needs no rarities. The eminence of such a man is not to be scaled; his depth is not to be plumbed. Borne on streams of light and plying the whip to flying rays, he traverses all space and pierces the floods. He exits through the zenith and enters through the nadir. He passes through the gateway of the Boundless and travels in fields of peace and beauty. He takes diversion in God (the Vague and Confused); he comes and goes far beyond all normal coming and going. He enthroats all the beautiful things at the very edge of the clouds; he tastes the six breaths of the universe at the red cloud accompanying the sun. He sojourns in God (the Obscure); he soars in God (the Infinitesimal). He travels the rainbow; he treads the celestial sphere. Such is the man who has found God.

Second to him stands the man who really knows how to be satisfied. Such a man can find happiness in uselessness and cultivate his affairs in the mountains and forests. He deploys his phoenix-dragon wings in the company of simple folk

and nourishes his overwhelming vitality (M 2A.2) in a $\quad$ *4a*
humble cottage. His garments may be patched and his belt a
rope, but he would not exchange them for all the glory of
the imperial robes. He may walk with a load on his back and
use a branch for his staff, but he would not change this for
the social cachet of four-horse teams. He lets gems remain in
Mount Sung's peak so that they will not be worked on the
grindstone. He lets tortoise shells sink into the dark depths so
that they will not suffer the drillings and scorchings of di-
viners. Whether active or resting, he knows when to stop;
he is satisfied wherever he goes. He casts aside the brief
bloom of radiant beauty; he shuns the dangerous routes
where vehicles overturn. As he hums and whistles among
the verdant cliffs, all creation becomes for him but dust and
evil air.

He relaxes under thick branches, and the red doors of
palatial homes are then seen to pivot on rope. He grasps the
plow to help in the tillage, and immediately the banners of
the military and the diplomas of office become no more than
the whip in his grasp. He drinks tea and rinses his mouth
from the spring, whereupon the suovetaurilia become as
mere herb soups. Grandly, in the seasons of leisure, he finds
pleasure in the arena of action that is perfect freedom. Joy-
fully, he equates honors and low estate where there is no
rivalry. As he partakes of pure drink and maintains simplicity, he is free from covetousness and worry. Maintaining
God (Truth) intact and staying uncommitted, he leads the
simple life. Partaking of its immensity and movement, he
makes his naturalness one with the whirl of all nature. Despite its vastness and confusion, he comes to terms with creation, whether dark, bright, murky, or pure. While seeming
dilatory, he is quick; he looks empty, but he is really full. He
refuses to quit his post of master craftsman for the worldly $\quad$ *4b*
tasks of corpse-representative or cantor; he refuses to disregard the cauldrons and other vessels of religious ceremony
and take the place of the ignorant cook (*Chuang* 1.25), and to

reject the guidelines and help with work that could hurt his hands (?M 7A.41). He does not engage in the sorrows and joys of an employee for a putrid pittance of a salary. Uninvolved, he finds no joy in the approval of the crowds; in his tranquillity, he does not fear being criticized for plagiarism. It is not for externals that he would dissipate the best of himself; it is not for profits and losses that he would soil his native purity. Therefore, since he cannot be lured from his chosen path by great riches or the highest honors, how can other things beguile him? Since he is not to be coerced by naked blades or boiling cauldrons, how can slander affect him? With never a thought for life's vexations, he is never one with created things.

To use Marquis Sui's gem to shoot a bird, lick the Lord of Ch'in's piles to amass vehicles, climb a rotten rope to view a nest, ford the weir of Lü to fish,[1] be a prince at dawn but one with the foxes and birds by nightfall — these are instances of irretrievable loss, where the beams have warped and the soup has been spilled.[2] One might say that men of the world act with precipitation and are eager to arrive, but the wise man acts with coolness and melancholy. Therefore, man in his highest form plays no official role in the state religious services and eliminates luxuries. Like a prince, he employs his own six rows of dancers in his religious services at that distant city of the mind Wu-ch'eng; therefore he need not take precautions against critics. Dragon that he is among men, he conceals his scales and horns at Useless where there is no need to trust to paltry lairs. When he looks down, it is not with a hoot of disdain; when he looks up, it is not with ambition which he will have cause to repent. Nobody recognizes him. He is far, far removed and aloof!

5a

[1] For Sui, Ch'in, and the fish, Ko Hung seems to have had in mind *Chuang* 28.29; 32.25; and 19.50. The reference to the nests remains unidentified.

[2] The references here are to *I ching*. See R. Wilhelm, *Buch der Wandlungen* (Jena, 1924), Vol. 1, pp. 82, 147; Vol. 2, pp. 118, 208. These are all references to stories of mean or futile desires.

2

Genii

Interlocutor: Is it possible to believe that gods and genii are immortal?

Ko: Even with the best of eyes it is impossible to see every material object, and with the best of hearing not every sound can be heard. Even with feet like those of Ta-chang and Shu Hai (two of Yü the Great's helpers) the land we tread would never be as vast as the untrodden. Though we possessed all the specialities of Yü's minister Yi and Ch'i Hsieh, what we know would never equal the bulk of our ignorance. What is there that does not exist somewhere in the multiplicity of creation (*Chuang* 11.55)? Why, then, should the genii, whose life histories fill books, not exist? Why should there be no divine process leading to immortality?

The interlocutor laughed and retorted: Whatever begins is sure to end; whatever exists is sure to perish. Therefore, even sages like the Three Augusti, the Five Emperors, Confucius, and the Duke of Chou 'died, as did also the technicians Hou Chi (Emperor Millet), Shu-li Chi, Chang Liang, and Ch'en P'ing; the persuasive discoursers Tuan-mu Tz'u, Yen Ying, Sui Ho, and Li I-ch'i; the stalwarts Meng Pen (8.9*a*5), Hsia Yü, and the Five who worked for the King of Shu. Death is

33

a constant in the human order, an important point certain to
be reached.

I have been taught only that after the frost a drying up
and perishing occur; that in the summer things lose their
freshness; that when the grain fails to head there is no flourishing; that before fruit forms the leaves of the flowers dry
up. I have never heard of anyone enjoying a myriad years of
life or everlasting vision without cease. That is why The
Ancients never learned in their studies to aim for geniehood,
and never talked about anomalies (Ana. 7.21). Anything
strange was blocked at its beginning, and only the natural
things were preserved. Setting aside the tortoise and the
crane as a special category famous for longevity, they felt
that life and death were matters of brief duration.

To eat out one's heart and to constrain oneself to the per-
formance of unprofitable activity are to do our engraving
on ice and our carving on dead wood, where there is no
prospect of success. It is best to engage in the planning of top
councils for the protection of our age and evoke prosperous
fortune for this very year. How fine it is to have the purples
and greens entwine the black bull caparisoned like a dragon!
To have the dragon-adorned carriage displace hastenings
about on foot! To have the cauldron of sacrificial stew replace the task of ploughing! (How fine to lead the official's
life!) I think ever of the section in *The Poems* (211) where
farming and its festival are described, but I give serious
thought to Confucius's witness that all things die (Ana.
12.7).

On the other hand, action that is perfect freedom holds
shapeless winds in its grasp; it seizes upon shadows hard to
hold; it seeks something unattainable; it travels a road which
is sure to lead nowhere. Quitting the niceties of civilized
living, it takes us through hardship and distress; relinquishing the easy, it strives for the extremely difficult. As in the
case of the man at the mulberry tree where one woman was
pursued and the other allowed to wander alone, there is sure

to be regret for a double loss. Shen Pao and Cheng Yi hoped for speedy accomplishment through one-sided action, but the result was disaster for the externals of the former and for the internals of the latter.[1] Neither Pan Shu nor Mo Ti could have sharpened a tile or stone into a needle's point (for they were specialists in ladders and kites), and metal-worker Ou Yeh could not have cast lead or tin into another *kan-chiang* sword. Therefore, even ghosts and gods cannot do the impossible; even all nature cannot achieve the unachievable. So where in our world could a miraculous recipe be found for restoring youth to the old or life to the dying? Yet you wish to prolong the cicada's span to a longevity of ages; you wish to tend the glory of the morning's mushroom until it has a growth of many months (*Chuang* 1.10). How misguided! The man who tries to add to the schools of old will soon revert to them in his confusion (A.11a1).

Ko replies: When a man has lost his hearing, he cannot discern even thunder; when his sight is gone, he cannot be made to see even the sun, moon, or stars. Would you say that rumblings and peals were mere whispers and that the luminaries in the sky were dim? The deaf man, however, insists that there are no such sounds, and the blind man claims there is nothing in the sky. How can such people, then, ever enjoy the refined sounds of the harmonies of woodwinds and strings, or the brilliance of interwoven figures on vestments? How can they appreciate the elegant harmonics of the expert tuner and the iridescence in bril-

---

[1] *Lieh* 8.7: I am laughing about a neighbor who was escorting his wife to her family's home. On the way, he saw a woman gathering mulberry leaves who so pleased him that he spoke with her. Then he looked back and saw that somebody was beckoning to his wife.

Chuang 19.30: In Lu a certain Shan Pao lived on a high cliff, drank only water, and did not try to make money as most people do. At the age of seventy he still had the complexion of a baby. Then, unfortunately, he met with a hungry tiger who killed and ate him. There was also a certain Chang Yi. Rich and poor alike flocked to him, but at the age of forty he died of a fever. Shan Pao looked after his internals, but a tiger ate his externals. Chang Yi took care of his externals, but illness attacked his internals.

liances? Therefore, if the deaf and blind right in the midst of concrete objects lend no credence to the thunder and the luminaries in high heaven, they will believe even less in things that are subtler than these. When ignorance befuddles the gods in a man's heart and mind, he will not believe that a Duke of Chou and a Confucius ever existed in antiquity; still less will he believe us when we tell him about gods and genii.

To be sure, life, death, beginning, and ending do form the grand framework, but there are differences and variations. What one man affirms, another will have reason to deny. In the myriads of changes and transformations of creation marvels may occur without limitation. What any individual thing seems to be, its activity may belie; the roots of a thing may be well balanced, but its branches may be deviant. We cannot treat all things the same way.

The majority of people claim that all that begins must also end, but one does not derive universal principles by lumping all the facts together and giving them all equal weight. It is said that in summer there is sure to be growth, but this is just when shepherd's-purse and wheat wither. It is said that in winter there is sure to be fading, yet it is the time when bamboos and thuyas flourish. It is said that beginnings must have endings, but heaven and earth never perish. It is said that all the living must die, but the tortoise and crane enjoy fullness of life. In midsummer it should be hot, but even summer weather is not without its cool days. Midwinter is rightly cold, yet in all its severity it does not lack intervals of warmth. Streams normally empty to the east, but there are some that rush to the north. Earth is quiescence in its highest form, but there are times when it trembles and things crash. Water is cool by nature, but there are also hot springs in Warm Valley. Fire should burn, but there exists the cold flame of Wormwood Hill (situated at sea). Heavy things sink, but in the sea to our south there is a mountain whose rocks float. Light things remain in suspension, but in

Tsang-k'o there is a stream in which feathers sink. Creation as a whole is not to be judged by one standard; this has been true throughout the ages.

Of all living things that have high intelligence, none surpasses man. One might well expect this creature who possesses such a noble nature to be of one uniform type, but — given their moral perfection and unenlightenment, perverseness and righteousness, beauty and ugliness, tallness and shortness, purity and impurity, chastity and prurience, poise and tenseness, sluggishness and alertness — men. differ in their preferences and in their sensual desires, just as heaven and earth or ice and glowing coals differ from one another. Why marvel that the genii are different and do not die as ordinary folk do?

If you claim that all breathing things follow one fixed norm, your thesis cannot be sustained, for the pheasant turns into a *shen* bivalve (see *Li ki*, part 6, "*Yüeh-ling*," and also HNT), the sparrow becomes a clam (*ibid.*), earth bugs assume wings, river frogs come to fly, oysters are changed into frogs(?), *hsing-ling* plants(?) become maggots, field mice become quail (*ibid.*), rotting grass turns into lightning bugs (*ibid.*), alligators become tigers, and snakes become dragons. If you claim that man, unlike other creatures, has an undeviating nature — that the destinies bestowed by August Heaven are not subject to vicissitudes — how can you account for instances where Niu Ai became a tiger, the old woman of Ch'u a tortoise, Hunchback a willow (*Chuang* 18.20), the girl of Ch'in a stone, the dead came back to life, males and females interchanged sex, Old P'eng enjoyed great longevity, but a baby son died prematurely? If such divergences exist, what limits can we set to them?

3b

If a genie nurtures his body with medicaments and prolongs his apportionment of life with special arts, illness will not arise from within him, nor will disease strike him from without. Though he attains everlasting vision and does not die, the body which he has long had undergoes no change.

There is nothing difficult about this provided one possesses the divine process. The shallow-minded, however, cling to popular beliefs and preserve the ordinary ways: They merely say that because they see no genii in their world it is not possible that such things exist. But what is so special about what our eyes have seen? Why should there be any limit to the number of marvelous things that exist between sky and earth, within the vastness of Unbounded? All our lives we have a sky over our heads but never know what is above it; to the end of our days we walk the earth without ever knowing what is below it. Our bodies are our very own, but we never come to understand how our hearts and wills become what they are. An allotment of life is ours, but we never understand how its actual measure is achieved. And this is even more true in the case of the more abstruse patterns governing gods and genii, and the dark mystery surrounding God and the natural life. Isn't it a sad spectacle to rely upon the surface perceptions of eyes and ears in judging the existence of the subtle and the marvelous?

Let us assume an intelligent individual of great ability who prefers to live quietly without official employment. He hides his lights and keeps his work under cover. He dispenses with falsity and avoids all drudgery for others. Clinging to his solid, native talent in an unsullied ambience, he *4a* leaves aside the petty pursuits of the crowd. Very rarely are the people of his day able to discern such a man, for they reason that a strong character, cannot be found cloaked in anonymity, and that gods will not dwell in a lowly body. So how can they possibly recognize the genie who pursues a vastly different path, considers riches and honors to be misfortunes, looks upon finery as so much filth, takes pomp and circumstance to be but dust, and thinks that all renown is as morning dew. He treads upon raging fire but is not scorched; he walks the dark waves with floating step. Beating his wings he moves through the limpid void, riding the clouds with the winds for his steeds; he peers upward and rises to the celestial pole or, peering downward, he comes to earth and nests in the K'un-lun mountains. How could men, who are but walking corpses, ever see them? If he chances in a playful mood to pass among men, he disguises his true self and conceals his extraordinary qualities, so that externally he resembles ordinary mortals. How is he to be known, even by those right at his side or just behind him? Genii can be recognized only if they have square eyes as did Chiao Hsien, ears rising from the top of their heads as did Ang Su, ride a dragon as did Ma-shih Huang, or drive a white crane like Wang Ch'iao; when they are scale-bodied or serpent-headed, carried in a golden chariot, or clothed in feathers. If no such sign is apparent, however, they can be recognized only by those with profound vision and heard only by those with penetrating hearing.

Since men of our day do not believe in them and are even highly critical of the idea that they exist, God's Men become angry and conceal themselves all the more. Further, just as the superior sort looks down upon the things that appeal to common people, so man in his highest form places no value on the things that ordinary folk esteem. Just as illustrious scholars and those of rare talent nurture their overwhelming vitality (M 2A.2) and take no pleasure in seeing inferior folk, so, all the more, why should the gods and genii yearn to have mere puppets (T 5) know that they exist? What do we expect, that we should think it odd never to have known them? From a distance of a hundred paces the eye cannot see too clearly; thus, when we wish to consider that which we see as existent, and that which we do not see as nonexistent, there will most certainly be a great many things that do not exist in the world! It is like saying that the sea is no deeper than the depth we can sound with a finger! Can an ephemeron judge the age of a great tortoise, or a hibiscus reckon that of the great *ch'un* tree?

Emperor Wen of the Wei (Ts'ao P'ei, A.D. 188–226) had read everything there was to read, and was extremely well-

4b

informed. He used to claim that there was nothing in creation with which he was unacquainted. He stated that a knife that would cut jade [abrasive-fed rotary steel knife?], or a cloth that could be cleansed in fire [asbestos], did not exist anywhere in the world. When the *Tien lun* (*Discussions on Our Institutions*) was compiled, his statement was cited. Before long, however, both of these things were brought to His Majesty, and, bemused, he had the *Discussions* suppressed. This instance may well serve to show that we can never be absolutely dogmatic about anything.

In his *Resolution of Doubts*, Ts'ao Chih [A.D. 192–232] states, "I used to say that the techniques of divine process are unquestionably baseless talk to entice the unenlightened. Yet when I watched my father (Ts'ao Ts'ao) put it to the test by setting apart Tso Tz'u and others and having them refrain from starches for almost a whole month — their complexions remained unchanged and their vitalities stayed normal, and they claimed they could continue their avoidance of normal foods for fifty years — how could I entertain doubts any longer? . . . He also had Kan Shih place a drug in the mouths of live fish and then cook them in boiling fat. Those without the drug cooked and were edible, but those which had been given the drug played around all day in the boiling fat as though they were in water. He also dusted mulberry leaves with a drug and fed them to silkworms, which were still not dormant in the tenth month. Furthermore he fed chicks and newborn puppies (4.13*b*9) on an age-arresting drug, and they grew no bigger. A white dog was fed on a nostrum for restoring hair color; after a hundred days, all its hair turned black. Thus I came to realize that we do not know everything about the things of this world, and we cannot allow mere opinions to decide questions. Personally, my sole regret is that I cannot abandon sensuous pleasures to devote all my heart and mind to a study of the divine process that leads to Fullness of Life."

These two Ts'aos, in their studies, had read every book

5a

that existed; in talent they were the most eminent of their day. Yet, that which they first claimed to be nonexistent later proved to exist. When they had come to know thoroughly the patterns of nature and life, they had their regrets. It is not surprising, therefore, that people inferior to those two do not believe in gods and genii.

Liu Hsiang [77–6 B.C.] was most erudite. He investigated the subtle and plumbed the extraordinary, and was conversant with the deep and the remote. In his thinking he was very clear regarding truth and falsehood; he made very sure whether a thing existed or not. In the *Biographies of Genii* compiled by him we find more than seventy individual genii mentioned. If no such activity as theirs existed; why should he invent it? How can we possibly see with our own eyes matters that occurred in high antiquity? In all these things we can rely only upon the writings in which they are passed down. What is recorded in *Biographies of Genii* certainly took place, but when a book does not originate from the Duke of Chou and did not pass through the hands of Confucius, people never trust it. By this reckoning, everything noted by the ancient historians would appear never to have happened! What could be unique about the problem of whether or not one certain book is reliable?

5b

The ordinary human being covets glory and profit. Ever mindful of renown and advantage, he presumes his own attitude to have been true also for the Ancients and no longer believes that there were once persons who shunned an imperial or royal crown, or disdained the honor of appointment as minister. They cannot believe in persons like Ch'ao fu, Hsü Yu, Lao–lai tzu, and Chuang Chou. Thus, to a still greater degree, how can we expect all men today to believe in gods and genii, which are far more difficult to know of than those heroes of old? The fact that most people claim that Liu Hsiang was not a sage and his book is not definitive, is cause for regret. My answer to them is that even if the recorders of Lu are not to be compared in virtue with heaven

and earth, still Confucius used their work to compile his
Annals; Ssu-ma Ch'ien [145–86 B.C.] is also not comparable
in brightness with the sun and moon, but Yang Hsiung
[53 B.C.–A.D. 18] affirms that he gives us a record of the facts.
So, why are the records of Liu Hsiang, a famous scholar of

6a   Han times and a worthy gentleman, to be rejected?

The people of our day do not believe that geniehood can
be studied and will not admit that life can be prolonged
simply because both the First Emperor of the Ch'in [259–
210 B.C.] and Emperor Wu of the Han [156–87 B.C.] failed in
their search for immortality, and because the endeavors of
Li Shao-chün and Luan Ta, magicians at the court of the
First Emperor, were ineffective. But this is the same as claiming that in antiquity there were no rich men like Fan Li and
I-tun because Ch'ien Lou and Yüan Hsien were so poor! Or
there were no beauties like Nan Wei and Hsi-shih because
Chung-li Ch'un and Su-liu were so ugly! Many who press
forward never arrive. Some crops are never harvested. Not
all merchants show a profit. Not every recourse to arms is
successful. So, to a still greater degree, why must all succeed
who undertake the difficult path to geniehood? Perhaps the
two monarchs and their two retainers were unsuccessful despite their searching because, although they began with
diligence, they turned lax toward the end. Or, perhaps they
did not find sufficiently enlightened teachers. How can such
evidence prove that no genii exist in the world (13.5*a*)?

When cultivating the best of divine processes in the search
for Fullness of Life, the secret lies in willpower, not in riches
or high position. If one is not of the right type, high position
and great wealth are serious incumbrances. Why? The
method in studying for geniehood consists of a true desire to

6b   attain calm and repose, to free oneself of covetousness, to see
and hear internally, and to be entranced and freed of
emotion. Emperors and kings, however, bear the weight of
the whole world on their shoulders; they regulate the count-
less details of administration. Their thoughts are harrassed by

thousands of schemes; their inner gods speed throughout the universe. A slightest error on their part, and the whole royal scheme of things declines. When their subjects go astray, they accept the blame. Potent wines trouble the harmony of their vital breaths; beautiful women hack at their very roots. The result is that their sperm is diminished, their thought processes weakened, and their calm and concentration destroyed. But I cannot discuss this in all its minute details. Suffice it to say that when mosquitoes bite our skin we cannot sit in peace; when swarms of lice attack we cannot sleep quietly. Surely a universal monarch is worse off still. How can emperors conceal their acuity, ration their breaths (12.1a11), undergo long rituals of purification, personally tend the furnace, rise with the dawn and go to sleep late in order to sublime the Eight Minerals (one list being cinnabar, realgar, laminar malachite, sulphur, mica, salt, saltpeter, and orpiment)? Emperor Wu of the Han enjoyed the longest reign because he derived some slight benefit from what he did to nourish his life. But gills of aid do not meet barrels of expense, just as an irrigation ditch could never carry away the water that leaks out of the sea at Wei-lü (Chuang 17.8) and prevents the sea from overflowing.

Methods leading to geniehood require calm, freedom of action, and obliviousness of our physical frames; but in the case of princes the bonging of huge bells and the thunderings of drums with their booming and rumbling upset their ethereal breaths and excite their hearts and minds. Innumerable arts and diversions kill his sperm and plug his ears. He travels fast in light vehicles, fishes the depths, and shoots *7a* birds on the wing.

Methods leading to geniehood, on the other hand, depend upon extending love to the things that creep and crawl, so that nothing which breathes may be harmed. In the case of princes there are bursts of anger and mass executions. After a single brandishing of his gilt halberd, after the ax of command is handed down for even a brief time, corpses lie prostrate over a thousand miles, blood flows in torrents, and beheadings go on and on in the market places.

Methods leading to geniehood call for avoiding the smell of animal flesh and for purification of the intestines by stopping the intake of starches; but in the case of princes, there is cooking and slicing of fat pork and slaughtering of living things of all sorts. The eight precious foods and the hundred mixed dishes are piled before them. Fried, simmered, and properly spiced, they add elegance to repletion. Methods leading to geniehood call for us to extend our love to the very frontiers of the universe and to view others as we do ourselves; but the prince absorbs the weak, attacks the ignorant, capitalizes on disorder, and spreads devastation. He opens new lands and extends frontiers. He destroys man's shrines. He herds the living and orders them into the valley of death. Their end is as forsaken wraiths in remote lands, bleached bones befouling the fields. On the Five Peaks he stations hosts with bloody blades; from the north gate of the palace hang Ferganese heads. In one instant, those buried alive and the slain captives amount to tens of thousands. Mounds of corpses pile up to the clouds; bleaching bones, thick as grass, form whole mountains and fill the valleys.

First Emperor of the Ch'in drove nine out of ten of his households to contemplate revolt. Emperor Wu of the Han made the whole world moan and reduced its population by half. While prayers were intoned for increase, the maledictions of the people brought decrease (Tso, Chao 20.6). The spirits of the dead, being capable of recognizing and rewarding virtue, surely took offense at these monarchs' meaningless offerings. With crowding vexations gnawing at their vitals, with men and ghosts matched in hating them, *7b* these two emperors had a hollow reputation for wanting geniehood, but they never experienced the reality of cultivating the divine process. They could not carry out completely even the superficial things of which they were aware, and they never did learn the truly marvelous and profound secrets. Further, they never found a man possessing the divine process, who could concoct the genie-drug on their behalf and administer it to them; so it is not surprising that they did not enjoy Fullness of Life.

I am only an ordinary person reduced to poverty. My home is as humble as that of Ssu-ma Hsiang-ju; my body knows the same pangs of hunger as that of the man noticed by Duke Hsüan when he halted under the leafy mulberry.[2] In winter, I suffer from the cold just like Jung Yi, who arrived after Lu's gates had been closed for the night;[3] in summer, I suffer from the full sun shining upon the small room prescribed by *The Rites*.[4] When I wish to travel far, I have neither boat nor vehicle at my disposal. When I plan some project, there is nobody to do the manual work. At home there are no silks and satins to delight the senses; outside, I have no opportunity to enjoy travel and sightseeing. Sweet and tasty things do not pass my mouth, nor do decorative colors pass before my eyes. Perfumes do not reach my nose, and my ears are not struck by music. All sorts of sorrows afflict my heart, and crowds of difficulties infest my home. In such conditions as these there is nothing to become attached to.

There are times when I obtain oral instructions for an important divine process or when I meet with an uncommon teacher, but even then I find myself clinging to my old wife and my little children; I still think lovingly of the hill where the fox and hare run in amity. Little by little the day of my demise draws nearer, and insensibly I grow older and weaken. Although knowing that Fullness of Life can be achieved, I am unable to undertake the work, for, even though I am concerned about the horrors of the popular practices about me, I cannot quit them. Why? Feelings of

8a

[2] *Tso tchouan*, S. Couvreur (1914), Vol. 1, p. 571.
[3] *Lü shih ch'un-ch'iu*, R. Wilhelm (Jena, 1928), 20.6a7, p. 351.
[4] *Li ki*, S. Couvreur (1913), Vol. 2, p. 606.

attachment and habit are involved, and it is never easy to realize the desire to break with common practice.

How much truer this was in the case of those two universal monarchs, whose amusements were of all types, and whose visitings were innumerable. Even if one had merely wished them to fast for a month or remain quiet for a few days, this would have been impossible. So, how could they possibly have banished all lascivious thought or rejected all the trappings of majesty? Wouldn't it be most unusual if they had managed to reject fine foods, neglect their desires, turn their backs on splendor, and go forth alone in search of the darkness and silence of divinity and geniehood? So, when we survey the list of those who attained geniehood in antiquity, we find that most of them were poor and in humble circumstances. They were not men of position and power. Further, Luan Ta had no profound knowledge. Hungering and thirsting after honor and position, and unabashedly accumulating wealth and presents, he huckstered false claims and madness to the imprudent, but forgot that calamity would be the price of failure. But is the dishonesty of one common, petty person sufficient witness to the nonexistence of genii in our world?

In olden days, Kou-chien's soldiers competed in walking on hot coals when he gave them an angry frog as a model of fierce courage. Duke Ling of Ch'u was fond of narrow waists; as a result many of his people died of hunger. Duke Huan of Ch'i had a craving for rare foods; so Yi Wu cooked his own son for him. The Lord of Sung approved of letting oneself grow thin in mourning (contrary to the rites), and the filial died of weakness in home after home. Whatever the master desires is always provided. Emperor Wu of the Han, by welcoming magicians and showing them excessive favor, encouraged such persons to indulge in false claims. If Luan Ta had possessed the divine process, how could he have been executed? For a man who possesses it looks upon high position as a cauldron of boiling water, upon the seals

8b

and ribbons of office as mourning garb, upon gold and jade as dirt or excrement, and upon painted halls as a paddock. Would such a man fawn on people and engage in meaningless talk to win glory for himself? A home with red pillars, innumerable gifts, a special seal of office, and the hand of a princess; wallowing in power and advantage, never attaining satiety, Luan Ta clearly did not possess the divine process.

We read as follows in Tung Chung-shu's *Biography of Li Shao-chün* [not extant]: "Li Shao-chün had a prescription for immortality but, his family being poor, he did not have the means to secure the necessary ingredients. He therefore presented himself to the authorities in order to acquire funds. Once the divine process had succeeded, he left." In *Notes on Activities at the Han Court* we read, "At the time when Li Shao-chün was on the point of leaving, Emperor Wu dreamed that he was ascending Mount Sung with him. When they were halfway up the mountain, an emissary mounted upon a dragon and holding a baton of authority descended from the clouds and said, 'T'ai-i (a god) requests the presence of Li Shao-chün.' When His Majesty awoke he told his attendants about it and suggested that Li Shao-chün would soon be abandoning him. A few days later, Li complained of illness and died. A long time later, His Majesty had the coffin opened, and it was found to contain only a gown and hat."

9a

The genii classics say that processors of the highest class raise their bodies into the void and are then designated Heavenly Genii. Those of the second class resort to the famous mountains and are designated Earth Genii. The third class sloughs off the body after death and is designated Corpse-freed Genii. It is clear that Li Shao-chün must have been a Corpse-freed. In more recent times (A.D. 23–220) Hsieh Yüan-i took Fei Ch'ang-fang away with him, leaving a bamboo effigy to be buried in his place. Processor Li I-ch'i was in P'i-hsien with two disciples, and when their families opened their coffins they found in each of the three a bamboo staff with red writing on it. All of these were Corpse-freed genii.

Formerly, Wang Mang quoted writings attributed to the Three Augusti and the Five Emperors to make his evil schemes palatable, but it would be inadmissible to argue from this that all scholars are usurping thieves. Through his playing of the lute, Ssu-ma Hsiang-ju stole the heart of the widow Cho Wen-chün, so that she ran away with him, but it would be inadmissible to conclude that musicians are the chief cause of immorality. It is inadmissible to curse the sowing done by God-farmer because some choke to death when eating. It is inadmissible to be angry with Firesticker for his fire-drilling because some burn to death. It is inadmissible to feel resentment for Yellow Emperor's invention of boats because some drown when they overturn. It is inadmissible to blame Tu K'ang's and Yi Ti's wine-making because some intoxicate themselves. Would you say, then, that it is admissible to claim no results for the pursuit of *9b* geniehood because Luan Ta was dishonest? This would be tantamount to saying that the heroes I-yin, Duke of Chou, and Ho Kuang had never existed because one had seen the scoundrels Chao Kao and Tung Cho in action. It would be similar to saying that there never were such filial paragons as Chang Po and Hsiao Chi, just because one had seen Shang-ch'en (who drove his father to suicide) or the parricide Mao-tun.

In the writings treating of gods and genii we find methods for summoning gods and denouncing the ghosts for their misdeeds. They also contain recipes for making people see ghosts. Ordinary people are unanimous in declaring them fictional. Some claim that there are no ghosts and gods in the world, while others claim that, even if they do exist, they can be neither summoned nor punished. Still others say that a man who sees ghosts is a shaman; a woman, a medium; but it is something in their natures, and not something one learns.

Both *Han History* and Ssu-ma Ch'ien's *Records* tell us that Emperor Wu gave Shao-weng, a man of Ch'i, the title Wen-ch'eng-chiang-chün. When His Majesty's favorite, Madame Li, died, Shao-weng caused him to see her as an apparition. He also caused His Majesty to see the Hearth God. This is clearly stated in the histories. Therefore, since there are techniques that can make a ghost manifest and also make it possible to see ghosts even when the inborn capacity to see them is lacking, we have the right to infer that all the other things are possible too.

Ghosts and gods frequently cause miraculous and strange things to occur among men. In our classics there is also much evidence regarding ghosts and gods. If then, in the light of all this evidence, people still do not believe that there are ghosts and gods in the world, why should they believe in genii, who live in high and distant places? The clear and the muddied waters flow in different streams, and once one has mounted to great heights one does not return to this world. But unless one possesses the divine process, how can the supernatural be experienced? The Confucianists and Mohists, knowing that such things could not be explained, have said nothing whatsoever about their existence; isn't it therefore to be expected that ordinary people do not believe in them? Such things can be known only to those capable of discerning truth, who have tried the recipes, secured the evidence, and thus found that they must exist. Such knowledge cannot be forced. Therefore, just because you do not see ghosts and gods and do not see genii, you have no right to say that there are no genii.

All men, wise or foolish, know that their bodies contain ethereal as well as gross breaths (18.4a3), and that when some of them quit the body, illness ensues; when they all leave him, a man dies. In the former case, the magicians have amulets for restraining them; in the latter case, *The Rites*

10a

(*I li*, 439) provide ceremonials for summoning them back.
These breaths are most intimately bound up with us, for
they are born when we are, but over a whole lifetime probably nobody actually hears or sees them. Would one conclude that they do not exist because they are neither seen nor
heard? Consider for a moment the ghost that returned a
kindness at Fu-shih (*Tso*, Hsüan 15), the ghost that evinced
the anger of T'ang the Victorious for Ch'i (LunH 21.10*a*),
Shen-sheng's ghost consorting and speaking with Hu Tu
(*Tso*, Hsi 10), the Marquis of Tu's repayment of the hatred
of King Hsüan of Chou (*Mo Ti* 39.2*a*), Master P'eng's assuming the form of a black boar (*Tso*, Chuang 8), Liu Ju-i's

10b   taking the shape of a blue dog (SC 9.4*a*5), Kuan Fu's ghost
beating T'ien Fen with a rattan switch (HS 52.5*b*8), Chuang
Tzu-i's ghost striking Prince Chien of Yen (*Mo Ti* 31.4*a*3),
the appearance of the god Ju-shou at Hsin (*Tso*, Chuang
32), Luan Hou's halting in a commoner's home, Su-chiang's
exposition of the divinatory texts, Hsiao-sun's composing of
an essay, Shen-chün speaking in Shang-lin Park (SC 12.1*b*),
and the god at Lo-yang serving the Wu court — these are
all matters dealing with ghosts and gods, documented in our
books; there are many more clear expositions of this sort.
So, if the ignorant still claim that they do not exist, how can
they believe in Fullness of Life, which is but rarely reported?
Hoping to compel their belief is like getting a gnat to carry
a mountain or like describing the sea to a hoptoad in a well.

Ordinary people who have never seen a dragon, *lin* unicorn, or *luan* or *feng* phoenixes say that such things do not
exist. They think that the Ancients invented these auspicious
signs so that rulers would exert themselves ceaselessly in the
hope that these rare auguries would appear. So, just imagine
what they will say when you would have them believe in
the existence of genii! The people of our day, because Liu
Hsiang was unsuccessful in the manufacture of gold, say that
he sought the unknowable and performed sorcery, and tried
to pass off figments of his imagination as truth; they claim

that his *Biographies of Genii* is wholly fictitious. Is this not sad? This is what is meant by the proverbs, "Reject a noctilucent gem a foot long because of a tiny crack," or "Lose a priceless sword because it has a defect the size of an ant's nose." Such was not the stuff of the jeweler Pien Ho's profound knowledge of jade nor of the swordsmith Feng-hu's recognition of the genuine. It was through such reasoning that Fan Li became melancholy and Hsieh Chu sighed so long (for they were perfectionists).

Accounts of the manufacture of gold are in the collections treating of gods and genii; Liu An [Prince of Huai-nan; died 122 B.C.] extracted them to compose his books *Huang-pao* and *Chen-chung*. Yet, even though the text exists, the essentials have been kept secret, and the text must be orally expounded as it is read. Only then can gold be made. Since the original names of many of the ingredients have been changed, the text is not to be taken literally.

Having been in charge of the case of Liu An, Liu Hsiang's father, Te, secured his writings, but they were not expounded to him by a teacher. Thus Liu Hsiang never understood the art of the divine process. When he happened to catch sight of these writings, he claimed that everything was contained in the written text itself; it is for this reason that he was unsuccessful in making gold. In composing his *Biographies of Genii* he condensed the writings of the Ch'in officer Juan Ts'ang and in some cases recorded his own personal observations. The content of the book is not imaginary.

Accounts of madmen and the ditties of children (believed to be portents) have been collected by our sages,[5] and there were times when they could not overlook the words of fuel-gatherers (*Poems* 254.3). But remember that we gather *feng* and *fei* plants, even though we may have no use for their lower parts.[6] Are we to say that our classics are not

[5] This could be a reference to Ana 18.5 and *Lieh tzu* 4.20.

[6] This is a quotation from *The Poems* 35.1. *Feng* and *fei* are not identifiable. The point, as in the previous sentence, is that the seemingly useless is not to be ignored.

applicable because we discover one percent of error in their wisdom ? Shall we say that the sun and moon, suspended in the sky, are not great luminaries because they have some-times been eclipsed ?

Some foreign country makes crystal cups that are actually the result of combining five types of ash. At present, in our southern coastal states,[7] many have acquired the method and make them, but when they use the word crystal for the sub-stance they make, people are quite unwilling to believe them. They claim that crystal is a substance found only in nature, like jade. And so, since gold also happens to be found in nature, why should people believe that there is a system for manufacturing it ? The ignorant do not believe that minium and white lead are the products of a transformation in lead, nor do they believe that the mule (called *lo* or *chü-hsü*) is born of a donkey and a mare, for they insist that each thing has a unique seed. So how can we expect such people to understand things still more difficult to comprehend ? It is normal for our world that when one has seen little, one marvels much. How very true ! Yet, though these matters are as evident as the sky itself, mankind hides beneath an overturned jar. How is it to recognize speech in its highest form ?

11b

---

[7] This includes what is now North Vietnam, Kwangtung, and Kwangsi.

3

Rejoinder to Popular Conceptions

Interlocutor: The existence of long-lived persons like Old P'eng is comparable to that of the pine and thuya among trees. It is something natural, hardly something attained through study.

Ko: Nobody in creation is cleverer than the human being. Possessed of the most accessible techniques, he can make all creation his servant; having attained the deepest, he can enjoy Fullness of Life and everlasting vision. Since he knows that the best medicines are potent for extending his years, he takes them in his search for geniehood. Knowing the great age attained by tortoises and cranes, he imitates their calisthenics so as to augment his own life span.

Notice that the branches and leaves of the pine and thuya are different from those of trees in general, and the bodies of tortoises and cranes are different from those of animals in general. In the case of Old P'eng, however, we are still dealing with mere men, not with creatures of a different species. It was through attaining the divine process that they enjoyed unique longevity, not through what they were by nature. Trees in general cannot choose to model themselves on the

53

pine and the thuya, and animals in general cannot imitate the tortoise and the crane; therefore they are short-lived. Man, however, possesses intelligence; if he can practice the same divine process as did Old P'eng; he can achieve the same results.

You claim that there are no genii in the world! Our wise predecessors have recorded almost a thousand individual genii, for all of whom not only their full names but also details of their deeds are given. These records are not imaginary. If you think that they were all specially endowed with extraordinary breaths, I would remind you that all their stories speak of learning from teachers and taking medicines. These individuals were not born with a knowledge of these things. If it is thought that the divine process cannot be acquired through study, I would remind you of bodily metamorphoses, sword swallowing, fire eating, disappearing at will, raising clouds and vapors, snake-charming, fish- and turtle-charming, instantaneous liquefaction of various minerals, melting of jade to syrup, reduction of gold to a paste, entering water without getting wet, walking on knife blades without being cut — more than 900 acts of thaumaturgy — all effective provided they are carried out according to directions. Why is it that geniehood alone is not believed possible?

The divine process leading to geniehood is achieved slowly and involves many taboos. It is not to be maintained without superhuman will and great energy. Some persons, inclined to be skeptical, give up halfway and then proclaim that the geniehood process and Fullness of Life simply cannot be achieved. On the other hand, the genii classics say:

> *Take the elixir and preserve Unity:*
> *With all heaven together end.*
> *Revert your sperm, breathe like fetus:*
> *Protract longevity peaklessly.*

These significant words refer to the perfection of the divine process.

Even Great Man here amongst us never turned against his own ideals and did nothing to shame his own shadow (the ever-present witness); he never deceived heaven nor went back on his word. And is this not truer still of God's Men of old? Why should they have created meaningless texts out of nothing to deceive future generations with matters that could certainly not be achieved? What would it have profited them? One who is not destined to these things is unwilling to believe in them. How can he be compelled to believe? 2a

Interlocutor: It might be that the longevity attributed to tortoises and cranes has no factual basis at all. Has anyone lived with those creatures from birth to death, so that he could know?

Ko: Once we have a first acquaintance with the essentials, what extends beyond the eight cardinal points seems to fit in the palm of our hand, and we seem to become contemporaries with men of a hundred generations back. They need not be inside our courtyards, or right within range of our vision, for us to know them. We read this in *★Yü ts'e chi*: "A tortoise a thousand years old is variegated. The two bones above its forehead rise like horns. It understands human speech. It floats on lily pads or lies at the foot of massed yarrow, and a white cloud always coils above it. A crane a thousand years old gives forth a cry at the proper times and can mount into trees, whereas one which has not yet attained a thousand years never perches in treetops. It is pure white in color, except for the crest, which is entirely red." Thus these animals can be recognized upon sight. Long-lived creatures, however, being very wise, conceal themselves deeply in secret, remote places and are seldom seen. 2b

In *★Yü ts'e chi* and *Ch'ang yü ching* these two creatures are not the only ones singled out for their longevity (17.2a1). It is said that thousand-year-old pines and thuyas have branches rising from all sides, while the top branches stop growing. Looked at from a distance, they resemble an inverted lid. In their tops live creatures; sometimes they resemble a blue buffalo, or a blue sheep (chamois), or a blue dog, or a blue human being; all of these are a thousand years old. Snakes also have an unlimited age. At eight hundred years the *mi*-monkey becomes a *yüan*-monkey, which after five hundred years more becomes a *kuo*-monkey. This last attains a further age of one thousand years. The hoptoad lives to three thousand, the unicorn to two thousand, the *t'eng-huang* horse and the *chi-kuang* animal to three thousand years. The thousand-year-old bird and the ten-thousand-year-old bird, with human faces and bird bodies, are known; their names correspond to their ages. The tiger and the deer-hare live to a thousand; and at five hundred years their coats turn white. When a bear is five hundred years old it can change into a fox. Wolves live to eight hundred, and at five hundred they can assume human shape. Rats live to three hundred, and on completing a hundred they turn white and with the aid of human mediums can foretell events. The one called *3a* Chung can tell good and bad luck for a whole year ahead, and what is happening a thousand miles away. This is the sort of thing contained in these two books, but of course I cannot reproduce it all.

However, the widely educated man knows the names of everything he meets; there are no principles in nature that can confuse the universally informed man. Why should it be necessary to be in constant association with tortoises and cranes in order to know about them? If one has no acquaintance with things, there will be plants and bushes in any garden and many birds and animals in any field or pond that one will not know, much less prodigies like the tortoise and crane.

The chapter on divination in *Shih chi* (128.3a1) reads: "When the men living between the Yangtze and the Hua are young, they place their beds on tortoises, and their families do not remove the beds until those boys have died of old age." Thus, these animals have lived at least fifty or sixty years, and, given that they can dispense this long with food or drink and still not die, it shows that they are far different from common creatures. Why should we doubt that they can last a thousand years? Isn't there good reason for the Genii Classics to suggest we imitate the breathing of the tortoise?

Ch'en Shih of Ying-ch'uan, also known as Chung-kung and Chief of T'ai-ch'iu, was a sincere scholar. In compiling his *Notes on Strange Things that I have Learned*, he says that a man of his district by the name of Chang Kuang-ting once fled his place when disaster struck. Having a daughter of four unable to walk or wade streams, whom he could not carry, he planned to abandon her. She would undoubtedly die of hunger, but he did not want her bones to lie uncovered. It happened that at the entrance to the village there was a large, old grave mound in the top of which had once been dug a hole. Attaching a rope to a large pot, he lowered his daughter into the tomb, where he left her with a few months' supply of dry food and drink and fled to await better times. Three years later he managed to return home and wished to gather up his daughter's bones for burial. When he went and looked, there was his daughter still sitting in the tomb. On seeing her parents, she recognized them and was very happy, but the parents at first were fearful that it was her ghost. Only when they had entered the tomb and approached her did they realize that she was not dead. When asked where she had procured food, she replied that when her supplies were first exhausted she became very hungry. On noticing a creature in the corner that stretched its neck and swallowed its breath, she tried doing the same thing, and gradually she became less and less hungry. She had continued to practice this every day. The clothes which had been left for her when her parents had departed were naturally still in the tomb, for, since she had not moved about, they were not worn out. Therefore she did not suffer from the cold. When her father sought the creature which she had mentioned, it

3b

proved to be a large tortoise. At first, on leaving the tomb and eating starches, her stomach hurt and she was nauseated, but after a while she became used to them. This proves that tortoises are in possession of a method leading to immortality; it constitutes evidence that when a processor imitates them he can live as long as they do.

Ch'en Shih and the author of *Shih chi* are not irresponsible story tellers. There are many crawling things and birds in the world, and since the Ancients mention only the tortoise and the crane, it is clear that they alone differ from their whole group. From a mere glance at this bit of evidence, my thesis can be established.

Interlocutor: Tortoises can hibernate in the earth and cranes can fly in the air, but man is unable to do either of these things even momentarily. How, then, can man imitate their longevity?

Ko: Many crawling things do hibernate, and the birds that fly are legion, but the only point under discussion in the case of tortoises and cranes is their longevity characterized by Fullness of Life. It is neither the hibernation nor the flying that causes their immortality. Therefore, God's Men merely ask us to study the method by which these animals extend their years through calisthenics and to model ourselves on their eschewing of starches through the consumption of breath, not to copy their hibernation and flying.

The man acquiring the divine process can stand on clouds and vapors, or swim in rivers and seas. The evidence for this is Hsiao Shih, who through his piping joined a phoenix flying in the air, and Ch'in Kao who rode a red carp into the depths of a stream. Why talk only of momentary hibernation or flying? Dragons, snakes, crocodiles, *ch'ih*-dragons, certain monkeys, hedgehogs, *t'o*-crocodiles, and termites all can pass the winter without eating, and are then sleeker than when they do eat. Nobody has been able to learn their method.

It is clear that in special areas many creatures far surpass

4a

4b

man; this is not only true for the tortoise and the crane. Accordingly, when weaving a net, Fu-hsi used spiders for his teachers. Shao-hao relied upon the nine quail to determine the seasons. Yellow Emperor awaited the cry of the phoenix in order to tune the pitch pipes. Yao observed the *ming-chieh* plant in order to know the months. The *chung-kuei* animal knows the past; the *kan-ch'üeh* knows the future. The silverfish can tell when water will be scarce; the ephemeron knows where springs lie hidden. A white wolf knew when the Yin dynasty was to flourish; a phoenix bird foresaw the rise of the Chou. Therefore, there is no reason to be surprised that the tortoise and the crane have a special understanding of calisthenics and diet. Further, in the Genii Classics there are several hundred items bearing on the divine process for Fullness of Life, which differ in speed and complexity. Everybody need not model himself precisely on the tortoise and crane. Gentlemen of the highest type rise in thought to God (the Spontaneous and the Mystery), but through the purely nearsighted interests of the ordinary man it is difficult to attain the farsightedness of divinity and geniehood.

Interlocutor: We know of no modern system for enjoying Fullness of Life. Why were the Ancients the only ones to know about this?

Ko: This would seem to be chatter from the ignorant; it is not the point of view of the wise. In divining the mysterious actions of heaven and measuring the varying motions of sun, moon, and the five planets, we discuss their trespasses in the realms of the constellations in order to determine prosperity or decline for the future. We look upward for signs in the clouds; we bend down to determine the good or evil forecast by the hexagrams and the cracks in the tortoise shell. We manipulate the Three Marvels to establish whether it is better for the army to march or to remain in camp; we study the nine tallies to learn the areas of good or bad fortune. By one multiplication or division we examine

5a

the state of the ghosts and gods. We blend the six emotions (joy, anger, grief, fear, love, and hatred) in order to probe the good or evil of fortuitous situations. For such pursuits it is possible to study the origins and seek out the organizing principles, but ordinary talents and common mortals are still unable to unlock their secret order, and simple, inexpert persons — wasting their keenness on garbage — cannot fathom completely their innermost subtleties.

Remember that mortise and tenon may be coarse work, but there are mysterious, untransmittable touches to the art of the wheelwright, and in the humble art of gathering grass-hoppers there is a divinely inspired dexterity even in the hunchback.[1] The practitioners of these arts work with the greatest of skills; so you can see how enormously far it is from easy to search out the roots and branches of the divine process leading to divinity and geniehood, where the effect is so deep-reaching.

People such as Ch'ih-sung tzu and Wang Ch'iao became genii, but even they did not necessarily fathom how they did it. How then can the man in the street ever expect to understand it? Since, however, it is meet to study such questions, the Ancients handed them down in records so that they could be transmitted to the discerning. If anyone understands these arts in his heart and is attracted to them, he may practice them in all faith. But those who entertain doubts about such things are of course not destined for such activity. There is no point in asking why the Ancients were the only ones to know about these things, while we are the ones who remain ignorant about them.

5b

I know in this very present that geniehood is obtainable. I personally can discontinue the use of starches and refrain from eating normal human foods. I aver that mercury can be distilled, and that gold and silver can be manufactured. What you object to is that despite my search for the under-lying logic of these things, I never actually got full knowl-

[1] *Chuang* 19.15; *Lieh* 2.16.

edge of it. And my reply to you is this: If the people of our day were to call that which they can conceive existent, and that which they cannot conceive nonexistent, then very little would be transpiring in this world of ours.

Therefore, when Lao Tan says that a cat's (or weasel's) head [a type of pea] can be used to cure abscesses [spelled with the word for rat] and "woodpeckers" [?a type of bean] can be used to prevent cavities in teeth, we can understand that here like is being used against like. But as for crabs affecting (the setting of) lacquer or hempseed (oil) spoiling wine, these are matters for which there is no categorical explanation. How can we ever rationally understand the profusion of thousands upon thousands of different things! Suppose you contract a serious illness and need the help of a potent medicine but will not take it without first knowing what (the patrons of medicine) Shen-nung or Ch'i-po had in mind when they used this particular herb to treat this specific illness! You would justifiably be called foolish.

Interlocutor: Life and death are predetermined by fate and their duration is normally fixed. Life is not something that any medicine can shorten or lengthen. A finger that has been cut off cannot be joined on again and expected to continue growing. Blood from a wound, though swallowed, is of no benefit. Therefore, it is most inappropriate to approve of taking such nonhuman substances as pine or thuya (seeds) to protract the brief span of life.

6a

Ko: According to your argument, a thing is beneficial only if it belongs to the same category as that which is treated. If that is so, since they originally belonged to the same body and not to some different species, why cannot the lost finger be put back again, and why may blood that has been shed not be taken as a medicine? As a matter of fact, I have often seen people graft on a lost finger with "Snake-jaw salve"(?), or use a mulberry sprout to replace a chicken's or duck's foot. Benefit from things of a different category, therefore, is not to be denied. If we followed your suggestion and mistrusted things of a different type, we would be obliged to crush flesh and smelt bone to prepare a medicine for wounds, or to fry skin and roast hair to treat baldness. Water and soil are not of the same substance as the various plants; yet the latter rely upon them for growth. The grains are not of the same species as living men; yet living men need them in order to stay alive. Fat is not to be classed with fire, nor water with fish, yet when there is no more fat the fire dies, and when there is no more water, fish perish. Cut down a tree, and the fungus dries up; mow down the grass, and the dodder perishes. If the river crabs did not return to the river, the *ch'i*-molluscs would perish (for they feed upon parasites that infest the crabs); if the mulberry trees were cut down, the silkworms' grubs would die. By reiteration of examples the point is established.

6b When gold and jade are inserted in their nine orifices, corpses do not decay. When salt and brine are absorbed into flesh and marrow, dried meats do not spoil. Therefore, when we take into ourselves things fit to increase the life in our bodies, why should we marvel that they produce Fullness of Life?

Interlocutor: The recipes for acquiring divinity or genie-hood are specious; they are certainly unreliable fabrications of wondermongers. They certainly never came from the hands of Yellow Emperor or Lao Tan, nor were they ever seen by Ch'ih-sung tzu or Wang Ch'iao.

Ko: According to your argument, they would appear inefficacious, but even the most minor of them is not without effect. I have frequently seen people obtain water from the moon at night by means of a speculum, and fire from the sun in the morning by use of a burning-mirror. I have seen people conceal themselves to the point of complete disappearance, or change their appearance so that they no longer seem human. I have seen them knot a kerchief, throw it to the ground, and produce a hopping hare. I have seen them sew together a red belt and thereby produce a wriggling snake. I have seen people make melons and fruit ripen in an instant, or dragons and fish come and go in a basin. All of these things occurred just as it was said they would.

According to *Han shu* (25A.10a12), when Luan Ta was first presented to Emperor Wu, he was tested by means of his "chessmen", which automatically fought one another. And *Hou Han shu*, in turn, records that Wei Shang could disappear at will and Chang K'ai could raise clouds and mists. All of these are records made by first-class chroniclers, and are credible evidence. Thus, although it is true that these recipes are given in books devoted to gods and genii, it can be accepted that they are not fabrications. If such minor things are attested, why then should it not be equally true that the divine process produces Fullness of Life?

7a

Interlocutor: If people could learn how to become gods and genii — suddenly ascending into the clouds, or avoiding common practice and quitting the world — when they no longer perform the ceremony of offering food, won't the ghosts of their forebears, which are conscious, go hungry?

Ko: I remember having been taught that it is the height of filial piety to keep the body intact. How much more then is it filial to acquire the divine process leading to geniehood along with full enjoyment of life and everlasting vision! Would not our being coeval with all nature be far superior to merely returning intact that which we have received whole? Let us say that we could mount into the air and tread upon the light, using clouds for our floor and the rainbow for the roof of our vehicle. We could taste dews fallen from the roseate clouds of morning and imbibe the pure essences of heaven and earth. Our drink would be jade juice and gold juice; our food, mushrooms of kingfisher blue and fruit of vermilion red; our dwellings, halls of beautiful stone and rooms of pink gems; our travels, fancy free in Paradise (15.10b10). Since the ghosts of our forebears are conscious of all this, they would share in our glory, either aiding the Five Emperors, or overseeing the various divine powers. They would attain their proper positions without any beseeching; for food they would chew upon flowers and rarities; in exercising their influence they would superintend Mount Lo-Feng (abode of the spirits); for prestige their cries would resound among the beams and pillars of the palace. If they truly follow this path, marvelous as it is, nobody would be letting them go hungry.

The most eminent by far of those with the divine process was Lao Tan (Po-yang). He had a son named Tsung, who became a general in Wei and was endowed with a fief, for services rendered, at Tuan-kan. It may be concluded, therefore, that those who study geniehood today can all, quite naturally, have sons and younger brothers who would carry on the family sacrificial rites. Why should they be interrupted?

Interlocutor: When those who wish to acquire the divine process have completed all the breathing exercises and followed the diets in all their essentials, with covered ears they will hear things a thousand miles away; with closed eyes they will see what is to come. Sometimes, abandoning a fine team of four, they harness up dragons. Other times, quitting the gods' country [China], they make their homes in P'eng-lai or Ying-chou, islands inhabited by genii. Still other times, they gradually return to normal living and move free as birds among men, rather than going to heaven and leaving no trace of themselves on earth. Since they all started by preferring the same thing, namely geniehood, why do they react differently afterward?

Ko: I learned from my late teacher that some genii mount to heaven and others remain here on earth. What matters is that they have all achieved Fullness of Life; they simply make their abodes wherever they prefer. According to the prescription to be followed when taking reverted cinnabar or Potable Gold only a half dose is taken and the rest put aside if one wishes to remain here in this world. Later, if one then desires to go to heaven, the remainder of the dose is taken. Once one's immortality has been confirmed, one is never again concerned about the fleeting of time. If one should return temporarily to wander on earth or in the famous mountains, what would there be to concern oneself about? Old P'eng claimed that in heaven there were so many important gods holding offices of high honor that the newer genii must hold the meaner positions. They must per- *8a* form all sorts of services, and their lot is harder than before. He saw no point in his striving persistently to go to heaven, so he remained among men for eight hundred years and more.

My teacher also said that those who attained geniehood of old would sometimes sprout feathers and wings, and be transformed into flying creatures. Having lost the fundamental characteristics of a human being, they acquired a form proper to a different species. This is like the natural metamorphosis of the sparrow into the clam, or that of the pheasant into the *shen* bivalve. It is not man's way. Man's way is to eat rich foods and wear light, warm clothing; to consort with women and occupy official rank; to remain keen of sight and hearing and strong of physique; to maintain a good complexion and not to decline in old age; to protract one's years and attain everlasting vision; to stay or go at will. To be immune from cold, heat, wind, and wet; invulnerable to ghosts, gods, and demons; unaffected by weapons and poisons; and never involved in the toils of grief, joy, slander, or praise: these are honorable. To turn one's back upon wife and children and make one's abode in the mountains or marshes, uncaringly to reject basic human usage and, clodlike, to become a companion of trees and rocks, is hardly to be encouraged.

Long ago, Master An-ch'i, Lord Ning of Lung-mei, Lord Hsiu-yang, and Yin Ch'ang-sheng took half doses of Potable Gold. They remained in the world for almost a thousand years, and only then did they leave it. To put it plainly, those who seek Fullness of Life merely do not wish to relinquish the objects of their current desires. Fundamentally, they are not yet overcome with any yearning to mount into the void, nor are they convinced that flying is always superior to being earthbound. If, by some good fortune, they can become immortal and yet go on living at home, why should they seek to mount speedily into heaven? When those who have achieved geniehood can shed their concern with the problems of livelihood, they have entered another phase altogether. This is what Old P'eng meant when he described them as still attached to human affairs.

Interlocutor: Those engaged in the divine process must first acquire merit. Is it not so?

Ko: Yes. In Chapter 2 of *Yü ch'ien ching* we read, "Doing good stands in first place; eschewing one's faults comes next. Followers of the divine process feel that saving people in trouble so that they can avoid disaster, and protecting others from illness so that they will not die before their times, are good acts of the highest class. Those wishing to seek geniehood should think of loyalty, filial piety, friendliness, obedience, the human ideal, and trustworthiness as basic. If they do not perform meritorious actions but solely pursue the esoteric techniques, they will never attain Fullness of Life. For the man who commits a wrong of great enormity, the Director of Fates will deduct a period of three hundred days (6.4*b*9); for lesser wrongs, a reckoning of three days. Deductions vary according to the degree of the transgression. In receiving his destiny each man is assigned a basic longevity. If this is large, it is not used up despite many deductions; so death arrives slowly. But if the assigned quantity is small and the wrongs are many, the deductions rapidly exhaust it and death arrives early."

Yü ch'ien ching says further, "Those wishing to become earth genii must do three hundred consecutive good deeds; those wishing to be heavenly genii must acquire twelve hundred. If, after acquiring 1199, one commits a single bad deed, all the ones previously acquired are lost, and one must begin anew." Therefore there is no question of the good merely outweighing the evil. Even though no wrong has been committed, if one merely speaks of one's own deeds and demands a reward for alms, the merit from the one vaunted deed will be lost immediately; but the whole series of merits will not be lost. It further says, "No benefit is to be derived from taking geniehood medicine before the full quota of merits has been acquired." If the medicine is not taken but the good deeds are performed, geniehood may not be acquired, but one can at least avoid the misfortune of sudden death. Personally, I am much inclined to suspect that Old P'eng and others like him were prevented from mounting to heaven because their full measure of merits had not yet been accumulated.

4

Gold and Cinnabar

THE VOLUMES I have studied as I examined writings on the nurturing of life and collected recipes for acquiring everlasting vision must number in the thousands; yet there was not one amongst them that did not insist that reverted cinnabar and Potable Gold were the things of highest importance. These two, it seems, mark the peak of the divine process leading to geniehood. If taking them does not make one a genie, then genii have never existed.

At the time when North China was being pillaged and all were fleeing in every possible direction, I was wandering through our country from the valley of the Huai south to Kuang-tung and Kuang-hsi and met several hundred migrant, worldly processors. Sometimes their reputations were known to me as being higher than the clouds and sun. As a group, however, they resembled each other in the depth and extent of knowledge, in which one was no better than the next. Though each of them owned a few dozen scrolls, they were in no case able fully to expound them; they had merely made copies of them so they could own them. Sometimes one of them would know how to circulate the breaths, dispense with starches, or take medical herbs. All the books *1b* of recipes they had read about the same. Not one of these

68

individuals had failed to possess the ★*Tao chi ching* (Book of Cosmic Activity, 19.4*b*3) nor to consider it the profoundest of secrets. They claimed that it had been composed by Governor Hsi, but I told them that it had been composed by General Wang T'u during the period A.D. 220–265 and that it did not come from the Ancients. Wang T'u knew nothing whatever about the grand medicines but merely wished to attain geniehood at home by circulating the breaths. Further, by composing this *Tao chi* and claiming that the divine process in its entirety was present there he was utterly deceiving others.

When I asked these processors about divine cinnabar and Potable Gold and also about methods for evoking the gods of heaven and the spirits of earth as given in ★*San huang nei wen*, not a soul among them knew a thing about them. Nevertheless the majority of them, boasting and exalting themselves, deceived others by claiming a great longevity and saying that they had once consorted with genii. With very few of them, however, was it possible to discuss the finer points seriously. Some of them had heard something about gold and cinnabar, but they did not believe that such things still existed. In fact they were unanimous in claiming that only the genii of antiquity knew about them. Some of them had sketchy accounts of the prescriptions, but they had not secured the true canons. Some had fragmentary prescriptions for elixirs and carelessly claimed that these contained everything pertaining to this method.

In the old days, while Tso Tz'u [A.D. 200] was giving careful thought to these matters in the T'ien-chu mountains [E. Shantung], a god gave him genii classics detailing both gold and cinnabar. At that moment the disturbances occurred that terminated the Han Dynasty [A.D. 220], and thus there was no opportunity to prepare them. Then, fleeing his mountain retreat, he crossed to South China, where it was his intention to settle in a famous mountain and carry out the divine process. There my paternal uncle (Ko Hsüan),

2a

known as the Genie, received the texts from Tso Tz'u. In all, he received *T'ai ch'ing tan ching* (4.7*a*9) in three scrolls, *Chiu ting tan ching* (Nine-crucibles cinnabars; 4.5*a*7) in one scroll, and *Chin i ching* (4.14*a*3) in one scroll. My teacher, Cheng Yin, was my uncle's disciple. He received these texts from my uncle, but, being of a poor family, lacked means to purchase the ingredients. I in turn was his pupil, doing the sprinkling and sweeping, for a long time, and in the Ma-chi mountains [NE Kiangsi] I received the scrolls from him under the seal of an oath at an altar, where I also received the secret directions, which may never be written down. Previously, these writings had not existed in South China. They derive from Tso Tz'u, who transmitted them to my uncle. The latter transmitted them to Master Cheng, who transmitted them to me. Therefore, while other processors know nothing about them, I have had them for over twenty years, but, my resources not being abundant, I have been unable to prepare them; for this I can feel only deep regret. On the other hand, those who have accumulated gold in their coffers and gathered mountains of cash do not know that these methods for attaining immortality exist, and even though they were told about them, not one of them in thousands would believe it. Nothing can be done about this situation.

After a highly sugared drink, one realizes how insipid marshmallows are; after seeing the K'un-luns, one feels how *2b* paltry the hills are. In the same way, having examined the divine process for preparing gold and cinnabar, a man can no longer look at paltry little prescription books. The great medicine, however, being hard to concoct satisfactorily, one is obliged to deal with lesser ones merely to maintain one-self. And yet, while the taking of gallons of other medicines can be to some extent beneficial, they can by no means bring one to Fullness of Life. Accordingly, Lao Tan's oral directions say that you will be troubling yourself for nothing unless you obtain reverted cinnabar or Potable Gold.

Even the grains are effective for keeping people alive. As long as a man gets them, he lives; when they are cut off, he dies. Think then what the situation is in regard to the highest quality of divine medicine! Wouldn't its benefit to man be thousands of times greater than that of the grains? Gold and cinnabar preparations are such that the longer they are heated the more marvelous are the changes they undergo. Even after a hundred firings, gold does not melt away, nor does it decay, no matter how long it is buried. By taking these two substances we refine our bodies, so that we neither grow old nor die. I suggest that this seeking of external substances to fortify ourselves may well be compared with a fire that does not die as long as the fuel maintains it, or with feet smeared with verdigris so they will not decay in water because the strength of the copper serves to protect the underlying flesh. On entering the body, however, gold and cinnabar permeate the blood and breath circulatory systems; it is not a case of mere external help, such as verdigris provides.

In our world hardly anyone believes in this highest of the divine processes. In the unlikely case that some man interested in strange things (14.5*b*8) comes along, he fails to become aware of these methods. If he does not find an enlightened teacher, there is no way of learning that the world possesses such a marvel. Therefore I am going to compile a digest on gold and cinnabar preparations as an inducement to future like-minded seekers after truth. May they diligently seek for the divine process and in so doing refrain from following inferior recipes and claiming that those are good enough to lead to geniehood! Those who do not find a teacher must soothe their minds with undying hope.

If a man wishes to encounter a revelation of the divine process, he must be aware that he will be emerging from the mire to float on a vast ocean; that he will be turning his back on lightning bugs and torches to face the sun and moon. For only on hearing thunder and lightning does one realize the

3a

weakness of signal drums; on seeing a whale, one realizes the minuteness of the minnow.

If, without first having been accepted by a teacher, one expected through mere cleverness to mount to heaven by using some cheap medicine, would that not be the same as spurring a lame donkey in pursuit of a strong wind, or crossing a mighty river by poling a reed boat? There are many minor recipes for edible cinnabar, which vary in effect because the skill with which they are prepared varies. Despite such variations, since the number of cyclical transformations is insufficient, they are like wine that has been fermented once; it cannot be compared with the pure, clear wine that has been fermented nine times.

3b

It is a fact, however, that the least of the minor cinnabars is far superior to the best of herbs. When roasted, all herbs turn to ashes, but cinnabar produces mercury, which after a number of successive transformations reverts to cinnabar. It is far superior to herbs. That is the reason it can produce Fullness of Life in people. The gods and genii alone perceive this principle. How infinitely different are they from the man on the street! Knowing little, ordinary people marvel much. Some of them do not know that mercury is a derivative of cinnabar. When we tell them about it, they will not believe it. They reply that since cinnabar is basically a red substance, how could it ever become a white substance like mercury! They also say that cinnabar is only stone, and since the roasting of stones produces at the best ash or lime, why should cinnabar be the only one to act as we claim it does? Since they cannot understand such a simple matter as this, isn't it to be expected that they guffaw on hearing about the divine process leading to geniehood?

Mindful of educable persons in times to come, God's Men of antiquity derived detailed prescriptions and methods in the hope that these would enable such persons to escape the misfortune of death; theirs may be called statements of the highest order. However, ordinary people, devoid of true faith, declare these writings lacking in substance. If this were true, how would one account for the fact that the nine transformations take place in a certain number of days exactly as the recipes prescribe? It is not for ordinary minds *4a* to try to find how God's Men came to know about these things.

Personally, from my youth I have been fond of prescriptions and recipes and went about on foot, a pack on my back, to make inquiries about them, undaunted by danger or distance. Every bit of strange information delighted me, and it did not worry me to be the butt of slander and ridicule, knowing as I did that the future held in store something far better than the present. I therefore compose this book solely to inform connoisseurs. Would I be so foolish as to glorify marvels and exalt unsubstantial talk with the purpose of making my book popular and winning the crowd over? The sun in all its glory cannot make dead wood blossom, and even the highest wisdom cannot convert the lowest stupidity. Writings are transmitted for the sake of those who will understand them; facts take on value in the eyes of the perceptive. When a peasant acquires a ceremonial red bow, he uses it to hunt birds; when a southern barbarian acquires a ceremonial gown, he uses it to bundle up faggots! The ignorant cannot be coerced into wisdom.

The uninitiated may eat their fill from dawn to dusk, but this is no guarantee that they have the diligence to study the doctrines of the Mohists and Confucianists or to fulfill the prerequisites of increased virtue. They merely give free rein to their fancy to while away their days. Their projects aim for either fame or profit. Some of them bustle about in the region of the capital, while others become addicted to the pleasures of food and drink. Some waste their time at music in the company of courtesans or debauch themselves with finery. Others practice archery, to the detriment of their sinews and bones. Still others waste their days at back- *4b* gammon. When talk turns to things of the highest order, they act as though drunk; the sight of a book about the divine process puts them to sleep. They make no attempt to keep their bodies in repair, and they would rather die than express curiosity about methods for nurturing life. It is by their own free will that such persons hack away at life, fry and roast it, torment and emaciate it, and press it dry. On the other hand, the man who has the divine process treasures what he knows as a secret. Since he has nothing to ask of others, why should he make any great efforts to tell them about the divine process?

It is common for people to argue that if Fullness of Life were possible, the rich and noble of antiquity would have achieved it, the fact that they did not do so is sufficient proof that there is no such process. Such people do not realize that the rich and noble of the past, like those of our own day, all disbelieved, and none sought the process; only their desire for things right under their own noses made them anxious. How could such as they ever have obtained the divine process?

Even if you cannot believe wholeheartedly that life can be protracted and geniehood attained, what have you to lose by trying it? The least success would extend your life by two or three hundred years; wouldn't that be preferable to the premature death experienced by the ordinary man? There are thousands upon thousands of activities in the world, but the techniques pertaining to the divine process are much harder to understand than any of the others. How is one with a mediocre heart and mind to decide that there *5a* is no such thing as the divine process leading to Fullness of Life? If you reason that it does not exist simply because the uninitiated do not believe in it, just ask yourself how many wise men there are in our world. And today, why must the person entertaining the idea of the divine process and devoting himself to seeking it be immediately considered the acme of stupidity and inferior to the rest of the world? Some who are thinking about seeking Fullness of Life fear that they will be ridiculed and thought ignorant if they turn out to be unsuccessful. If, however, in the very unlikely case that common opinion should be wrong, and it should turn out that there is after all a divine process leading to immortality, wouldn't they be laughed at by those who have succeeded? There are things which even the sun and moon cannot illumine completely; why should common opinion merit our entire trust?

We read in *Huang ti chiu ting shen tan ching* (Nine-crucible cinnabars) that Yellow Emperor rose into the sky and became a genie after taking this elixir. It adds that by merely doing the breathing exercises and calisthenics and taking herbal medicines one may extend one's years but cannot prevent ultimate death. Taking the divine elixir, however, will produce an interminable longevity and make one coeval with sky and earth; it lets one travel up and down in Paradise, riding clouds or driving dragons. Yellow Emperor transmitted this divine process to Hsüan tzu with a warning: "This is a highly essential divine process and must be transmitted only to those of the highest caliber. Although an improper person offer jewels piled up mountain-high, you are not to divulge it."

5b

He who receives it must throw a golden human statuette (9 oz.) and a golden fish (3 oz.) into an eastward-flowing stream as a pledge and take an oath by smearing his lips with blood of a victim (white chicken). No person who lacks the constitution of a god or genie may observe the process. The preparation should be carried out at an uninhabited place on a famous mountain. You shall have no more than three companions. Previously, you shall have undergone rites of purification for one hundred days, and washed your body and hair in fragrance, to attain a state of cleanliness. Do not approach anything that soils, nor associate with common people. Let no disbelievers know of your plans, for if they blaspheme the divine medicine, successful preparation will be prevented. Once it has been successfully consummated, you and your whole household, not just you alone, will become genii.

The uninitiated do not mix the divine elixirs, but they have great faith in herbal medicines — although they are subject to decay when buried; to softening when cooked; and to scorching when roasted. Since these substances cannot even maintain themselves, how can they give life to others? The nine elixirs are indispensable for Fullness of Life, but they are not something that any random person should be allowed to observe or hear of. The masses, in their frantic creeping about, thirst only after riches and honors. They may well be called walking corpses.

During the mixing, religious offerings are also required; for these one chapter of illustrations and directions exists.

The first cinnabar is known as *Flowers of Cinnabar*. It is begun by preparing some "tin oxide" (a preparation using tin and mercury [TT 884.1.3*b*], used to coat the crucibles inside and out after the Six-One lute has been applied [879.1.15*b*]). From several dozen pounds each of realgar solution, kalinite solution (TT 929.1*a–b*),[1] Turkestan salt, lake salt, arsenolite, oyster shells, red bole, soapstone, and white lead, prepare Six-One cement (TT 884.7.5*a*), with which to cover both clay crucibles (TT 884.7.4*b*) inside and out. The crucibles are then dried slowly in the sun for ten days (TT 879.1.15*a*). The cinnabar (or elixir) will be ready after being fired for thirty-six days, and if you take it for seven days you will become a genie.

6a

If a pill is made of this cinnabar, by mixing it with human feces(?) and then placed in a raging fire, it will turn to gold in a moment or two. Gold can also be produced by mixing 240 scruples of it with one hundred pounds of mercury and firing it. If the gold forms, we know the medicine is done.

---

[1] The Chinese alchemists prepared solutions of a large number of minerals, usually by dissolving them in weak nitric acid made from niter and vinegar, this solvent being called *hua ch'ih* ("flower trough"). One of their manuals has been ably translated by Ts'ao T'ien-ch'in, Ho Ping-yü, and Joseph Needham in *Ambix* 7(1959). 122–155 [N. Sivin].

If it does not form, reseal the medicine and heat for another thirty-six days. This never fails.

The second is called *Divine Cinnabar* or *Divine Amulet* (15.10*a*6). Take it for one hundred days and you will be a genie. To cross streams or pass through fire, smear the soles of your feet with it and you will be able to walk on water. After taking only three spatulas of it you will see that the Three Corpses and the Nine Worms in your body (6.4*b*–7*a*) will disappear, and all your illnesses will be cured.

The third is called *Divine Cinnabar*. Take a spatula of it for one hundred days and you will be a genie. It will also confer immortality if given to livestock. It can also ward off all weapons. If you take it for one hundred days, genii and fairies as well as the ghosts and gods of the streams and mountains, will come in the guise of human beings to serve you.

6b

The fourth is called *Reverted Cinnabar*. Take a spatula of it for one hundred days and you will be a genie. Vermilion birds and Phoenixes will soar and hover above you, and fairies will come to your side. If one spatula of it is mixed with one pound of mercury and fired, it will immediately turn into gold. If your coins and goods are smeared with it, they will all return to you the very same day they are traded. If it is used to draw signs above anyone's eyes, ghosts of all sorts will flee from them.

The fifth is called *Gustatory*. After you take it for thirty days you will be a genie, ghosts and gods become your servants, and fairies appear in your presence.

The sixth is called *Refined*. After taking it for ten days you will be a genie. When mixed and fired with mercury, it too turns to gold.

The seventh is called *Tender*. After taking a spatula of it for one hundred days, one becomes a genie. If it is taken mixed with raspberry juice, men of ninety can beget children. Mixed with lead and fired, it becomes gold.

7a

The eighth is called *Fixed*. On the very day you take it

you become a genie. When you hold a piece of it slightly larger than a jujube seed in your hand, every sort of ghost will flee. If it is used for writing over a doorway, no evil powers will dare approach it; thieves, bandits, tigers, and wolves will be put to flight.

The ninth is called *Cold*. After taking a spatula of it for one hundred days you are a genie, and fairy children will become your servants. You will fly and levitate without need of wings.

By acquiring any one of these nine you will become a genie; there is no need to prepare all nine. Which one is prepared depends entirely on one's preference. If you wish to mount to heaven after taking any one of them, you will go. If you wish to remain a while among men, you will be able to leave and enter anywhere, no matter what the barriers. Nothing will be able to harm you.

Translator's note: Since in composing the above résumé Ko Hung reports nothing about the actual preparation of any of the nine cinnabars, I translate here what TT 884.1.4*a*–5*b* says about the first: *Recipe.* Use one, two, or ten pounds of pure cinnabar, the amount depending upon the wealth of the candidate. Place the cinnabar in a crucible (which is placed mouth-to-mouth with another crucible). Seal the joint hermetically with Six-One lute. Examine it carefully to see that there is no crack even as fine as a hair, for otherwise all the medicine will evaporate and its essence be lost. In such a case no benefit can be derived from taking the residue. When the sealing has been completed, dry it for some ten days before using the reaction vessel.

First, warm the vessel for nine days and nights with a fire of dried horse manure kept five inches from it; then move the fire closer for another nine days and nine nights. After this, surround the bottom half of the vessel with fire for another nine days and nine nights. After thirty-six days in all, one may halt the firing and allow cooling for one day in order that all the medicine may sublime into the upper crucible. It will resemble either mottled serpentine, shooting stars, or frost. It will be pure red like cinnabar, blue, or scarlet. Remove only one pound minus four ounces of it by brushing with a feather.

If any of the medicine has remained unaffected by the firing, it must be resublimed. After mixing it with mercury (or brine?) and raspberry juice (or dew from mulberry leaves, or white dog gall?) until it is liquid, place it once more in a red clay crucible lined with lead amalgam, and thoroughly seal (with another crucible) exactly as you did before. Sublime it by means of a raging fire for thirty-six days; now the medicine will be ready, having required a total of seventy-two days.

When you are ready to take it, wash and bathe both body and hair, and burn incense for five or seven days, then at 6 o'clock in the morning bow eastward and, while kneeling, take a dose the size of a large grain of wheat or millet, or even of a gram. If a truly superior processor takes it thus for seven days, he will rise to heaven. If a lesser one takes it for seventy days, he will also attain geniehood, but an uninitiate would require a whole year for this same result. After this it is best to use the very same vessel in which you have made the Flowers of Cinnabar, to sublime the other eight cinnabars.

In the words of the Celestial Female (from whom Yellow Emperor received the divine process), "After Flowers of Cinnabar has been made, test it by projection to make gold. If the gold succeeds, the medicine is ready; otherwise, not. The medicine is not to be taken until it has been affected by the firing. Sometimes the sealing of the vessel with Six-One lute has not been carefully done; sometimes there has been a violation of taboo. If so, it must be resublimed and retested. Make a pill of it the size of a gram by means of raspberry juice (?). Place over a raging fire, on which you must blow with a bellows, and within a mealtime it will turn to gold. Gold can also be produced by mixing twenty-four scruples of Flowers of Cinnabar with one pound of mercury; this gold is then used to make a tube to be filled with the medicine. One scruple of Flowers of Cinnabar added to one pound of mercury or lead will produce gold if a strong fire is gradually increased to very intense heat through the use of a bellows. You must be careful to see that the quantities are not exceeded, else the gold will be too hard. If not enough is used, the gold will become too soft; neither of these types is malleable." Finally, she added,

> "Gold is formed, to last you're able.
> Gold not formed, your life's unstable.
> Effort in vain, protection whence able?"

There is also *T'ai ch'ing shen tan*, a method coming from Primal Lord, who was Lao Tan's teacher. The *T'ai ch'ing kuan t'ien ching* was originally in nine fascicles, and we are told that the first three could not be passed down from master to disciple. The second set of three was permanently submerged beneath the Three Pools, since nobody in the world was found worthy to have them transmitted to. The last three constitute this *T'ai ch'ing shen tan*, in three scrolls marked top, middle, and bottom, respectively.

Primal Lord is chief of the gods and genii, and can claim

to harmonize yin and yang, and to give orders to ghosts, gods, wind, and rain. He drives nine dragons and twelve white tigers. All the genii in the world are his subordinates, and yet he claims to result from a study of the divine process and the taking of cinnabar. If even he did not achieve his status automatically, how much more must ordinary mortals make these efforts!

According to this classic, when a first-class processor is successful, he becomes an official in heaven; a second-class one joins the others on Mount K'un-lun; a third-class one enjoys Fullness of Life in this world. The uneducated, having no faith, assert that all these claims are false, and engage solely in death-seeking occupations from morning to night. They do not seek life at all. How then can even heaven itself force such people to remain alive? The only things that ordinary mortals know are fine food, nice clothes, sensual pleasures, riches, and honors. Take care not to speak of the divine elixirs with those who give free rein to emotion and lust, and are bound to die in a little while. It will make them mock the divine process and malign God (the True). If you transmit the alchemical classics to the wrong sort of person, you are sure to suffer bad luck yourself. If, however, you find a true believer, the finished medicine may be shared with him. But the recipe itself is not lightly to be passed on to him.

8a   What use has the possessor of the divine process for kings and lords? As soon as the divine elixir has been made, not only is Fullness of Life obtained, but even gold can be made. When this last has been achieved, a hundred pounds must be expended on a large-scale religious ceremony, for which a special method is given in one scroll, different from the one used in the aforementioned Nine-crucibles cinnabars. Separate sums are to be allocated for the different parts of the service, as follows:

To honor heaven	20 pounds
„ sun and moon	5 pounds
„ the Great Dipper	8 pounds
„ T'ai-i	8 pounds
„ the Well God	5 pounds
„ the Hearth God	5 pounds
„ Count of the River	12 pounds
„ earth	5 pounds
„ ghosts and gods of doorways, house, and village, and Paradise Lord, five pounds each	20 pounds
	Total 88 pounds

8b

The remaining twelve pounds are to be placed in a sound leather pouch, and on a propitious day, at the peak hour of the market in the city, to be dropped silently among the crowd; and the place is to be left without a glance backward. Any gold over and above the hundred pounds may be expended as you please. But if the first part of the gold is not used to serve the gods, you will surely incur disaster. This classic further says:

> "*The divine process leading to Fullness of Life*
> *Does not depend upon offerings in honor of the ghosts and gods*
> *Nor upon calisthenics, bendings, and stretchings.*
> *The principal requirement for rising up to becoming a genie is divine cinnabar.*
> *Knowing how is not easy, and doing it is harder yet.*"

If you can achieve it, you can enjoy fullness of existence.

Recently, at the end of the Han [A.D. ·220], Master Yin Ch'ang-sheng mixed this *T'ai-ch'ing* elixir and attained geniehood. He began as a pupil of the Confucianists, and was very gifted. He composed poetry and also a eulogy on the *T'ai ch'ing tan ching*. In the preface to the latter he gives a very clear account of his early studies of the divine process under a teacher and of his forty-odd acquaintances who also attained geniehood.

The making of this *T'ai-ch'ing* elixir is somewhat more difficult than that of the Nine-crucibles cinnabars, but it is a

9a   superior method for mounting to heaven in broad daylight.
Here the fire may be lighted only after you have prepared
the fortified vinegar, red crystal salt, calomel, "dark-white"
(a mixture of lead, gold, and mercury), Express Amulets,
and Three-Five Divine Solution.

An elixir of the first cyclical transformation culminates in
geniehood after being taken for three years; of the second,
in two years; of the third, in one year; of the fourth, in half
a year; of the fifth, in one hundred days; of the sixth, in
forty days; of the seventh, in thirty days; of the eighth, in
ten days; and of the ninth, in three days.

Place the elixir which has been cycled nine times in a reaction vessel and expose it to the sun after the summer
solstice. When the container becomes hot, introduce a
9b   pound of cinnabar beneath the lid, and even while you are
watching, with the full power of the sun shining upon it, the
whole content will suddenly glow and sparkle intensely with
all the colors of divine light. It will immediately turn into
reverted elixir. If a spatula of it is taken, one will straightway
rise to heaven in broad daylight. Further, the nine-cycle
elixir must be sealed in an earthen crucible and heated by a
chaff fire, at first gentle but gradually made intense.

Cyclical mutations one through nine are thus differentiated by the varying speeds of their effectiveness. If these
transformations are few, the medicine will be found weak,
it will have to be taken for a longer time, and geniehood will
be attained slowly. If, however, it is transformed through
many cycles, the medicine will be strong, it will be taken for
fewer days, and geniehood will be attained quickly.

There is also the Ninefold Radiance Elixir, which uses a
method similar but not quite like that of the Nine-cycle
Elixir. Various ingredients are mixed and fired separately
with each of the five minerals, cinnabar, realgar, arsenolite,
laminar malachite, and magnetite. Each mineral is put
through five cycles and assumes five hues, so that altogether
twenty-five hues result. Separate containers are each filled

with one ounce of each hue. If you wish to raise a body that has not been dead for fully three days, bathe the corpse with a solution of one spatula of blue elixir, open its mouth, and insert another spatula full; it will revive immediately.   *10a*

If you wish to summon the Traveling Canteen,[2] smear your left hand with a solution of black elixir; whatever you ask for will be at your beck and call, and everything you mention will arrive without effort. You will be able to summon any thing or any creature in the world.

If it is your wish to become invisible, or to know the future, or to live without growing old, take one spatula of yellow elixir and you will immediately enjoy Fullness of Life and never grow old. Methods are to be found only in chapter two of *T'ai ch'ing shen tan* for knowing effortlessly, as though one were actually present, all the good and bad luck that occurs a thousand miles away, or for knowing all the horoscopes of human beings as well as their prosperities, declines, longevities, premature deaths, riches, honors, poverties, and indignities.

Next comes *Wu ling tan ching* (Classic of the Five Supernatural Elixirs) in one chapter, which provides five methods. It employs cinnabar, realgar, orpiment, sulphur, malachite, arsenolite, magnetite, Turkestan salt, and brown hematite. In addition, Six-One lute, a two-part sealed reaction vessel, and religious services and libations are used to compound them, and they require 36 days for completion. Five-Emperor amulet designs, written in elixir of various hues are also employed to prevent death. Nevertheless, these elixirs are inferior to *T'ai ch'ing* elixir and to the Nine-crucibles cinnabars previously mentioned.   *10b*

There is also a *Min-shan tan fa*, found in a cave by Chang Kai-t'a as he was giving careful thought to such matters on Mount Min. This method forges yellow copper alloy to make a speculum for gathering water from the moon. It is

---

[2] Y 109.12*b*; cf. H. Maspero, *Le Taoisme*, 48: fragrant foods served in plates of gold and cups of jade.

then covered with mercury and its interior heated with solar essence (gathered by a burning-mirror; 3.6*b*5–6). The taking of this substance over a long period will produce immortality.

This same text also teaches us to place this elixir in a copper mirror coated with realgar, cover it with mercury, and expose it to the sun for twenty days, after which it is uncovered and treated. When taken in the form of pills the size of grams, washed down with the first water drawn from the well at dawn, for a hundred days, it makes the blind see, and by itself cures those who are ill. It will also turn white hair black and regrow lost teeth.

Wu-ch'eng tzu's method puts some mercury made from Szechuan cinnabar on an eight-inch copper plate. A brazier is filled with coals, and a trivet placed over it to hold the copper plate, whose content is then sprinkled with sulphur solution, so that the cinnabar maintains the consistency of mud. If this is taken for a hundred days, immortality will ensue.

Hsien-men tzu's method mixes three quarts of wine with a pound of cinnabar and exposes it to the sun for forty days. After it has been taken for one day the Three Worms and all illnesses are immediately purged from the patient. If taken for three years, it will confer geniehood and one is sure to be served by two fairies, who can be employed to summon the Traveling Canteen. This elixir can exorcize ghosts. When the unburied dead everywhere are possessing people and harming them, inflicting injuries upon our homes, and throwing up earthworks to obstruct people, no harm will come to us if this elixir is hung pointed toward the sources of disaster.

There is an Instantly Successful elixir, for which nine recipes exist. It is similar but inferior to the Nine-crucibles cinnabars. Its one important difference is that it has us roast orpiment and realgar, to reduce their copper content, and cast it into vessels. Cover them with three-year-old strong

11a

vinegar. After one hundred days red nipples several inches long, in some cases looking like variegated coral, will have grown on them. If these are compounded and taken, Fullness of Life can be achieved. This preparation may also be mixed with dodder. (By this term we mean the first sproutings of roots that resemble dodder.) Dig them up, extract their sap, and mix it with this elixir; the moment you take it you will change into whatever you may wish. When it is mixed with Vermilion Herb, you can travel through the void as soon as you take it. Vermilion Herb resembles small jujube plants and is three or four feet long. Its branches and leaves are red, whereas the stalks look like coral. It grows best at the foot of high cliffs in the famous mountains, and when it is cut its sap flows like blood. When jade, one of the Eight Minerals, or gold or silver is thrown into it, they can immediately be formed into soft pills, or after a longer time, turn liquid. After being so treated, the gold is called "gold jam"; jade is called "jade wine." All of these are able to produce life in all its fullness.

11b

Then there is a *Ch'ü fu tan fa*, where we read that all the streams of the world named Vermilion (*tan*) are like Vermilion River in Nan-yang [C. Shantung, north of mountains] in that they all contain vermilion-colored goldfish. These are to be looked for at night ten days before the summer solstice, at which time they will swim to the water's edge, their reddish brilliance reflecting upward like fire. They may be taken with a net. Take as many as you wish, but not all of them. When their blood is extracted and smeared on the soles of the feet, it becomes possible to walk on water or to live in the depths for a long time.

Ch'ih-sung tzu's recipe has us steep cinnabar in sap from *Vitis flexuosa* and the alum-peach in an impermeable vessel. This vessel, its mouth sealed with floss and honey, is then buried three feet deep in the earth. After a hundred days its content is taken mixed with juice squeezed from the red fruit of the mulberry tree. It will make a man's face, eyes,

and hair turn red while he enjoys Fullness of Life. Was it not
because he had taken this mixture that, of old, Genie Chung-
huang had a red beard?

Master Shih's elixir was made by feeding unfledged birds
on cinnabar mixed with beef. When they were grown and
their feathers had come out red, he killed them and dried
them in the shade for one hundred days. After that he
crushed them, feathers and all, and took a spatula of the
powder every day for one hundred days; by so doing he
12a   attained a longevity of five hundred years.

K'ang-feng tzu's elixir is prepared by taking some blood
from the chick in a crane's egg and the juice of aconite from
Mount Shao-shih and mixing them to make the elixir. Place
in a swan's egg, seal with lacquer, and submerge in mica
solution. When, after a hundred days, it turns red, take a gill
of it and increase your longevity by a hundred years; a quart
will increase it by a thousand.

To make Ts'ui Wen-tzu's elixir place cinnabar in the
stomach of a duck and steam it. When taken, it prolongs
life; and if taken for a period of time, immortality results.

Liu Yüan's elixir consists of cinnabar mixed with Potable
Gold.* After a hundred days it will turn purple and can be
taken in the hands without soiling them. Mix with mica
solution, place in a tube, and seal it with lacquer. Throw it
into a well. After a hundred days it will turn to a red liquid.
Take one gill and live to a hundred. If taken over a period
of time, it will confer Fullness of Life.

Yüeh Tzu-chang's elixir is a malachite and minium
mixture with mercury and cinnabar, placed in a copper
cylinder. Seal by means of dry tile and white talc, set it in
white sand, and steam for eighty days. If you will take some
the size of a gram every day for three years, you become a
genie.

To prepare Li Wen's elixir, wrap cinnabar in plain silk
and cook in bamboo juice. A product called Red Spring will

* *Hsüan shui*, literally "mystery solution." This identification is only a surmise.

then float on the hot liquid. Steam this and mix with Potable Gold. Take a gill for one year and become a genie.

For Yin tzu's elixir mix cinnabar with mica solution and *12b* seal it carefully in "golden flowers" (cinnabar solution?) for one year, then remove. Take it one spatula at a time until you have consumed one pound, and you will live for five hundred years.

In T'ai-i's elixir for Summoning Gross and Ethereal Breaths the five minerals [cinnabar, realgar, arsenolite, malachite, and magnetite] are used and sealed with Six-One lute as in the Nine-crucible cinnabars (4.5*a*—). It is particularly effective for raising those who have died of a stroke. In cases where the corpse has been dead less than four days, force open the corpse's mouth and insert a pill of this elixir and one of sulphur, washing them down its gullet with water. The corpse will immediately come to life. In every case the resurrected remark that they have seen a messenger with a baton of authority summoning them.

Palace Lady's elixir. Hare's blood is mixed with cinnabar and honey and steamed for one hundred days. Take a pill the size of a cola nut three times daily for one hundred days, then two goddesses will come to attend you and obey your orders.

Chi-ch'iu tzu's elixir. Mix clear wine, hempseed oil, honey, and raspberries (?or white-dog gall, or ?mulberry dew), and seal with Six-One lute. Heat for ten days in a chaff fire. When it is ready, take one pill at a time the size of a gram, and when you have taken the whole batch, you will live to five hundred.

Mo Ti's elixir. Place mercury in a copper vessel with solutions of the five minerals. Heat on the fire, stirring with an iron spoon, for ten days. As soon as it reverts to cinnabar, take it. One spatula will cause all possible illnesses to leave you. If it is taken for a long time, immortality will result.

Chang Tzu-ho's elixir. Combine lead, mercury, and *13a* malachite solutions. Seal and steam together with red panicled millet for eighty days. When it is ready, use jujube paste to make pills of it. If you take pills the size of a soybean for one hundred days, you will live to five hundred.

Ch'i-li's elixir. First sublime the five minerals and jade dust. Combine with cinnabar and mercury (or mercury prepared from cinnabar) in a large copper vessel and cook for a hundred days. Take when it appears in a great variety of color, and immortality will ensue. Combine a hundred spatulas of this compound with one hundred pounds of lead, and heat, and it will turn into silver. Combined and fired with realgar solution for a hundred days, it becomes gold. If the gold is too hard, cook with lard. If it is too soft, cook with white plums.

Yü-chu's elixir. Mix cinnabar with fortified vinegar. Place it on a bed of, and cover with, powdered malachite and sulphur, insert into a cylinder. Place this in sand, and steam for fifty days. If taken for one hundred days, fairies, and Liu-chia (yin) and Liu-ting (yang) goddesses will come to attend you, and through them you will have knowledge of everything happening in the world.

Handy elixir. Mix cinnabar with "gold flowers." Seal within dry tiles and steam for eighty days. Then place the mixture in a dish in the sun and stir. When it emits rays which rise to blend with those of the sun, take some the size of a gram, and you will enjoy Fullness of Life. If mixed with "male copper" (arsenic-copper alloy) and fired, gold will be formed.

Duke Li's elixir. Let cinnabar and solutions of each of the five minerals, one quart each, be mixed to a paste and fired in a crucible for thirty-six days. Remove and mix with sulphur solution. Take this for ten years, and you will last as long as all nature.

Master Liu's elixir. Mix cinnabar with juices from white chrysanthemums, gromwell, and ailanthus. Steam for thirty days, and crush in a mortar. If taken for a year, it will result in an age of five hundred. If an old man takes it, he will be-

13b

come so much younger that he cannot be recognized; if a young man takes it, he will never grow old.

Lord Wang's elixir. Let Szechuan cinnabar and mercury be placed in chicken eggs and sealed with lacquer. Have a chicken incubate three of them. Take them on the lucky days,[3] and you will never grow older than you are now. Small boys may not take this, for it would stop their growth. When given to chicks and puppies, they stop growing (2.5*a*5). Its effect is the same on all birds and animals.

Master Ch'en's elixir method. Place white honey and cinnabar in a copper container. Seal it and sink in a well for a full year. Take it, and you will not feel hunger for a whole year. A whole pound will produce a longevity of one hundred years.

14a

Han Chung's elixir. Varnish honey and cinnabar. Fry. When taken, it can protract your years and confer ever-lasting vision. In full sun you will cast no shadow.

There are several dozen additional recipes, but I cannot give a complete account of them.

It was by taking Potable Gold that T'ai-i became a genie; it is in no way inferior to the Nine-crucibles cinnabars. To compound it, use one pound of gold by the old scales (15*a*10). Use also mercury (? or selenite, or vinegar and raspberries), realgar, Turkestan salt (? or glauberite), sulphur (?), magnetite solution (?), Epsom salts, and cinnabar. Seal them together until they liquefy. The book devoted to this preparation says, "When potable gold enters a man's mouth, his whole body takes on a golden hue. When Lao Tan got it from Primal Lord, the latter said, 'This divine process is very important. It appears but once every hundred years. Let it be kept in a stone chamber. Those who prepare it shall purify themselves for one hundred days, and abstain from contacts

---

[3] Literally, "king and prime minister days." These are the two days of each ten which correspond to the same one of the Five Agents as does the season. For example, in spring the lucky days are the first and second, for they, like spring, belong to wood. [N. Sivin].

with ordinary people. Let a cell of retreat be erected on a slope of a famous mountain where a stream flows east. After a hundred days it will be ready. On taking an ounce you will become a genie . . .' If you do not wish to leave the world as a celestial genie just yet but would prefer to be a land or water genie, merely fast for one hundred days. All who wish to mount to heaven must first dispense with starches for a year, and then take this preparation. By taking one half-ounce you will enjoy Fullness of Life and become immortal.

14b   Not a single harmful thing or poison will be capable of injuring you. You will be able to have a wife and family and hold official position. All your wishes will come true. If later you wish to ascend to heaven, you need only fast, take another ounce, and then soar away as a genie."

A recipe for making "black amber sesame" from Potable Gold is to combine Potable Gold with mercury and cook for thirty days. Remove, and fill a clay bowl with it. Seal with Six-One lute, place in a raging fire, and cook for sixty double-hours, by which time it all turns to elixir. Take a quantity of this the size of a gram and you will immediately become a genie. A spatula of this elixir mixed with one pound of mercury will immediately turn it to silver; a pound placed over a fire, which is then fanned, will turn into a reddish gold termed "vermilion gold." If daggers and swords are smeared with it, they will ward off all other weapons within ten thousand miles. If plates and bowls are made of vermilion gold and used for drinking and eating, they will produce Fullness of Life. If these dishes are used to gather exudate of the sun and moon, as specula are used to gather lunar water, the exudate will produce immortality when drunk.

When Potable Gold is mixed with loess earth and placed in a bowl coated with Six-One lute and cooked in a raging fire, it will become real gold, and can be used as such. If it is then again cooked in fire, it will all turn into elixir, and, if a quantity the size of a gram is taken, it will enable one to go to famous mountains or great streams and thus become an earth genie. When a spatula of this elixir is powdered in *15a* mercury, silver will be immediately formed, one ounce of which can turn a pound of lead into silver.

When taught this *Chin i ching* (Potable Gold Classic) one must throw an eight-ounce gold statuette of a man into an eastward-flowing stream. Only after taking an oath and drinking the blood of a sacrificial victim is one given the oral directions. When the basic rules are not followed or the recipe has been stolen, all concocting will be in vain (4.5*b*).

The medicine you make may be given to ordinary people who have great faith in it, but the writings are under no circumstances to be transmitted lightly, for both parties would be sure to suffer harm from such a transaction. The gods of heaven keep far closer watch on human beings than people realize.

The Nine-crucible cinnabars are by far the best methods for making genie medicine, but the ingredients used in their preparation are extremely varied. When goods flow freely from all parts of the empire, they can all be bought in the markets (TT 884.1.2*a*7 or 10.6*b*8 enjoin us not to haggle!), but when the provinces are cut off from each other such things are unobtainable. Also, the fire must be kept going for several dozen days and nights, and one must watch over its intensity, which must not be allowed to fall short of the requirements. This is taxing and extraordinarily difficult. Therefore, these elixirs are not as easily prepared as is Potable Gold.

When concocting Potable Gold, it is only the gold that is hard to obtain. A pound of gold by the old scales (14*a*4) is the equivalent of two pounds by our present scales, the whole amount being worth not more than some 300,000 coppers. The various ingredients employed in this recipe are relatively easy to obtain. Further there is no fire to tend. The mixture is merely placed in a solvent vinegar bath for a sufficient number of days to prepare it. The whole operation *15b* may cost 400,000 coppers, but then one batch can suffice to produce eight genii. However, if the amounts of ingredients are even slightly less than specified, they will lack the activity to react with one another, just as wine can never be made when only a few quarts of rice are fermented.

There are also methods for nibbling gold. These may be inferior to Potable Gold, but they are vastly superior to other medicines. Sometimes the gold is refined with wine and the skin and fat from the back of a hog. Other times it is prepared with the bark of ailanthus. It may be dissolved with Ching wine and magnetite, drawn out into a sheet, or liquefied and taken that way. Sometimes taboos must be observed; therefore it is inferior to Potable Gold. Other times it is mixed with realgar and orpiment and then taken. This product can be drawn out or stretched like a skin. It leads merely to earth geniehood.

Silver and large pearls from oysters can all be dissolved and taken, but they must be taken over such a long period of time that they may not last. They are therefore also inferior to Potable Gold.

Since the preparation of Potable Gold and the Nine-crucible cinnabars requires money as well as exile on a famous mountain, very few can undertake it. Further, only one person in a million possesses these classics at any given time. Therefore, practically none of the writings on the divine process expound gold and elixirs.

16a

The principal prohibition is that no profane unbelievers are to be given an opportunity to criticize or malign the work, for that would be sure to cause failure. Lord Cheng, my teacher, said that the reason for this is that the preparation of these important medicines always required concomitant religious ceremonies which would cause T'ai-i, Primal Lord, Lord Lao, and Heaven-fairy to come and supervise the preparation. If the operator would fail to sequester himself in a concealed retreat and permitted stupid, profane persons to pass by his place of operation and hear and see him, the gods would immediately blame the operator for failing to follow the injunctions of the classic and letting evil persons have an opportunity to malign the work. The gods would withdraw aid from him, evil influences would gain entrance, and the process would fail.

One must go up a famous mountain, undergo rites of purification for a hundred days, eat none of the five pungent flavors (onion, garlic, leek, absinthe, mustard) nor fresh fish, and not associate with profane persons. Only then may one undertake to prepare the great medicine. Only when it is ready may the fasting and other measures for ritual purity be discontinued; performing them at the beginning is not enough.

Lord Cheng said that Lord Tso had told him that *Chin i shen tan* could not be prepared on the little, ordinary mountains, these do not have their own gods to govern them. In such places one finds only tree and stone spirits, creatures a thousand years old, and vampires. All these are evil breaths, and are not intent upon good fortune for men. They can *16b* only bring misfortune, and they are clever at testing processors, who are then obliged to use recipes to dispel them from themselves and their accompanying disciples. Yet there will still be times when they will succeed in ruining your work. Whenever doctors today are preparing some beneficial medicine or salve, they never want any fowl, dogs, children, or married women to watch them, for if their precincts are violated the preparations will prove ineffective. Further, dyers dislike having those with the evil eye observe them at work, for it makes them fail to secure the perfect color. So why should we not exercise even greater care when preparing the great divine medicines leading to geniehood? Therefore, when the processors of antiquity were mixing divine medicine, they made sure to go up a famous mountain and not to linger in the ordinary hills.

According to the genii classics, the following are the mountains where careful thought can be given to the com-

pounding of genie-producing medicines: Mounts Hua,
T'ai, Huo, Heng, Sung, Shao-shih, Ch'ang, T'ai-po, Chung-
nan, Nü-chi, Ti-fei, Wang-wu, Pao-tu, An-ch'iu, Ch'ien,
Ch'ing-ch'eng, O-mei, Jui, Yün-t'ai, Lo-fu, Yang-chia,
Huang-chin, Pieh-tsu, the larger and the smaller T'ien-t'ai,
Ssu-wang, Kai-chu, and Kua-ts'ung. These are all mountains
which have gods of their own. Sometimes earth genii are to

17a   be found there too. Magic fungi and herbs grow here. They
are good places in which to sit out war and catastrophe, not
merely to prepare medicines.

If those having the divine process will ascend these
mountains, their gods will most certainly assist and bring
luck. The medicines will be sure to succeed. If, however, it is
impossible to go to these mountains, the larger islands along
the coast, e.g., Tung-weng, Tan, or Chu-yü in Kuei-chi;
Hsin-chü, T'ai-kuang, and Yü in Hsü are next best. The
famous mountains in North China cannot now be reached,
but the following famous mountains south of the Yangtze
may be used: Huo in Chin-an, Ch'ang and T'ai-po in Tung-
yang, and Ssu-wang, larger and smaller T'ien-t'ai, Kai-chu,
and Kua-ts'ang; all of these are in Kuei-chi.

Personally, I have the honor to be both the son and the
grandson of high ministers of state. My talents may not have
been sufficient for governing the state or managing affairs,
but many, driven by love of man or industry, and surely not
much wiser than I, have risen to the Milky Way with a flap
of their wings, their radiance a sunrise lighting up the clouds.
I have broken, therefore, all contact with my native village
and quit the glories of our present world, because I felt
obliged to go afar and ascend a famous mountain to finish
my philosophical essays, and afterward to prepare the divine
medicine with a view to enjoying Fullness of Life. Every

17b   member of the crowd is amazed that, forsaking my family's
village and leaving disinterestedness behind, I undertook to
cultivate thickets and to grow callouses on my hands and
feet. They consider me mad. The divine process, however,

does not flourish in the midst of mundane activities. If such human activity is not abandoned, how can an ambition such as mine be cultivated? And once this has been clearly perceived and one's resolution is made, what fear can there be of condemnation? Can one be moved by arguments pro or con? Meanwhile, I write what is in my heart in order to inform those of the future who may share my intention and preferences. My staunch, like-minded friends of the future will, I am sure, reject the same things that I have rejected.

The Lesser Divine elixir (cf. 11.16a10). Take three pounds of real cinnabar, six pounds of white honey, stir together, expose to the sun, and cook until it can be shaped into pills. Every morning take ten of these pills about the size of a hempseed. In less than a year, whitened hair will become black, lost teeth will regrow, and the skin of your whole body be moist and rejuvenated. Those who take it will not age, and old men will regain their youths, enjoy Fullness of Life, and become immortal.

The Lesser elixir (11.17a2). Take one pound of cinnabar, pestled and sifted, three quarts of strong vinegar, and two quarts of lacquer. Mix these three thoroughly, and cook over a slow fire until the compound can be shaped into pills. Take three, the size of a hempseed, twice daily for thirty days, and all abdominal illnesses will be cured, and the Three Corpses that are in your body will depart. Take for one hundred days, and your flesh and bones will become strong and sturdy. Take for one thousand days, and the Governor *18a* of Fates will strike your name from the Book of Death; you will last as long as all nature, and the sun and moon will always shine on you. You can change shape continuously. You will cast no shadow in the sun, for you will radiate your own light.

The Lesser Recipe for Nibbling Gold (11.16b2). Dip refined gold in and out of clear wine about two hundred times until the wine bubbles. Knead it until it comes through the fingers like mud. If the wine will not bubble and the gold will not come through the fingers when you squeeze it, remelt it and dip it in pure wine innumerable times. When ready, take some pills the size of one or two crossbow pellets, dividing them into smaller pills, over thirty days. You will then be immune to cold and heat, and gods and fairies will attend you. Silver may be nibbled in the same way as gold. If those who take these two substances can dwell in a cave on a famous mountain, they will levitate to become celestial genii within one year. If they take them while living among other men, they will become earth genii. Don't transmit these recipes heedlessly.

Liang-i tzu's recipe for nibbling melted gold (11.16b7). Prepare three pounds of the skin and fat from the back of a hog and one quart of strong vinegar. Place five ounces of yellow gold in a container and cook on an earthen stove. Dip the gold in and out the fat one hundred times; likewise in the vinegar. Take a pound of this, and you will outlast all nature. Take a half pound, and you will live to 2,000; five ounces, to *18b* 1200 years. It may be taken in any amount, but it must be made on lucky days to be miraculously effective. Let this recipe not be given to others nor shown to them, otherwise the elixir will be unsuccessful and ineffective. If you wish to banish [the Three Corpses] from your body, you should take cinnabar.

5

The Ultimate System

How CAN MY intelligence be superior when, God (the Subtle and Marvelous) being hard to know, the vast majority of people are in doubt and confusion regarding God? I happen to have a specialty — like the crane that knows when it is midnight and then trumpets (*Mo Ti* 19.10*a*4) or the swallow that recognizes the days *wu* and *chi*[1] and does no nest-building on those days since they are equated with the agent earth (*Shuo wen* 5288*a*2) — but that is no guarantee that I know anything else. Among specialists, there are also some who know purely from the evidence that Fullness of Life is achievable, and that genii are not a special species. The

[1] A cycle of sixty disyllabic terms has been employed in China since before 1000 B.C. Used for the hours, days, months, and years, it is formed by revolving a cycle of ten monosyllables concomitantly with one of twelve. The denary list is *chia, i, ping, ting, wu, chi, keng, hsin, jen,* and *kuei*. The duodenary is *tzu, ch'ou, yin, mao, ch'en, ssu, wu, wei, shen, yu, hsü,* and *hai*. Chinese fortune-telling correlates these two lists with the Five Agents (Elements), Five Directions, Four Seasons, Five Planets, Five Colors, Five Savors, Five Musical Notes, and Five Internal Organs of Man. Frequent reference is made to them by Ko Hung. The duodenary has long been used to designate the twelve double hours of the day, beginning at 11 P.M. At the same time, in Chinese fortune-telling everybody has a serial number determined by eight of these monosyllables drawn from the sexagenary cycle marking the year, month, day, and hour of his birth. *Wu* and *chi* are the fifth and sixth days of each ten-day "week."

The cycle of Five Agents can be viewed as creative or destructive. Its creative order is wood, fire, earth, metal, and water. The destructive order is wood, earth, water, fire, and metal. Cf. especially 17.5*a*11–*b*9; 11.8*a*5, 15*b*5.

marvelousness of God, however, is not to be told exhaustively through anything written, and nothing even
approximating God can be expounded.

In the past, Keng-sang Ch'u (*Chuang* 23.2) giving himself
callouses, and Yin-wen tzu, using sumptuary regulation
(*Chuang* 33.35), worked earnestly and hard for a long time
to attain social and economic formulas acknowledging God
about which they were most uncompromising. What
breathing human being, however, does not rejoice in life
and fear death? Glory and power seduce their minds; white
faces and jade-like flesh bewilder their eyes; clear and liquid
strains of music confuse their ears; love, hate, profits, and
losses agitate their inner gods; reputations and citations bind
their very bodies. These are all things that come naturally,
unsummoned; they take form without any study on our
own part. Unless naturally fated to respond to geniehood
and to give themselves utterly to the arranging of a unique
view; unless their understandings adapt themselves to what
1b is out beyond the empiric world, and they themselves move
in the purity of paradise; unless they are conscious of the
relationship of forms to names, and grieve over the lightning-
like passing of life, how can they abandon society to cultivate
something distant, repress their covetousness, or diminish a
very present desire in order to cultivate a far-off goal that is
hard to achieve?

It is through perfect freedom that the empiric comes into
existence; form requires the inner gods in order to be. Then
the empiric becomes the palace of perfect freedom, and
bodies become the abodes of the inner gods. Therefore, to
adopt a comparison with a dike, remember that when the
dike crumbles, water is no longer retained. Take for comparison a torch, and remember that once the torch has been
destroyed, fire no longer dwells within it. Similarly, when a
body is overworked, its inner gods are scattered; when the
breaths are exhausted, life itself ends. When the roots are
worn out and the number of branches is excessive, vigor

departs from the tree; when the breaths are worn out and desire gets the upper hand, the inner spirits leave the body. There is no time set for the return of the departing, and the decayed lacks the principle of life. These are facts sincerely regretted by the man who knows God.

Wouldn't you say that there is reason to disdain marks of distinction and to stress quietude? This is the reason that those who nourish life in the hills and forests, and those who achieve their own purposes by disdaining common custom, equate exalted position with warts and tumors, and all creation with a cicada's wings. Do you think it without reason that they boast and show their disdain vigorously for the affairs of our world? Understanding only too well what they see about them, they simply abandon it as something not worth remembering. For this reason, they settle far away, stay in hiding, conceal their shining scales, and veil their elegance. They repress the eye's desire to see; banish the beauties that weaken vision. They plug the ear's very thought of sound; put afar the music which only confuses hearing. They cleanse the dark mirror of the mind (T 10), maintain a feminine approach, and embrace Unity (18.1a3). Concentrating upon the breaths to produce softness, they fortify themselves with calm and impartiality. They dismiss the evils of joy and sadness; they are alien to the glory and disgrace associated with successes and failures; they lop away rich living that later turns to poison. They silence verbosity at the pole of all things. Listening in reverse, they hear most clearly; looking inward, they see free of blemishes. They nurture the roots of their inner powers on God (the Mystery that is Creation); they dispel affection for the things contacting them. By eschewing everything shallow, governing through joy and love, and acting through perfect freedom they maintain the natural order intact.

They chew and inhale breath to bathe their inner gods in Paradise.
They disregard astrology (the five planets) and concentrate on preserving within themselves the nine gods.

*They affix a lock to the sperm in the lower abdomen (Gateway of Life);
keep their eyes on the pole of the universe.*

*Drawing the light of sun, moon, and dipper to within their foreheads (Hall
of Enlightenment), they enter trances in order to confine their bodies.*

*Gathering there life-giving exudate from the golden beams of Paradise, they
slow down the race toward old age and retain their youth.*

*They maintain immutable the transparency natural to the centers within
their heads, chests, and abdomens, and conduct their saliva to the lungs,
heart, spleen, liver, and kidneys.*

*As they tend the fire below the bubbling crucible, multicolored birds are
inspired to look up toward them and chirp (Chen kao 8.11a8).*

When they pluck the best products from the brew, a unicorn sounds its note.

*Then, cherishing both sun and moon in their hearts, they conceal the
gathered light within their own heads.*

*After their stomachs have been filled, the effects show in their faces; the
nose becoming drenched, the effects pass to the blood vessels.*

Imbued with heavenly contentment, they summon the Six-Ting gods

To sit or lie in their hearts and chew upon the juices there.

2b *Flourishing become their inner working parts: showing flowerings of vermilion and shoots of blue. Clear white becomes their fat: oozing and
dripping.*

Thus, hunger controlled and thirst ended, no illnesses burgeon in them.

Spleens completely at ease, they enjoy tranquillity and peace.

*Their inner spirits under firm control, their bones become filled, but their
whole frames remain light.*

That is why they can live long as they give spur to the wind and clouds and ride the vast spaces in God's (Undifferentiation's) own carriage. Big wooden beams, however, do not grow a foot thick by time as measured by the clock; water from the mountain does not penetrate in regular stages. Those frightened by such teachings are not believers; believers do nothing about them or, if they do, they do not persist to the end. Those who are successful are very rare and conceal themselves; those we see about us everywhere are the many who failed. It is only the latter that the world sees, not the former; hence the false conclusion: There is no divine process in the world leading to geniehood.

Where the dike is strong, there is no loss of water; where the fat is abundant, the fire suffers no loss of light.

The sword Lung-ch'üan was always sharp because it had never cut anything; ordinary axes are quickly dulled by daily use.

Hidden snow will last through the summer because it is kept from heat; stored ice lasts through the hot spells because it is lodged deep.

When covered by even a single thickness of silk a mirror will not shine; weeds, of no value, survive the winter through cover.

Muddied earth quickly loses its shape, but when fashioned into tiles it can last as long as all nature.

3a

Oak decays easily, but when it has been roasted into charcoal it will last for thousands upon thousands of years.

The yamen's pig dies old because it has been well cared for; but the best of horses will perish early if abused by steep climbing.

Insects in cold climates seek no longevity once their end comes, but the forests in the south grow and flourish because there the climate is warm.

When touched by the breath of death, things perish in the ice and frosts; planted where there is warmth and coziness, things thrive like thickets and branch luxuriantly.

All things are one in origin, but varying qualities bring them differing functions.

Is reaping restricted solely to autumn, and is storing only for winter?

Man's fated moments of birth and death are not to be compared with what happens to plants in cold weather. The system governing the protracting and nurturing of life in man, and the recipes that must be followed to repair and save him are not merely superficial benefits accruing from warmth. Why should earnest efforts directed toward Lasting Vision be unfruitful? The people of our world, however, very narrow-minded and defending only what is nearby, think that the divine process leading to geniehood is an idle boast. They claim that Yellow Emperor and Lao Tan talked nonsense. Isn't this sad?

In their stupidity, people choose not to believe in infusions, medicines, acupuncture, and moxibustion. How can they believe in what is even more profound than these? They all ask why Yü Fu, Ch'in Yüeh-jen, Doctors Ho and Huan, Ch'un-yü Yi and the like ever died, if it is so certain that they could cure illness. Then they add, "Do the rich and honored lack medicines and recipes? Yet they are noted for short lives. This can only mean that life is a purely natural thing." To get people who criticize in this fashion to believe in geniehood is like getting a buffalo to climb a tree, or a horse to go as fast as a bird.

3b

The minor elixirs for recalling a man's ethereal breaths, the pills for countering the three Messenger-corpses, and lesser medicines made from the Five Brilliances and the Eight Minerals (2.6*b*) will sometimes melt hard ice instantly or keep one afloat in water. They can intercept ghosts and gods, lay tigers and leopards, and disperse accumulations in the digestive system and our organs. They dislodge the two lackeys of illness from the heart region and the diaphragm (*Tso*, Ch'eng 10.5); they raise those who have just died; return frightened ethereal breaths to the body they had quit. All these are common, everyday medicines. And, if they can still restore the dead to life, why should the superior medicines not be able to make the living immortal?

Ch'in Yüeh-jen revived the Crown Prince of Kuo after his death; a foreign shaman restored life to Su Wu after his breathing had ceased (HS 54.7*b*7); Ch'un-yü Yi knew how to open a cranium to rearrange a brain; Hua T'o could open the abdomen to drain the stomach. Wen Chih exceeded his promise to cure a case of royal anxiety (by making the patient angry when he suggested a specific means for his own destruction); Chang Chi pierced a breast to insert a red tablet. If these paltry arts of the physicians can still achieve cures, what is impossible for the divine process which comes to us from the gods and genii?

Man's death ensues from losses, old age, illnesses, poisons, miasmas, and chills. Today, men do calisthenics and breathing exercises, revert their sperm to repair the brain, follow dietary rules, regulate their activity and rest, take medicines, give thought to their inner gods to maintain their own integrity, undergo prohibitions, wear amulets and seals from their belts, and keep at a distance all who might harm their lives. In this way they may avoid the six baneful things just listed that can cause death.

Physicians today have pills that activate and brighten the kidneys, powders that benefit the circulation, roasted box-thorn for strengthening bony structure, and infusions of yellow Hedysarum as a general tonic. Those that take these things give themselves a flourishing appearance. Fan Ah took such ordinary herbs as lacquer-tree leaves and beet greens, and lived to be two hundred, his ears and eyes remaining sharp enough for him to hold the acupuncture needles to treat illnesses. These are facts of recent times, recorded and commented upon by highly reliable historians.

These same writings add that a certain Wu P'u received of Hua T'o "The Sport of Five Animals" [tiger, deer, bear, monkey, and birds] to replace calisthenics, and still lived for more than a hundred years. If such are the effects of these humblest of medicines, think what can be done by those that are truly marvelous! Today, however, the crowd says it is not true when we report that the infusions *li-chung* and *ssu-shun* can prevent cholera; that coltsfoot and aster counter spasms of coughing; Eulalia and male fern are vermifuges; spikenard and peony are good for cramps; *Gendarussa vulgaris* and *angelica* are carminatives; sweet flag and dried ginger check rheumatism; dodder and *Aeginetia* are tonics; ipecac and *Draba* dispel mucus; Trichosanthes and gold-thread cure diabetes; *Aenophora* and licorice are antiseptics; rhubarb and "Increasing Heat" stop the bleeding of

4a

4b

wounds; and *Ephedra* and *Justicia* are febrifuges. In matters of life and death, the crowd prefers to ask for good luck, divide the stalks of milfoil, or inquire about demons. Unwilling to believe in treatment by excellent physicians, they turn to the mumbo jumbo of shamans. Imagine then, if you will, their reactions when they are told that gold and cinnabar bring geniehood or that excrescences and Brilliances can protract lives!

In old times, Chang Liang, the Marquis of Liu, was a deviser of extraordinary schemes. None of his contemporaries could equal him in sagacity. There was nothing shallow about him, and yet he affirmed that immortality could be achieved. His intelligence and wisdom were in no way inferior to those of his contemporaries, and yet he could say, "I shall now quit human affairs and associate with Ch'ihsung tzu." Thereupon he practiced calisthenics and gave up starches for a whole year. While following a divine process leading to levitation, he suffered oppression at the hands of Empress Lü, who asked him for a plan to protect the interests of Crown Prince An. Despite his own higher interests, Chang Liang then devised the scheme of summoning the group of Four Graybeards. Everything naturally turned out as they predicted, and Empress Lü, valuing Chang, had him fed forcibly. This is the only reason he was not successful in the divine process he was pursuing. K'ung An-kuo's *Pi chi* reads, "Chang Liang secured Huang-shih kung's recipe for immortality (for his writing was not restricted to military strategy) . . . He originally had the Four Graybeards for his teachers, that is Master Lu-li, Youngest Brother Ch'i-li, and the others, all of whom were genii. From them he got divine prescriptions, and although he was forced by Empress Lü to eat and drink he later resumed the practice of the divine process leading to geniehood and secretly did attain immortality. The people of his day, ignorant of this, merely said that he had died." Thus, according to K'ung An-kuo, Chang Liang achieved geniehood.

5a

A prime minister under the Han, Chang Ts'ang, happening to learn a minor recipe, lived to 180 by sucking his wives' milk. This may be the lowest form of the divine process, but Chang Ts'ang attained three times the average life span by following it. Therefore, when one practices the secrets and marvels of the more elaborate recipes, why shouldn't Fullness of Life be possible ? All of these facts can be found in *Han History* 42.3*a*6. They are not idle talk.

The taking of medicines may be the first requirement for enjoying Fullness of Life, but the concomitant practice of breath circulation greatly enhances speedy attainment of the goal. Even if medicines are not attainable and only breath circulation is practiced, a few hundred years will be attained provided the scheme is carried out fully, but one must also know the art of sexual intercourse to achieve such extra years. If ignorance of the sexual art causes frequent losses of sperm to occur, it will be difficult to have sufficient energy to circulate the breaths.

5b

Man exists in the midst of breath, and breath is within man himself. From heaven and earth on to all creation there is nothing that does not require breath to stay alive. The man who knows how to circulate his breath maintains his own person and also banishes evils that would attack him. The crowd, however, makes daily use of breath without understanding these things. Among the people of Wu-Yüeh there is current a method for casting spells that is very effective; it consists merely of rendering breath more abundant.* He who employs it can go even where there is plague and sleep with the sick without becoming infected. His companions, to the number of several dozen, can also be rendered immune. This is an example of the effectiveness of breath against natural disasters.

Sometimes evil demons or mountain spirits attack us. They throw tiles or stones at us or they burn homes. At

---

* There are probably some words missing from the text in the latter part of this sentence.

times they can be seen going to and fro, while at other times only their noise or voices are heard. When, however, exorcizers use breath against them, all their activity ceases (8.3*a*). This shows that breath can be used against ghosts and gods.

Many valleys in the mountains and forests are the lurking places of poisonous vipers and snakes. Whenever ordinary people cross through them they are apt to be struck, but if an exorcizer charms them with breath he can make them flee for several dozen miles square and keep his companions unharmed. In the same way it is also possible to charm tigers and leopards as well as snakes and wasps, making them all

6a   crouch immobile.

Bleeding from knife wounds can be stopped by breath; it can be made to halt the moment it appears. Such charms can also repair bones and sinews, and can be used against bare blades so that one can walk on them unscathed or remain unpierced when they are jabbed at us. If bitten by a snake or viper, one can be cured immediately by using a breath charm.

Not too long ago, people such as Tso Tz'u and Chao Ping charmed streams by means of breath, so that the water receded as much as ten or twenty feet. Further, they lighted a fire on a thatched hut to cook their food, but the hut did not burn. They drove a spike into a post for seven or eight inches, then, when they blew upon it with their breath, the nail darted out. They charmed boiling water with breath and threw some one hundred coins into it; then they had someone pull them out with his bare hands without scalding them. They placed charmed water outside in a courtyard and it did not freeze, even though the weather turned very cold. They could cast a spell on the cooking of a whole district so that nothing got done. They charmed dogs, preventing them from barking.

Anciently, the state of Wu sent General Ho Ch'i to punish bandits who were infesting the mountains. Among these bandits there was an exorcizer who saw to it that when the battle was about to be joined the swords of the government troops could not be drawn, and the arrows which they shot returned to their source and were ineffective. General Ho, a man of wide knowledge and great talent, remarked after some reflection, "I have heard that spells can be put on the edges of weapons and on the poisons of insects. However, no spells can be placed on things without an edge or without poisons. They can place a spell on our weapons, but they certainly cannot put a spell on things without an edge." Then he prepared many bare staves of strong wood and, selecting five thousand exceptionally strong and excellent soldiers as a vanguard, armed them with the staves alone. Since, confident in their exorcists, the bandits had taken no defensive measures whatever, the government troops attacked them with the bare staves and inflicted a severe defeat, for the exorcists could no longer operate, and some thousands were slain. Since breath emanating from a body can be put to such effective use, how can we doubt that illness can be cured, our years protracted, and our very existences nurtured by abstaining from the normal starchy foods?

6b

Chung-chang T'ung was a man of great capacity. He composed the *Ch'ang yen* in 24 chapters, in which he discusses the possibility of dispelling hunger and illness by circulating breath. In his words, "At first I did not believe this, but once I had practiced it I found it to be true. Extremely simple though the recipe for nurturing one's very life is, yet I had not been able to pursue it. Is this not because my heart and mind were turned toward wordly matters and I was keenly intent upon the normal human pursuits? And all others who have been unable to circulate their breaths will certainly share my complaint.

"Anciently, a wise master (*Lieh* 8.22—) knew of a divine process leading to immortality, and the lord of Yen sent a man to study it. Before he could settle there, however, the master died. This made the lord of Yen so angry with his emissary that he was going to have him put to death. But

7a

the emissary argued that, the greatest of worries being death and the greatest of prizes being life, since that master lost his own life, how could he possibly have given the prince immortality? Thus the man was not executed, for he had argued a good case for himself. If, however, that master's possession of a prescription for immortality was in any way similar to the rule for circulating breath which I have learned, his death is not a definite indication that he did not know a divine process. It only means that he was unable to quit worldly affairs in order to carry it out. Even though he may have known the divine process, it was of no benefit to him. But this does not mean that he had no method.

"At Mi in Ho-nan there lived a certain Shang-ch'eng who had studied a divine process for a long time and finally took leave of his family. His first steps were only slightly elevated, but then he rose into the clouds and was never seen again. This is what is known as lifting one's own body, becoming light and buoyant, and rising to heaven in broad daylight. He was a genie of the highest type.

"Ch'en Shih and Han Jung were both illustrious processors of Ying-ch'uan, which is close to Mi. The two of them believed that there were genii in the world, probably for the simple reason that their fathers and grandfathers had seen Shang-ch'eng become a genie and mount to heaven."

7b This is yet one more proof of the existence of genii.

6

The Meaning of "Subtle"

I HAVE BEEN taught that those who accept common opinions and conform to established patterns are trusted without a word, whereas those who travel a different path or pursue different interests are doubted despite their protestations of loyalty. Among the little townsfolk who have never been beyond the confines of their own village, petty matters vying for their acceptance or rejection sink or swim more readily than metals or feathers. For such people, things are either black or white, as rice flour and ink; but doubters are far more undecided than that. This is particularly true when you wish to persuade them about things transcending normal worldly experience or to instruct them about the infinitesimal. They just guffaw. This has been going on for a long time; it is not a new problem.

So long as vision can be applied, though it be on dark and obscure places or on tiny and barren things, it is felt that it is not difficult to see. However, in the case of things which are unattainable, though it be the brilliance of sun and moon and magnificent heaven, or the heights of Mounts Sung, T'ai, Kan or Yün, people still find it impossible to examine them! The profound knowledge and unique views of those Saints of God, Yellow Emperor and Lao Tan, have been revealed in secret texts from the famous mountains or in genii classics handed down by the gods. Removed from the impediments and dust of our human world, these texts contain no shackles; mounting the greatest heights, they carry us to the empyrean itself. (The reading of such texts brings nothing but elation.) Metal and stone cannot equal

1b them in hardness; they enjoy longer lives than do turtles and cranes.

Mindful of the future and anxious lest believers in these things lack texts, those Saints transmitted prescriptions which are brilliantly clear. The minor ones produce lesser effects; the important ones will produce strong effects. Shallow-minded persons, however, observe only the most paltry things. Thinking only of infusions of sow thistle or smartweed as sweet, they remain ignorant of sugar and honey; preferring the poorer wines, they disdain the excellent. They know how to cherish life, but they are ignorant of the divine process that nurtures it. They know enough to fear death, but they will not believe that there are methods that can produce immortality. They know the many illnesses that result from excesses of eating and drinking, but they are unable to moderate the fats and sweets entering their mouths. They know that overwork and covetousness produce desiccation, but they are ignorant of methods to curb their desires. In the same way, I may declare that divinity and geniehood are obtainable, but how can I command credence?

Interlocutor: Your own person bears none of the lineaments of superiority, nor do strange hairs cover your frame. You have not reached the age of either An-ch'i or Old P'eng. Your eyes have never set upon a god or genie, nor have your ears enjoyed a unique hearing of strange tales. How do you know that Fullness of Life is achievable or that there is any evidence of life being nurtured? You will not yet admit that you feel God (the Mystery and the Marvelous) in your heart and mind or that you enjoy a unique view of extraordinary sights. Your clothes are not sufficient to cover your hide, and your general resources are not enough to last from one day to the next, yet you talk mightily of arts that only a millionaire like Fan Li could practice; you associate yourself with schemes appropriate to a wealthy man like I-tun. It is only logical that you bring criticism upon yourself. You are sickly, yet claim to have the essence of the arts of Doctors Ho and Ch'in Yüeh-jen. You have frequently run away, but claim to understand thoroughly the calculations of the strategists Sun Wu and Wu Ch'i. If people do not believe you, it is because you do not show any effects of your own claims.

Ko: Floating in its well, the tiny grub declares there is no such expanse in the world as the four seas; twisting within a kernel, the worm believes that the six extremities of the universe are restricted to his one fruit. If you were to tell these insects about the boundlessness of great expanses of water or the vastness of the universe, they would find your words meaningless and utterly incredible.

When my eyes have square pupils and my ears grow from the top of my head; when, driving a flying dragon and riding a cloud of good fortune, I shall mount above the darting lightning and reach Lighted-from-below, how will you be able to interrogate me? If you see me, you will then cry out that it is a heaven or an earth deity, or a strange sort of man. It will never occur to you to say that I am something produced by mere study! Meanwhile, being the first one to be awakened to these truths I can draw along those who are like-minded, but how can I compel people like you to believe me? If there were a genie in your own household, right under your eyes and standing at your very side, you would never suspect it even if you consulted the lots. But once his course was completed, he would do his walking in the blue yonder and sojourn on Purple Summit. Then, unless you were attuned to such things, you would neither see nor hear him. You must be an earless fellow!

People of the world have faith only in their own opinions and rely upon their own shortsighted views. They claim that nothing differs from what they personally have experienced. They accept all the everyday things, but are amazed at the unusual ones. They prick their ears and point fingers at everything they do not understand. This attitude has been around for a long time; there is nothing new about it.

Another person: Having frequently listened to what you had to say, I cannot doubt the existence of genii. Nevertheless, I personally feel that I simply could never become one. Are there any other significant divine processes that could be pursued more simply?

Ko: Any pursuit of the divine process begins in the shallows before attaining the depths; facility is acquired only after difficulties. If your will is firmly formed, you can reach any shore; if you are hesitant, nothing is achieved. It is a complex matter. You cannot expect a tree's branchings to tower high into the clouds unless its roots go deep into the soil, nor can a stream flow mightily for thousands of miles if its springs do not run deep. Therefore, unless effective secret action is accumulated ahead of time there can be no influencing of the gods; without a meeting of sincere hearts and minds there can be no winning of a teacher's friendship. Unless there is hard preparatory work there can be no question of the Grand Attempt. If you search for the important divine process before consulting an intelligent teacher, you will not succeed. The Nine-crucible cinnabars and the Potable Gold are by far the chief of the divine processes leading to geniehood, but they are so elaborate and the expense is so heavy it has not been possible to carry them through to the end. There is the greatest urgency that sperm be valued and breath preserved. In addition, by taking the lesser medicines to protract one's life and studying the lower recipes to avoid evils, progress is gradually made into the subtleties.

Still another person: There are so many prescriptions that it

3a

is very difficult to carry them out fully. Aside from the gold and cinnabar processes, which are the best of the others?

Ko: Before acquiring those of the highest importance a man has no choice but to become widely acquainted with the lesser ones (TT 884.5.1*a*—). It might be said that one must rely upon the whole mass of recipes jointly to produce Fullness of Life. To compare the situation with a similar one of significance, it is similar to a king's governing of his domain. Not a single one of the many civil or military rites and standards can be dispensed with. Or to compare it with some lesser undertaking — it is like the cartwright's work, where neither the shafts nor the rims nor the axles nor the hub-locks may be missing. The recipes we follow stimulate the gods within our bodies so that a prolongation of life may be acquired more quickly, and externally they exorcize evils so that no misfortunes interfere. One might compare all this with a lute, from which we must not expect the Five Notes if there is only one string left. Or we might take for comparison the lorica and helmet, which require more than a single plaque to withstand a point or blade. Why? There must be nothing missing if you would have a harmonic use of the Five Notes, and the place where points and blades strike must have all its parts.

3b

In everything pertaining to the nurturing of life one must learn much and make the essentials one's own; look widely and know how to select. There can be no reliance upon one particular specialty, for there is always the danger that bread-winners will emphasize their personal specialties. That is why those who know recipes for sexual intercourse say that only these recipes can lead to geniehood. Those who know breathing procedures claim that only circulation of the breaths can prolong our years. Those knowing methods for bending and stretching say that only calisthenics can exorcize old age. Those knowing herbal prescriptions say that only through the nibbling of medicines can one be free from exhaustion. Failures in the study of the divine process are due to such specializations. People with shallow experience who happen to know one particular thing well will immediately declare it a panacea. But those ignorant of the true divine process, though possessing potent prescriptions, continue to do more and more searching, without end. Their days are lost in wasted effort, and they lack certainty about their labors. All of this type are suffering double loss. Sometimes, since they are naturally stupid, what they know is extremely superficial, and, feeling compelled to enter a famous mountain, they tread upon or are struck by the bite of some poisonous animal and suffer a wound from it. Then they are ashamed to try a second time. Or they may be devoured by a tiger or a wolf; slain by a *wang-liang* demon (in the form of a brown child with red eyes, long ears, and a fine head of hair); or become hungry and remain without a method for dispensing with starchy foods; or become cold and lack a method for warming themselves. Wouldn't it be stupid to die in a mountain valley?

4a

Selection of the right teacher is more important than hard study. If the teacher is not widely schooled, he will not teach his subject exhaustively, and will go on to claim that pursuit of the divine process does not reside in quantity. This declaration merely signifies that, given the possession of all the essentials pertaining to gold and cinnabar, no use will be made of the rest. Very few people, however, know these matters. How can you stand around waiting for instruction in what is not necessarily the big thing, without meanwhile practicing the lesser recipes which are also quite beneficial? This would be as though a householder said that he would not use other things, for he had been told that the handling and preservation of gold, silver, pearls, and jade could of themselves provide for generation upon generation. Yet, if he lacked such things, how could he help but sow the various grains and provide by accumulating abundant stores of fruits and vegetables?

Therefore, by giving up starches (8.2*b*2) one can become

immune to weapons, exorcize demons, neutralize poisons, and cure illnesses. On entering a mountain, he can render savage beasts harmless. When he crosses streams, no harm will be done to him by dragons (cf. Chap. 17). There will be no fear when plague strikes; and when a crisis or difficulty suddenly arises, you will know how to cope with it. All these are minor matters, but one must not fail to be aware of them. How can you then fail to learn things that are more important than these?

Interlocutor: Would you mind listing the taboos for one wishing to carry out the divine process leading to Fullness of Life?

4*b*

Ko: Taboos are most urgent for avoiding harm and losses. *Inner Commands of the Book of Changes, Ch'ih-sung tzu's Classic,* and *The Life-dealing Amulets of the Ho-t'u-chi* are unanimous in saying that the gods of heaven and earth who are in charge of misdeeds make deductions from people's three-day reckonings (3.8*b*) according to the degree of their wrongdoing. As these reckonings decrease, a man becomes poorer and falls ill; frequently he suffers anxiety. When no more are left, he dies. Since there are hundreds of things that may give rise to deductions, I cannot give a complete account.

It is also said that there are Three Corpses in our bodies, which, though not corporeal, actually are of a type with our inner, ethereal breaths, the powers, the ghosts, and the gods. They want us to die prematurely. (After death they become a man's ghost and move about at will to where sacrifices and libations are being offered.) Therefore, every fifty-seventh day of the sixty-day cycle they mount to heaven and personally report our misdeeds to the Director of Fates. Further, during the night of the last day of the month (6*a*1) the hearth god also ascends to heaven and makes an oral report of a man's wrongs. For the more important misdeeds a whole period of three hundred days is deducted. For the minor ones they deduct one reckoning, a reckoning being three days. Personally, I have not yet been able to determine whether this is really so or not, but that is because the ways of heaven are obscure, and ghosts and gods are hard to understand.

5a We do know that both Viscount Chien of Chao and Duke Mu of Ch'in received a gold plaque from Emperor-up-there; the site god himself was witness. We know that there are spirits in mountains, rivers, plants, trees, wells, hearths, water holes, and also pools. Even within the bodies of us human beings there are gods. Therefore, since heaven and earth are the biggest things in creation, it is logical that they should also have spirits. And if they do have gods, it is also logical that they reward good and punish evil. Yet, given their physical size and the looseness of their organization, they simply must not be expected to respond mechanically.

Accordingly, when we examine the moral injunctions of the various teachings, we find all of them agreeing that those desiring Fullness of Life must strive to accumulate goodness, win merit, be kind and affectionate to others, practice the Golden Rule, love even the creeping things, rejoice in the good fortune of others and commiserate with their sufferings, help those in distress, aid the poor, harm no living thing, utter no curses, look upon the successes and failures of others as their own, not be proud, not vaunt themselves, not envy their betters, and conceal no evil intentions with flattery. In this way they become men of exalted character and receive good fortune from heaven. Their undertakings are sure to be successful, and they can seek geniehood with hope of success.

On the other hand, when goodness is disliked and slayings preferred, lips approve while the heart disapproves, things are said behind a back that would not be said to a face, the upright are opposed, subordinates oppressed, superiors deceived, those being served are rebelled against, when there is no gratitude shown for favors, bribes are accepted when the law is applied, crooked dealing is acquiesced in and honesty corrupted, private interest is given precedence over the public, the innocent are punished, the homes of 5b others destroyed and their valuables taken, harm is done to others and their positions usurped, those of high caliber are plundered, those who have surrendered are put to death, genii and sages are maligned, harm is inflicted on processors, flying birds are shot with pellets, the pregnant disemboweled and eggs broken; when there is hunting by fire during spring and summer, gods and powers are cursed, people are taught to do evil, the virtues of others are concealed, others are jeopardized in order to bring security to oneself, the credits of others are seized, the good deeds of others are destroyed and the things they love taken from them; when one separates others from their families, one's victory is pressed to the point of disgracing others, one borrows full strings of cash and repays with deficient strings, floods are caused and fires set, spells are cast on others, the weak are oppressed, evil is returned for good, one takes or requests forcibly, plunders for enrichment, is not objective and fair, is licentious and base; when orphans and widows are oppressed, bequests are amassed and gifts extracted, deception and falsehood are practiced, the secrets of others are betrayed and their vices abetted, Heaven and Earth are invoked, justification is sought through the help of the gods, things are borrowed but not returned, exchanges and loans are not repaid, one's demands and desires are insatiable, loyalty and honesty are repulsed, a superior's orders are not obeyed, the teacher is not respected, another's good deeds are mocked and his crops destroyed, the things of others are damaged, those with no ability are given employment, the impure is considered clean and given to others to drink and eat, light weight is given and short measure, the bolt of cloth is short in width and length, truth is interspersed with falsehood, dishonest profits are amassed, goods are taken under false pretenses, associates are surpassed, even including one's 6a father — then there will be singing on the last of the month but weeping (4b8) on the first. Every one of these constitutes one fault, and according to its severity the Director of Fates deducts a reckoning or a period (4b); when no more reckonings remain, death ensues. When there is only evil intention but no overt act, only one reckoning is deducted, but if another suffers as the result of your wrongdoing, a whole period is deducted. In all cases where suicide is committed before the allotment is exhausted, misfortune will befall the sons and grandsons.

Whenever you interfere with or appropriate another's property, your wife, children, and other members of your household may be reckoned in as compensation even if this requires their deaths, which however may not occur immediately. And if your wrongdoing does not bring death upon the members of your household, floods, fires, burglaries, and other losses will continuously occur among your belongings. Or you may be obliged to provide personally the medication for the district magistrate's illnesses and meet the costs of the animals for the sacrificial services until you have compensated for the wrongs you have committed. Therefore, the Taoists say that whenever a person has been wrongfully slain, there will follow mutual slayings with weapons; wealth acquired through improper acts will create resentments. It is like satisfying hunger with putrid corned meats or slaking thirst with poisoned wine; death ensues despite your momentary satiation.

6b   These are the rules governing atonement for wrongdoings of the past: if there have been wrongful slayings on your part, thought must be given to rescuing those deserving death in order to absolve one's own fault; if the property of others has been wrongfully seized, thought must be given to donations for the poor and needy; if others have been inculpated in your wrongs, thought must be given to recommending those of high caliber for office. All these propitiatory actions being diametric opposites of the wrongs done, they will promptly bring enjoyment of good luck and profit; this is the way to turn misfortune into good.

If one violates none of the prohibitions, one's years are sure to be protracted, one's longevity increased, and one's study of the divine process quickly concluded. Heaven is high, but its hearing reaches low, and every creature is under its observation. If good is done unremittingly, one is sure to be rewarded with good fortune. Yang Hsü accumulated good works and was charitable; therefore in his old age he received gold dropped from heaven. Ts'ai Shen was so highly filial that all the gods reacted favorably to him. Kuo Chü was willing to kill his son for the sake of his own mother and got as rich reward an iron token inscribed in gold. However, goodness being difficult and evil easy, the unthinking among us hold that heaven and earth cannot distinguish good from evil because of the misfortunes suffered by such persons as Hsiang T'o[1] and Jan Keng. They do not realize that one with a good reputation is not necessarily deserving of it internally; that the man praiseworthy for one thing need not be absolved of guilt for the very opposite. It is like observing the life-and-death cycle of shepherd's purse and wheat (2.2b5; 9.8b11) and then not believing that the grand breaths of yin and yang have effect from great distances. It is probably for similar reasons that superior officers barely escape punishments despite earnest efforts, and ordinary men do not get their wishes fulfilled. *7a*

Interlocutor: Before God and the natural life have been achieved, or before all trace of oneself has been obliterated in a famous mountain — the present being different from antiquity and bandits being very numerous — how are we to banish sudden anxiety and obviate sure disaster?

Ko: Always gather Six-*kuei* superior earth on a friendly day, and after mixing it with a hundred leaves of fragrant plants paint a square foot of your door with it. No bandits will then come. A human form may also be fashioned of a

---

[1] Cf. M. Soymié, *Journal Asiatique*, Vol. 242 (1954), pp. 311–392; *ChanKT* 7.6a2.

mixture of Market-south-entrance earth, Sui-p'o earth, and Yüeh-chien earth, and then placed to the south to check robbers. In an emergency, place yourself in a nucleus (life-site); then there will be nothing to fear. There is a nucleus to the world, a province, a prefecture, a subprefecture, a town, a neighborhood, a house, and even a room.

Interlocutor: Isn't that getting quite small — a room?

Ko: The classics tell us that in the greatest of emergencies one can hide in the crossbar of a vehicle, so you see that there is a nucleus even in a vehicle. Why shouldn't there be one in a room?

Interlocutor: I have been taught that when carrying out the divine process in search of life one should know the two mountains, but I have never been clear as to where they are located. I should like you to enlighten me and allay my doubts.

Ko: They exist, but they are neither Mount Hua and Mount Huo, nor Mount Sung and Mount Tai.

> *T'ai-yüan's mountain, hard to know but easy to seek.*
> *It is neither in heaven nor on earth; it is not sunk under water, nor does it float.*
> *It is exceedingly steep and long-lasting; rocky and rough-pathed.*
> *Pleasant and wholesome; our inner gods and thoughts like it there.*
> *Jade-like wells run deep there with clear water, irrigating the mountain without cease.*
> *There is an administrative force of one hundred twenty, well coordinated.*
> *Since it is situated on a line with east and west, there are black growths by the thousands.*
> *Particularly, the peach grows there, all the fruit exceptional.*
> *There are rocks of gold and jade, and springs of new wine flowing from the corners.*
> *Officers of the past have quaffed from its pure streams.*
> *If you can find it, you will join the company of Wang Ch'iao and Ch'ih-sung tzu.*

This is one of them.

*Ch'ang-ku's mountain, fllled with fragrances and looming ever
  larger and larger.*
*The breath of God blows in breeze after breeze there; exudates
  of jade continuously fall in flakes.*
Golden pools and crimson rooms in its crevices.
Any ignorant person accidentally straying there will surely die.
*The officer in possession of the divine process who climbs it will
  not weaken.*
*Having gathered and taken knotgrass (11.2a1), he acquires ability
  to fly heavenward.*

This is the second of them. Give careful thought to them,
for they are the places which the Ancients of high caliber
kept secret.

Interlocutor: I should like to learn the recipe of God's Men
for protecting one's person and refining one's well-being.

Ko: Your question probes to the very depths. Here are the
oral directions I received from my late teacher:

At the foot of Shih-ch'ing (Beginnings-Azure) are the moon and sun.
Like two halves, they mount jointly to become one.
An emission from the Jade Pool (mouth) enters the Golden Room (lungs)
  [cf. 8.2*b*7].
Large as an arbalest's pellet, yellow as an orange;
Within it has an excellent taste, sweet as honey.
When you have been able to secure it, be careful not to lose it.
One does not pursue that which has already passed, otherwise the body
  would perish.
The pure, white breath becomes thoroughly sublimated.
Proceeding to the Somber Gateway (kidneys), it bends and twists thrice.
The Cinnabar Field of the center portion of the body sparkles as never
  before.
When the emission comes to a halt at the Gateway to Life (belly), the
  physique will not perish.
Profound is this marvel, and hard to call in question.[2]

8a

As I say, these are the oral directions I had from my late
teacher. He who knows them will fear no ghosts at any time,
nor weapons.

[2] Further search may some day reveal precisely what this means, but oral traditions abound in esoterisms. The reference seems to be to the hoarding of breaths
or nasal mucus. Cf. H. Maspero, *Journal asiatique*, Vol. 229 (1937), pp. 229–377.

Interlocutor: I have been taught that he who can fully carry out the correct sexual procedures can travel alone and summon gods and genii. Further, he can shift disaster from himself and absolve his misdeeds; turn misfortune into good; rise high if in office; double his profits if in business. Is it true?

Ko: This is all deceptive, exaggerated talk found in the writings of mediums and shamans; it derives from the enlargements and colorings of dilettantes. It utterly belies the facts. Some of it is the work of base liars creating meaningless claims to deceive the masses. Their concealed purpose is to seek service from others; to gather about themselves pupils solely with a view to obtaining advantages for themselves in their own time.

The best of the sexual recipes can cure the lesser illnesses, and those of a lower quality can prevent us from becoming empty; but that is all. There are very natural limits to what such recipes can accomplish. How could they ever be expected to confer the ability to summon gods and genii and to dispel misfortune or bring good?

8b

It is inadmissible that man should sit and bring illness and anxieties upon himself by not engaging in sexual intercourse. But then again, if he wishes to indulge his lusts and cannot moderate his dispersals, he hacks away at his very life. Those knowing how to operate the sexual recipes can check ejaculation, thereby repairing the brain; revert their sperm to the Vermilion Intestine (?for small or large). They can gather saliva into the Pool of Gold (?gall bladder); conduct the three southern and the five northern breaths to their Flowered Rafters (?lungs). They can thus cause a man, even in old age, to have an excellent complexion, and terminate the full number of his allotted years.

The crowd, however, learning that Yellow Emperor mounted to heaven after having a harem of 1200, proceeds to claim that this was the sole reason he attained Fullness of Life. They do not know that Yellow Emperor mounted to heaven on a dragon only after having successfully sublimed the Nine-crucibles cinnabars on the shores of Tripod Lake at the foot of the Ching mountains. Yellow Emperor could naturally have a harem of 1200, but his success was not due to that sole fact.

In sum, there is no benefit from taking all sorts of medicines and eating beef, mutton, and pork, if one does not know the arts of sexual intercourse. The Ancients, therefore, fearing that people might treat existence itself lightly or arbitrarily, purposely lauded these arts beyond complete credibility. Sexual intercourse may be compared with water and fire, either of which can slay man or bring him life, depending solely upon his ability to deal with them. On the whole, if the important rules are known, the benefits will be proportionate to the number of one's successive copulations. If, however, the procedure is employed in ignorance, sudden death could ensue after only one or two copulations. Old P'eng's methods contain all the essentials.[3] Other books on the subject teach only many troublesome methods difficult to carry out, and the resulting benefits are not necessarily as claimed. Man is scarcely able to follow the directions, and there are thousands of words of oral directions. Whoever does not know them would still be unable to attain Fullness of Life, even though he took many medicines (8.3*b*6).

9a

[3] H. Maspero, *op. cit.*, pp. 380–398.

7

Objections Countered

Interlocutor: The August Vault, being divinity in its highest form, should be just in the fates it metes out. Yet if such ordinary persons as Wang Ch'iao and Ch'ih-sung tzu achieved immortality, why did the Duke of Chou and Confucius fail to receive the favor of lasting vision?

Ko: Whether one's predestined life is long or short is a matter of chance: On receiving breath and taking form in the womb we all belong to a star or celestial asterism. God (T'ien-Tao) acts in perfect freedom, and in every case something natural occurs. There is no question of close or distant relationships; no subjectivity to the event.

When a man's destiny comes under a star of life, he is sure to like the divine process leading to geniehood, and when he seeks it he is sure to be successful. But when the fated life comes under a star of death, that individual will not believe in this process and will not train himself in it. What a man likes depends upon his endowment, and heaven can do no shifting, changing, granting, nor canceling. All this may be compared with the smelting of ores and casting of metals, or with earthenware formed on the wheel and fired in the kiln. Although they may all be treated in the same way to achieve a shape, the quality of the copper or iron utensils, as well as that of the earthenwares, depends upon chance. There is no sense in blaming the furnace or the kiln.

Interlocutor: The works of the craftsman are the result of his skill, and in the same way heaven is intelligent enough to do anything. You, on the other hand, claim that each man is the result of chance and has not been fashioned by Grand Azure up high. In my stupidity you have me quite confused. I cannot accept your explanation.

Ko: God (Primal Chaos) was split into two: the clear and the muddy. Some of this mounted and became active; some descended and lay still. Heaven and earth themselves do not know how they came to be what they are; and the acquiring of breath by everything in creation was also something spontaneous, each thing — and that includes heaven and earth — constituting one object. There was, however, precedence in these doings, and there are large as well as small constitutions. It is only comparative size that makes heaven and earth seem big, while individual creatures seem tiny. We may compare heaven and earth with our abdomens and backs which may embrace our five internal organs, and yet the abdomens and backs did not make the five organs. Or, our flesh and skin may embrace the blood and breaths, and yet they did not make them. So, heaven and earth may surround all creation, but they are not the producers of all creation. It is like the plants and trees that sprout and grow in the mountains and forests, even though the mountains and forests play no part in their sprouting and growing. Or, compare fish and turtles resorting to waters for birth and growth, while the waters themselves have no part in the process. Ordinary people, however, notice only that heaven and earth are large and the various created things relatively smaller. They conclude, therefore, that heaven and earth are the parents of created things, which are then the children. But just because lice live on us it does not mean that we created them. They do not live without us, but we are not their parents, nor are they our children or grandchildren. Gnats are reared by vinegar; mushrooms grow on wood and stone; waterbugs multiply in wet places; lichens flourish on pines, but none of these hosts fashion their parasites. Is it not in just this same way that created things fill all heaven and earth?

Heaven possesses sun, moon, cold, and heat; man possesses eyesight and breathing; and, if I may do some comparing between the distant and the near and draw inferences from one regarding the other — since man cannot know of himself why his own body, whether old or young, suffers pain and illness, neither can heaven know of itself why its own body, whether expanding or contracting, suffers calamities and omens. If man cannot keep his ears and eyes constantly keen and prevent his blood and breaths from diminishing, neither can heaven prevent eclipses and diminishings of the sun and moon, or departures from the proper sequence of the four seasons.

Proceeding then analogically, great longevities are not within the province of heaven and earth, and whether one becomes a genie or not depends entirely upon one's fortune. To be sure, our fathers begat us and our mothers bore us, but they cannot assure us a desirable body, elegance of facial expression, undisturbed constitution, lofty intellects, and an abundance of breath and energy that will protract our lives. Sometimes we are small and puny, or dark and ugly, or deaf, blind, stupid and crafty, or disjointed and crippled. What is gotten was not desired, and what was desired is not gotten. How much more would this be true in the case of heaven and earth which are so vast and distant! They are farther removed from us than our parents.

Once our bodies are in our own possession, we cannot make them remain eternally at the prime nor prevent them from growing old. We cannot keep them forever strong and free from illness. We cannot see that our joys and angers are always justified, and our schemes and plans free from regrets. Accordingly, the providers of the breaths and the characterizers of our bodies are the parents, while the receivers and possessors are our own persons. And there is nothing closer and more intimate than this; nothing more regulating and controlling. But neither our parents nor ourselves can take or add anything to our respective roles. How then could heaven and earth possibly share in any knowledge of what is happening?

Most certainly, if men and creatures were the products of heaven and earth, they should all be fair and free from unpleasantness; they should all be perfect — no failures. Throughout creation there would be no anomalies, and the overturned willow would not be bemoaning its death in the spring. Since heaven could not cause Confucius and Mencius to enjoy immortality, you should come to realize more and more that our endowments are part of a natural process; they are not consignments from heaven and earth. The excellence of these sages was the pinnacle of excellence. If heaven had been able to provide them with this and still made them incompatible with their environment, so that their work did not become established, their positions did not become that of hegemon or king, and they did not live to be a hundred — this is clear evidence that heaven had nothing to do with it. If heaven was not the slayer in their deaths, neither was it the producer of their births.

The most capable are not certain to live long lives, and the stupid are not certain to die before their time. Goodness does not vouchsafe imminence of good fortune, and evil does not guarantee imminence of misfortune. Birth is not in a predetermined year, nor death at a constant moment. Wise men teeming with excellence may flourish and then produce no fruit (*Ana.* 9.22); but the artisan Tou (a musician: HS 30.5*a*7) lived to almost two hundred years. Jan Keng became helplessly ill, and Pu Shang lost his eyesight weeping for a son who had died; but robber Chih, the basest of men, lived to be white-headed; Chuang Chiao, the epitome of

3a

evil, also lived to an old age. It is clear that heaven has
nothing to do with these things.

Interlocutor: Confucius has said that everything finally
dies (12.7), but Lao Tan (?T 59) claims that divinity and
geniehood can be acquired through study. The words of the
sage Confucius are credible and supported by evidence; but
the declaration of the Taoist is exaggerated and hard to
apply.

3b

Ko: Confucius is a sage in the eyes of the scholars, but Lao
Tan is a sage for those who have attained God. The teachings of the Confucian scholars, being empiric and easy to
grasp, are honored by the great majority; but the idea of
God, being abstruse and hard to understand, is compre-
hended by a few only. God is the source of all differences;
but Confucian doctrine is the stream of piety. Long before
the three Augusti, God reigned; beginning at the time of
the emperors and kings, the scholars have been instructing.
Listen to any conversation and you will hear anyone ac-
knowledge the sincerity and simplicity of the great past
ages but criticize the evils and laxity of custom in these
latter days. Why, then, value only Confucius, and treat Lao
Tan lightly? This is like enjoying the flowers on the twigs
and failing to recognize the trunk from which they spring.
How is it any different from valuing a bright pearl but
despising the watery depths; or liking Pien Ho's circular
jade but hating the Ching mountains? A person who does
this is ignorant of the fact that the depths are the source of
the bright pearl, and that it was the Ching mountains which
produced that circular jade.

It must be noticed that the things done to nourish life are
but the fragments of Taoism, just as ritual and music are the
things of least importance in Confucianism. Thus Confucianism is valued for the improvements it brings about in
habits and customs, and not only for its bowings and
wheelings; Taoism is honored because it transforms conduct
without uttering a word, and not just for the sole matter of

nurturing life. While there is, of course, a temporal sequence between Confucianism and Taoism, Confucius is not to receive all the confidence, and Lao Tan is not to be followed to the exclusion of Confucius (12.6a8). After paying his respects to Lao Tan, Confucius wanted to compare himself with Old P'eng (*Ana.* 7.1). Further, admitting to a knowledge of fish and birds but to no acquaintance with dragons, he compared Lao Tan to a dragon (*Chuang* 14.61; SC 63.1*b*); this was probably a way of expressing his own humility and not a meaningless statement. His remark was in no way different from what Yen Hui made of Confucius (*Ana* 9.11): "When I catch sight of his doctrine before me, it suddenly is behind me; it is too hard to penetrate and too lofty to see."

Interlocutor: If Confucius spoke face to face with Lao Tan, why did he fail to study God with him?

Ko: This makes it increasingly clear that endowment is ordained by God (Spontaneity); preferences possess an unalterable existence. Confucius realized that Lao Tan's God (the Mystery and Marvel) was to be honored and marveled at, but he was unable to draw and pour from God (the Unprejudiced and Uncommitted). The Grand Ancestor, prime origin of all, rises from beyond the nonempiric and becomes part of Ultimate God, but Confucius, through his inquiries, could learn only about political economy. How could he inquire about methods for seeking geniehood? It may be conjectured that his heart and mind kept syphoning solely for transformation through instruction; they did not concentrate upon recipes. Confucius may be a sage in worldly matters, but he was not competent to plunge into and find quiet in God (the Mystery and Silence) and thus protect himself with perfect freedom of action. That is the reason Lao Tan warned him (SC 63.1*b*4): "Things of the highest value are stored deep and seem nonexistent; Great Man teems with the natural life and looks unintelligent. Give up your pride and covetousness, your airs and wanton will. They are of no benefit to your person." This is enough to

4a

4b

show that Confucius was not devoid of human failings and was not a student of geniehood.

Settling now here and now there, wandering hither and yon, Confucius' energies went into saving his times. He listened longingly for the cry of the phoenix (9.9); he complained about being an empty gourd that might be unsaleable (17.6). When one mournfully contemplates entering public service, how can one quit the task of giving the world good order and cultivate the abandon which nurtures life?

Interlocutor: Of Confucianism and Taoism, which is the more difficult?

Ko: Confucianism is difficulty in the midst of facility; Taoism is facility in the midst of difficulties. The difficulties of Taoism are these: abandonment of social intercourse and renouncing wife and family; rejection of fame and loss of income; removal of brilliances from one's sight and suppression of the tinkling marks of office from one's ears; the silence and retirement where one's sole profession is preservation of one's own integrity; not to be depressed by criticism nor elated by praise; to look upon honors without desiring them and to dwell humbly without shame. But Taoism also has its attractive side: no visits of congratulation or condolence, and no critical glances and looks at one's abode; no troubling of the internal gods with the Seven Classics and never a concern for the calendar; no bother about the advancings of asterisms and no enslavement to a craft or to letters; all annoyances lifted, and an inner harmony that grows of itself; perfect freedom of action and thought, no fear, no grief. Therefore, I describe Taoism as facility in the midst of difficulties.

5a

Everything done in Confucianism is modeled upon precedents. Leaving and staying have their set rules; speech and silence depend upon the hour. If a teacher is desired, he can be found in practically any house; if it is a matter of written material, there are plenty of commentaries to resolve the doubts. This is what is easy in Confucianism. Its difficulties are these: grasping the profound and rendering present the distant (*Changes, Hsi tz'u*), and also confronting and reconciling the regulations coming from the rulers of old; embracing the documents of *The River* and *The Lo* (A.3*a*6), and acquiring a wide knowledge of all those many things said by the various schools of philosophy; constantly accumulating good works among the people, and giving the last drop of loyalty to one's lord; being able to interpret any signs conferred by heaven, and giving thought to the meanings of winds and clouds; to be considered unsuccessful for not knowing some solitary matter, and to have to face criticism for one word of imprecision; to have one's every step taken as a model by the world, and to have one's every utterance repeated by all. This is what I mean by difficulties in the midst of facility. But to put it honestly, Confucianism is difficult because of its multiplicities, while Taoism is easy with its conciseness. Being afraid of difficulties, I evade them and pursue what is easy. The critics of my choice come in droves; none do I find sympathetic with my decision. However, as for those who will come to share my purpose in the future, I will not at this time predict that they will be but few.

5*b*

Interlocutor: I have surveyed the exalted persons enjoying high renown and the eminent Confucianists of vast learning, and naturally found that most of them had made an exhaustive study of life in all its ramifications and had thoroughly studied the empiric and the nonempiric. Nowhere, however, did I find any of them saying that our years could be protracted or that geniehood could be obtained. I cannot believe that you, whose brightness does not equal that of the sun and moon, and whose intelligence is not superior to that of thousands of others, place reliance in a divine process leading to Fullness of Life.

Ko: I am only an ordinary person of modest talents. My views are shallow and my learning slight. How could I dare admit that I surpass the men of my generation in eminence

and unique knowledge? However, having found that the
evident is to be sought in the obscurities and the easy obtained from the difficult by comparing the slightest clues,
big effects become known; on seeing what is already there,
one learns to understand what has not yet been tried.

We should not undertake to rectify those of our generation who do not believe there are genii in heaven and earth.
All these have a talent for governing the masses and the art of
efficient administration. They study the books and writings
with pedagogical value and thereby conclude that the principles governing man are shallow and facile. When the confusions of all are under discussion, they say, "We are able of
ourselves to resolve the doubts felt by the masses. We can
feel things before the omens of them occur. This means that
we enjoy complete sympathy with the affairs of all creation.
6a   We reach into everything hidden or obscure. When we say
that genii do not exist, then they certainly do not." Such has
long been their obduracy.

Whenever I notice the ignorant, stolid disbelief of ordinary
Confucianists regarding matters of the highest importance,
I am always sorry that with so much intelligence they bind
themselves in prejudice and burden themselves with petty
things. I do not claim that they are utterly in profoundest
ignorance, but simply that they cannot distinguish between
beans and wheat. To adopt only the narrow point of view as
though peering through a tube and shut off everything that
hearing and sight do not attain — how does that differ from
using eight feet of rope to draw from a depth of eight hundred feet and, without realizing that the implement is too
short, to claim that there is no water in the well? When the
ignorant man hears the roar of a bright fire whipped by a
savage wind, he says that it is thundering in the winter.
When he sees clouds moving westward, he says that the
moon is rushing eastward. When told what is happening,
he does not understand or believe, so self-confident is he.

For listening to sounds, we all trust our ears, and for seeing objects, we all trust our eyes. Yet sometimes what is heard or seen is said to be so and so when in fact it is not, and it becomes clear that even our ears and eyes are not to be trusted. How much greater then is the difficulty in matters of thought, where nothing is visible or audible, and yet people, thinking the products of their own thought are assuredly the most profound in the world, go on to claim that gods and genii are empty talk? How ignorant can they get?

6b

Beauty and ugliness are accepted categories, but, given the differences introduced by emotion, no two pairs of eyes see them in the same light. The elegant and the depraved are natural categories, but, given the differences introduced by likes and dislikes, no two pairs of ears hear music in the same way. There is substance to the categories of true and false, but, given the varieties in preferences, no two hearts and minds counsel in the same way. There are people who consider the ugly beautiful, the muddy pure, and failure success. These situations are so simple that the contrariness in them can be clearly understood; yet the parties concerned can in no way reach a common decision. How much truer is this in the case of divinities and genii! Despite the marvelousness of this matter, no logical procedure yet exists for achieving our desire to have all men believe. What could be more valuable in the eyes of the initiated than to have all men know about divinity and geniehood? But to expect the masses to cease from incoherent talk is like expecting that the Yellow River will soon run clear! If I do not remain silent, it is simply because I hope it may prove possible to attract not only those with whom one may talk of the highest things but also those capable of only the lowest. The Ancients have already found it impossible to do anything about those who refuse to be persuaded.

It is not just today, but already for a long time, that there has been no faith in gods and genii, the highest logic not being easy to elucidate. In highest antiquity these things

7a

were known naturally; after that, they were understood only when proclaimed by authority, and whenever loud laughter was induced among the listeners, they were being accepted far and wide.[1] But now that I am discussing these matters, I am saddened by many defeats in my efforts to convert, and I often blame myself for wasting words! But we do most harm to creatures when we avoid association with them. It would be well to remember that, just as even a maximum of *yang* cannot make a dead tree grow, a divine intelligence can effect no change in the natures of those who are bogged down. Tuan-mu Tz'u (LSCC 14, end) himself was unable to persuade the country yokel who had taken Confucius's horse for cause, and a duke of old (M 1B.15) was unable to dissuade the northern barbarians who wanted his lands. There are places where facts and logic are not congruent, where persuasiveness is ineffective. There is no sale for our ceremonial hats among the southern barbarians, and our red shoes find no use among the uncivilized who go barefooted. How can we compel acceptance?

Remember that someone saw a piece of jade and, pointing to it, called it a stone. This does not mean that the jade was false, but the facts could not be ascertained before Pien Ho (the jeweler) arrived. There was also the man who saw a dragon and called it a snake. This does not mean that the dragon was not divine, but the difference could not be established until Ts'ai Mo passed that way. In the same manner, God is esteemed because additions Thereto cause

[1] In God, and the things pertaining Thereto, contraries become identical. Cf. T 41:

> *The best gentleman is diligent in doing something*
> *about God, once he has been taught.*
> *The middling type reacts haphazardly, and*
> *the lowest type bursts out laughing: and*
> *we can be sure that it is God that we have*
> *taught him.*
> *One may sum up in this fashion: Beaming God*
> *resembles darkness; God advancing resembles*
> *retreat; flattened, God resembles the rough*
> *places. . . .*

no increase, and diminutions bring no decrease. The natural 7b
life is valued because, when maligned, it feels no shame;
when praised, it feels no pleasure.

When others feel certain that there are no genii in the
world, and I alone, feeling that they really do exist, were to
argue with them, the longer we argued, the more firmly
they would persist in their denial. In this way the confusion
would be prolonged to no avail and there would be no way
out of the impasse. Quite naturally, then, we must acknowl-
edge the situation to be that of the gimmal, which could be
separated only by an act of violence.

8

Resolving Hesitations

Interlocutor: Of the many things constituting human life, search for geniehood is the most difficult. Unless we abandon it, our affairs will be thrown utterly awry. How can we destroy all arts and letters, the duties evoked by sorrow and joy, and the hierarchal relationships of the good society?

Ko: In all essentials, God is no trouble because there is so little we can do. The only thing to be feared is that there be no will to God and no sincere belief. There is no reason to fear that the human order will be abandoned. What objection can there be to concomitant cultivation by the fully endowed, as we inwardly treasure the divine process for nurturing life, and outwardly work with our generation? By regulating our own bodies, they will long remain active, and by providing order for the state, the state will enjoy a veritable millennium.

Let the Six Classics be taught to the common run of gentlemen, but the recipes transmitted only to our intimates. When the latter wish to remain on earth a while, let them serve their generation as they temporarily halt their work with the recipes. When they wish to ascend, let them mount lightly into the empyrean. These would be the gentlemen of the highest class. Below them would rank those who live to their full potential but, being unable to lead the double life, abandon normal human pursuits and concentrate upon God and the natural life. Anciently, Yellow Emperor bore the hard burden of empire, but this did not prevent his elevation to geniehood at Ting-hu (6.8*b*6). Old P'eng was a grand officer for eight hundred years, after which he went west to the Gobi. Lao Tan was a state recorder; Ning-feng chief of the potteries. Fang Hui was a village official; Lü Shang a grand tutor. Master Chiu served the Yin. Ma Tan held office in the state of Chin. Fan Li became the leader of the state of Yüeh and then floated away to sea. The lutist Kao held a post under King K'ang of Sung. Ch'ang-sheng forced himself into a humble job. Duke Chuang stored his capacity in a small office. It is evident, therefore, that many of the Ancients continued to work at public office after attaining the divine process; they practiced it in the shadows of the court, presumably because they had an excess of energy.

Why, then, must the divine process be carried on in the mountains and forests, and achieved only after completely abandoning wordly affairs? There are persons whose hearts and minds find security in solitude and quiet; who have a natural dislike for noise; who take joy in relaxed living; for whom the glories of office would be grief. They wear rope belts, dress in rags, eat herbs, and work the ploughshare. They delight in the three joys of being human, male, and alive (cf. Ana. 16.5, and M 7*A*.20); and this norm they defend until death. They have no intention of living to no avail; they do not stand in fear of sudden death. They decline gifts worth a thousand in gold; they disdain the honors of being state minister. And thus they ever continue without any specific projects. How much more, then, would such people be unwilling to slave for their generation were they to be informed of this divine process leading to divinity or geniehood! Each then to his own will! All are not to be described under one classification.

2a   It is said that one word can be so good that it is worth more than a thousand in gold. What this signifies is probably only success in military matters, or the quality of personal conduct. But when a person is given the oral directions for enjoying Fullness of Life or a prescription for immortality, it is worth far more than the right word of the ordinary man. Why is it valued at only a thousand in gold? If a man lies at death's door with illness and a person is able to cure him, everyone says that he has had a mighty favor or an enormous gift. Today, if the Nine-crucible cinnabars are sublimed and gold or jade liquefied, the whole world can be made immortal — a favor involving not the life of just one individual. The excellence of Yellow Emperor and Lao Tan is certainly immeasurable; it is a pity that none can understand it and it is therefore considered madness!

If you wish to seek divinity or geniehood, you need only acquire the quintessence, which consists in treasuring your sperm, circulating your breaths, and taking one crucial medicine. That is all! There are not a multitude of things to do. In these three pursuits, however, one must distinguish between the profound and the shallow. You cannot learn all about them promptly unless you meet with a learned teacher and work very, very hard. Many things may be dubbed circulation of the breaths, but there are only a few methods for doing it correctly. Other things may be dubbed good sexual practice, but its true recipe involves almost a hundred or more different activities. Something may be dubbed a medicine to be taken, but there are roughly a thousand such

2b   prescriptions.

In teaching these things one always begins with the superficial; only then, if the student's will does not lag and he shows that he can work hard, does one tell him the significant parts. Through circulation of the breaths (cf. 6.4a8) illnesses can be cured, plague need not be fled, snakes and tigers can be charmed, bleeding from wounds can be halted, one may stay under water or walk on it, be free from hunger and thirst, and protract one's years. The most important part of it is simply to breathe like a fetus. He who succeeds in doing this will do his breathing as though in the womb, without using nose or mouth, and for him the divine process has been achieved.

When first learning to circulate the breaths, one inhales through the nose and closes up that breath. After holding it quietly for 120 heartbeats it is expelled in tiny quantities through the mouth. During the exhalations and inhalations one should not hear the sound of one's own breathing, and one should always exhale less than one inhales. A goose feather held before the nose and mouth during the exhalations should not move. After some practice the number of heartbeats may be increased very gradually to one thousand before the breath is released. Once this is achieved, the aged will become one day younger each day.

The circulating of the breaths must be done at an hour when breath is alive, not when it is dead. It is a reference to this when we read, "The genii take the six breaths." In one whole day and night there are twelve [double] hours. The six hours from midnight to noon are the hours when breath is alive; from noon to midnight it is dead. No benefit is derived from practicing the circulating when breath is dead. To use exhalations adroitly, *hsü* at water, and it will flow backward several yards for you; *hsü* at fire, and it will go out; *hsü* at tigers or wolves, and they will crouch down motionless; *hsü* at snakes, and they will coil up motionless (5.5*b*). If someone has been wounded by a weapon, you may stop the bleeding by *hsü*ing it. If you learn of someone bitten by poisonous insects, even though he is not in your presence, far away as you are, you may *hsü* and pray upon your hand; in the case of a male *hsü* your left hand, for a female, the right. All these persons will get better immediately even though they may be a hundred miles away. If stricken suddenly by a severe illness, just swallow breaths in three series of nine, and there will be an immediate improvement.

3a

It must be admitted, however, that it is man's nature to engage in multiple pursuits and he is little inclined to the peace and quiet requisite to the pursuit of this process. For the circulation of the breaths it is essential that the processor refrain from overeating. When fresh vegetables, and fatty and fresh meats are consumed, the breaths, becoming strengthened, are hard to preserve. Hate and anger are also forbidden. Overindulgence in them throws the breaths into confusion, and when they are not calmed they turn into shouting. For these reasons few persons can practice this art. My ancestral uncle, Ko Hsüan, merely because he was able to hoard his breaths and breathe like a fetus, would stay on the bottom of a deep pool for almost a whole day whenever he was thoroughly intoxicated and it was a hot summer's day.

On the methods of correct sexual intercourse at least ten authors have written (HS 30.33*a*7—). Some claim they show how to replenish losses, cure illnesses, gather more yin or increase the yang, or increase the years and protract longevity. The essential here lies solely in reverting the sperm to repair the brain. God's Men have transmitted this method orally without any writing. Though one were to take all the famous medicines, without a knowledge of this essential it would be impossible to attain Fullness of Life. Man may not, however, give up sexual intercourse entirely, for otherwise he would contract melancholia through inactivity, and die prematurely through the many illnesses resulting from depression and celibacy. On the other hand, overindulgence diminishes one's life, and it is only by harmonizing the two extremes that damage will be avoided. Unless the oral directions are available, not one man in ten thousand will fail to kill himself by attempting to undertake this art. It is probable that people like Hsüan-tu, Su tzu, Jung-ch'eng kung, and Old P'eng had some rough acquaintance with it, but they consigned none of its really important parts to paper. However, those bent upon immortality will devote their energies to seeking them out. Personally, I had in-

3b

4a

struction along these lines from my teacher Cheng Yin, and I record them here as information for future believers in the divine process. It is not personal opinion that I am chatting. I must admit that I have not yet personally gotten all the directions involved in the art. Sometimes, narrow-minded processors try to observe solely the recipes regarding sexual intercourse in order to control the gods and genii without utilizing the great medicines of gold and cinnabar. This is the height of folly!

Only a few Taoist writings come from Yellow Emperor and Lao Tan themselves; most are enlargements upon the personal knowledge and experience of later curiosity-seekers, and their bundles and scrolls have accumulated like a mountain. The Ancients were simple and largely un-sophisticated. Since they do not go into details when dis-cussing the inner workings of things, it is not clear what evidence they are using; therefore, with all the essentials lacking, they are hard to understand, and what under-standing of them we do have is not very profound. One cannot expatiate with them upon the subtleties, nor inform the strugglers, encourage the willing, and instruct the beginners, so that the paths of God (the Mystery-Marvel) and the courses followed by good and bad fortune may be-come known. Chant through them thousands of times, and you get simply nothing. No matter how extensively one may wish to study this material, it is advisable to choose carefully the best and concentrate one's attention on them. It is not worthwhile to unravel the less important Taoist writings.

Those with little learning sometimes cannot distinguish between the shallow and the profound authors. As soon as any book is called Taoist they proceed to copy it and fill their cases and baskets with them. But to give all of one's heart and mind to the searching out of their contents is like looking in a swallow's nest for the egg of the phoenix, or searching the bottom of a well for a sturgeon. No matter

4b

how hard one works, what one seeks is not there and nothing that is sure to be useful can be found. There is not an ounce of profit in wasting months and days without rime or reason and working oneself to exhaustion with nothing to show for it. In such a way all the effort of the present is lost, and no Fullness of Life results. And then everyone sizes up the situation by saying, "The fact that these people worked so diligently at the divine process without achieving genie-hood signifies, naturally, that there is no method leading to immortality." They do not realize that those people were seeking immortality like a man who gazes upon the river wishing for fish but using no net. It does not mean that there are no fish in the river.

The Five Thousand Words (*Tao te ching*) may actually come from Lao Tan, but it is only a general discussion and a rough outline of our topic. Its contents in no way allow a complete exposition of the matter from beginning to end that could be employed as support for our pursuit (10.2a3). Merely to recite this classic blindly without securing the essential pro-

5a

cess would be to undergo useless toil. How much worse in the case of texts inferior to *Tao te ching*! Such persons as Hsin Chin (Wen tzu), Chuang Chou, and Governor of the Pass, Yin Hsi, prepared writings that may well be based upon Yellow Emperor and Lao Tan, but they expound the modeling of ourselves upon God (Mystery and Uncommittedness) only in general terms and are very far from speaking exhaustively. They may equate death and life and say there is no difference between them, treat existence as toil and death as repose, but they are an uncalculable distance away from the problems of divinity and geniehood. Why should we toy with them? Their metaphors and similes can be garnered as rubble to fill unexpected deficiencies. Isn't it a pity, though, that the eloquent rogues and base scoundrels of these latter days should be allowed refuge in Lao Tan and Chuang Chou?

Interlocutor: With a wise emperor on the throne, only

those of the highest caliber are treasured, but those studying for geniehood are unwilling to enter office. If everyone pursued the divine process, who would remain to help with political affairs?

Ko: For turning their backs upon a sage prince and resorting to the mountains, Ch'ao fu and Hsü Yu have been called illustrious. Because he turned hermit on meeting someone with the divine process, Chuang Po-wei was honored. When Yellow Emperor was presiding over the world it could well be called highly well-ordered, but his teacher Kuang-ch'eng would have none of it. When Yao was ruling the world it could be said to be in a golden age, but even though Wo-ch'üan did not assist him the effects of his excellence were in no way diminished, and the talented were not lacking because Wo-ch'üan failed to help.

5b

When T'ang the Victorious waged his revolution, Wu Kuang drowned himself in the river by clasping a stone. When Wu of the Chou cut off the Shang, Po-i and Shu-ch'i starved themselves to death in the western mountains. When Duke Huan of Ch'i came to power, Hsiao-ch'en Chi secluded himself in his narrow alley. When Duke Wen of Wei flourished, Tuan-kan Mu continued as a hermit in Hsi-ho. The Four Graybeards remained like phoenixes at Shang-lo, but that did not prevent the Han from having an abundance of personnel. Chou Tang remained like a unicorn in the bush, but he was not condemned for lack of filial duty and loyalty.

In the course of a thousand years there will sometimes be persons unaffected by favors and honors; unmoved from their goals by promises of riches. They will not stoop or deign to wash their hats in the Ts'ang-lang (M 4A.9). They will look upon a fragrant forest as a high terrace, a cave high in the cliffs as a fine house, blue irises as a rope bed, and green leaves as curtains (A. 4a6). For them, rags will replace imperial robes, and herbs fulfill the role of exquisite cuisine. Their hunger will not be satisfied unless they do the farming with their own hands; they will clothe themselves only with what their wives have woven. They may even abandon their families to the community or clan; quit their homes without a glance back. They may turn against pomp and circumstance like renegades; break with every desire that was ever in the heart. They may traverse the peaks of Mount Sung to travel alone; have no company but shadows and echoes in the famous mountain. They may gaze inwardly upon the land where shapes enjoy perfect freedom; turn the ear inward to the deepest of silences. Throughout the whole universe there are very few such at any given moment, yet you fear that the sovereign will have no ministers! Don't you think you're excessively worried?

Interlocutor: Those preparing for geniehood purify only their own persons and forget the confusion they are causing in their families and in public relationships. Neglecting the sovereign, they are slothful in their failure to serve in office. I fear that on failing to achieve Fullness of Life they will later be caught in the net of the criminal code.

Ko: Northerner, Stonehouse, Curluper, and the Tzuchous were all men of great capacity (*Chuang*), but they nurtured the overwhelming vitality that was theirs by fleeing and relinquishing public life. Nevertheless, national prosperity did not fail because of them, and China's civilizing influence did not falter. There is no guarantee that those studying for geniehood have any capacity for governing or supporting a dynasty. If the government were to win them over they would add nothing to the achievements of their day; and in losing them, not the slightest loss is felt! Right now, if in a surge of public unity people came from far and wide to serve in government, there would be such a store of eminent public servants that there would be not enough posts for them to fill. Gentlemen would be caught in a backlog for assignment; office functions would never be subjected to temporary suspension. Those who had worked long and hard would be complaining of slow promotion; those of

6a

superior service would find praises and rewards difficult to come by. There would be no appreciation for accumulations of helpful deeds; and there would be no lack of mediocre officials.

Anciently, Crown Prince Chin (=Wang Ch'iao) worked as master chef and abandoned the weighty duties of heir presumptive, but King Ling of the Chou did not charge him with being unfilial. The Chou did not condemn Yin *6b* Hsi for disloyalty when he repudiated the duties of his office and fled the responsibility of taking corrective measures. Why? Because these men showed by their sincerity that they were not disdainful of their generation, nor were they slighting their sovereign; they merely were different in their preferences, for even an ordinary person is resolute of will. The sovereign who understands the right principles may have unpleasant experiences but must be skilled in reciprocity. He knows that the hearts of men cannot be identical, and that an innate quality is required for public or private living. He neither constrains nor forbids in order to exalt the glories of a particular service. When the sovereign is not inclined toward jealousy and hatred, his subjects experience the supreme joys of satisfaction, with the result that the splendor of his abilities is praised and noised abroad without end. And on learning of it, the avaricious man blushes with shame. As I was taught it, if the wind is from the south, furs and braziers lie at rest; if the age is one of decline, the best gentlemen will withdraw.

Once our present losses and upheavals have been allayed, the buffaloes given rest and the horses put to pasture, the shadows of the signal fires and smoke signals extinguished, shields and spears stacked, the bows in their sheaths and the hunting dogs in the pot — Chang Liangs will return to their hamlets from the camp, and Han Hsins and P'eng Yüehs, removing their loricas and helmets, will once more take up their fishing.

In the light of all this, why should the state and families

have regrets for the less than one candidate for geniehood in ten thousand of population? His endeavour, it is to be remembered, lies in lessening preoccupation and emptying his desires; his occupation consists in keeping his person whole and prolonging his allotment of life; his work decries the odor of disputes; it causes no harm to other people. What crime could he be charged with? Moreover, given the great size of Mounts Hua and Huo and the vast depths of the azure sea, those heights have no need of the additions of swirls of dust, and those depths do not await the emptyings of the flowing waters. Any soil such a candidate might take would not diminish their peaks, and the cup of water he draws would not lessen the breadth of the waters. In any generation there are only a few genii, so how could they lessen the availability of political controllers?

Interlocutor: If the divine process leading to geniehood can really be had by seeking, why is there no mention of it in the Five Classics? Why have the Duke of Chou and Confucius said nothing about it? Why didn't the sages become genii? Why do not those with the highest wisdom enjoy Fullness of Existence (Ana. 16.9)? If neither the Duke of Chou nor Confucius knew anything about it, they cannot be considered sages. If they knew about it but did not study it, then there can be no divine process leading to geniehood.

Ko: Every man is born under a particular star, for which I shall give the details in another chapter (12.3a4—). You are going about with a basin over your head if you do not see the brilliance of the seven big luminaries when you look skyward. He who stretches his neck toward the big rivers for only a moment knows nothing about the marvel of depths upon depths. There is no limit to what is not contained in the Five Classics, and there are a great many things about which the Duke of Chou and Confucius say nothing. My object now is to expound roughly one ten thousandth of this other material to you, and I will not be stopped even though you may ridicule me. It would be

7a

difficult to set forth a complete description of the whole process, and I therefore wish only to have you listen to a rough account.

Heaven and earth are the biggest things in creation. *The Changes*, composed jointly by nine sages (cf. SS 32.13b12), is sufficient to embrace completely yin and yang (the physical universe), but nothing more. Today, when we ask those who study this classic about the size of the sky, the breadth of the four seas, the extent of the universe in miles, where up and down end, who is doing the pushing or pulling when things revolve, the speeds of the sun and moon, on what the nine paths of the moon are mounted, the durations of darkness and light, the successive positions of the constellation Hydra, the swellings and shrinkings of the five planets, the "hats and pendants" to the sun or partial and total eclipses of the sun and moon, the trespassings upon the 28 celestial mansions, the source of comets, the anomaly of vapor dartings, the omen in lucky stars and in Canopus, the failure of the north star to move, the solitude of Saturn in the east, the heat when the sun emits rays but chill when the moon reflects inward, the Milky Way's sparkling appearance when we look up at it, the waves and tides moving back and forth in varying magnitudes, the foreboding of joy or anger by the Five Notes and the Six Regulators (11.15a9—) in the Ten Trunks of the sexagenary cycle, the good and bad times indicated by the movements of clouds and the risings of vapors; certain comets, shooting stars, meteors, dartings, reddenings, comets over any of the four revered mountains, thundering meteors, and strange celestial phenomena sometimes proclaiming success and at other times failure — when we ask the specialists in *The Changes* about these things they cannot answer us. And when after that we turn to the specialists in *The Annals* (all four parts), *The Poems*, *The Writings of Old*, and *The Three Rites*, we again receive no answer. They say that there is no mention of these things in the standard classics.

Complete accounts of these things have been handed down only by Shaman Hsien, Kan Te, Shih Shen, Hai Chung, Ch'i Meng, and *The Seven Luminaries*. Were I to ask our classicists whether these six authors contain classical instruction, they would deny it. Were I to ask whether such people as Kan Te and Shih Shen were sages, they would again deny it. Since this is so, given that we are men with heaven above us, that we move on to old age with earth beneath our feet, that when we ask about these things of the Five Classics there is no reply, and that when we put our questions to the writings of the Duke of Chou and Confucius we get no satisfaction, should they not be considered worthless for our present day? If we cannot understand such supremely large things as heaven and earth which we see on lifting our eyes, what are we going to do about "the mystery within the mystery" (T 1) or "the pinnacle of marvels within the marvelous"?

When the ordinary man is asked about the country where there is riding upon clouds and birth from a cocoon, the people whose livers and hearts never decay, the dwellers in nests or caves, the one-eyed, the three-headed, the bird-clawed, the dog-pawed, the long-armed, the cross-legged; the yellow pool and the absence of males; people with holes through the breasts and mouths to one side; the Accepted Sovereign obtained through the grotto and floating off in an earthen boat (HHS 116.5*a*2—); Sha-i bumping a log and giving birth to a herd of dragons (HHS 116.7*b*6—); Nü-kua coming out of the earth and Tu-yü falling from heaven; the flying brick and the talking dog; the shifting mountain and the altar to Earth that moved by itself; the armed host that was completely transformed in a single morning, the gentlemen turning into cranes and the petty fellows into sand; Nü-ch'ou leaning against the dead tree; Erh-fu being seized and tied down; the insects that take up a temporary abode; the shell-quitters and the walking flesh; two-headed snakes; the string that became a bow; the timber that does not turn to ashes; the fire that is not hot; the birds of Ch'ang and Shu; the eyeless animals, the bodiless heads, the headless bodies; the *ching-wei* birds filling up the sea; the *chiao-jang* tree growing alternatively; the cloth which is washed in fire; the knife that will cut jade; Yen-mei spitting flames, Mo-ni sweating water; the metamorphoses on Mount K'u-kuan; the mountain demons with their heels in front; the nine-headed creatures on Mount Shih-hsiu; the *pi-fang* bird with the human face; Shao-kan's complaint against Po-shuai; the sage administrator exacting work of the Su-shuang horses; the Western Ch'iang prospering by means of a shadow (HHS 117.2*b*11); the Hsien-pi growing strong through a turtle-rider (HHS 115.2*a*10); Lin-i acquiring the kingship through Shen-lu; Yung-Shu acquiring the emperorship through a floating corpse; the goddess of Salt River, rebuffed, becoming an insect and flying about; the vertical eyes that change every generation in the caverns of Ching; the five stalwarts making the mountain tumble when they pulled out the snake; the *jou-shen* fish moving its fins in the three seas; the jade writing on a plaque of gold uncovered beside Yü's well; the chapters *Cheng chi and *P'ing heng of the *Ling pao ching* being cut from a joined stone, and altogether probably a thousand such marvels — ask the ordinary man about these things, and he will invariably reply that there are no such things since they are not mentioned in the Five Classics and not expounded by the Duke of Chou or Confucius.

9*a*

And there are many things which the Duke of Chou and Confucius could not do: people to our south can insert a stick through their ears so that it protrudes from each ear; Lieh Yü-k'ou was able to balance a cup of water on his elbow as he shot his arrow (*Chuang* 21.55; *Lieh* 2.8); Po-hun Mou-jen raised his heels over an abyss thousands of feet deep (*ibid.*); the man at Lü-liang sang as he swam because he had confidence in the water depths (*Lieh* 2.15; *Chuang* 19.50); a man of Sung could fashion a leaf that could be mistaken for a genuine one (*Lieh* 8.4); Kung-sun Pan (M 4*A*.1) soared with a wooden kite, Li-lou spotted a hair or a spike of grain from a hundred yards away; Meng Pen (2.1*a*10) and Wu Huo had backs strong enough to lift thousands of pounds; Ch'in Yüeh-jen successfully used his acupuncture needles when Crown Prince Su was thought dead; Shu Hai took strides of several thousand yards; an ax was brandished at the lime on the nose of the man from Ying (*Chuang* 24.48); and finally, Wang Chung-tu bared his body to the cold. Are we to conclude that these things never existed because the Duke of Chou and Confucius could not do them?

If there are certain things that the sages could not do, we should not be surprised that they did not attain geniehood; but that does not mean that they were not sages. To be a sage is to be peerless. How could they lead in involvement with minutiae? Sages were sometimes indifferent, and either quit or kept their posts automatically. They had bodies, but they did not treat them as their own private possessions; they were alive, but they did not make plans regarding life. Since their survival or death depended upon the long or short life that heaven or fate had conferred, how can we be surprised that they did not study geniehood?

9

What We Mean by "God"

GOD EMBRACES both heaven and earth but has no particularizing designation (T 25). When we discuss this lack, comparison with shadows and echoes provide criteria, but the
multiplicity of created things forces a preference for no
designation at all. Measure-regulator Li-shou would be
unable to calculate God's quantity, and Li-lou (the sharp-
sighted) himself would be unable to scrutinize all the
resemblances. Wu Cha and Chin Yeh could exhaust all the
keenness of their hearing without noting all of God's sounds
in the midst of the quietude and darkness of the universe.
The fleet creatures moving with all possible speed could
never follow God's traces out beyond our world. When we
would use the term "near" in speaking of God, we find that
God moves within an autumn hair and still has room
to spare. Use the term "far," and the Grand Void proves
insufficient to embrace God. God is the sound in sounds, the
echo in echoes, the shape in shapes, the shadow in shadows.
The quiet in the square comes from God, as does the movement in the circle. Through God, descent bends low and rise
mounts. The particularizing designation of "God" is in itself belying; how much more is this the case when, with
thousands of diminutions, hundreds of divisions, myriads of

splits, and thousands of analyses we give God names and appelations without end! These remove us from God about *1b* as far as possible.

Unable to understand that God is the basis for the grand beginning of all things, the common man busies himself with the inferior subdivisions. Good fortune, however, will come a man's way without his asking, and misfortunes will depart without any exorcizing, if he can remain quiet and indifferent; unblemished and unmoved; nurture his heart and mind on freedom from desire; feed his inner gods on the pure; brush and wash away emotional considerations and confine them in rectitude; banish all difficult thought; let fall the bonds harmful to God (the True); disdain the evils of joy and anger; and extinguish all buddings of love and hate. Why? Because life is situated within man; it has no attachments to externals; and it is in the here and now that God exists, with no attending upon a there.

How distressing! Unable to preserve God (the True 18.2*a*1), the ordinary man lacks the restraints that would bar him and pursues the agitations of covetousness. Rushing about and ever in motion, he becomes bewildered and never gets back. Affected by the things of nature, his activity becomes involved in externals; his skill and knowledge abound from contact with worldly affairs. He is seduced by the desirable, so that all orderly arrangement in nature is extinguished. Since he is confused by what he sees and hears, the primal purity and unity are removed from him; his heart and mind become slaves to prodigality and amusement; his feelings are disturbed by indecisions. At that point, when destructive calamities and unshakable misfortunes arise, all he can do is cook pork, pour libations of wine, brandish weapons and wave shields, sing and dance, strike *2a* his forehead in deep bows, or continue his requests and sit doing nothing as he beseeches the smile of good fortune and hopes to be sure of getting it. To the day of his death he remains unenlightened. Isn't it sad?

Thus his inner spirits are troubled with worry, his blood and breaths destroyed by toil. He tortures and roasts his body and its breaths; he hacks away at his natural harmony. Accepting no restraints in the struggle for distinction, he breaks his very head begging for his lord's commands. When something occurs in the region of his heart and diaphragm, he offers sacrifice and addresses prayers to seek cures. As he undergoes winds or lies in dampness, he begs forgiveness of gods. After drinking and eating beyond measure he blames his misfortunes upon ghosts and demons. These anxieties, however, are brought by the body in its paltriness upon itself. How can the gods of heaven and earth provide help? What amends can be made to his troubles by cooking sacrificial victims that exhaust the herds? Good fortune is not to be invited by an excess of politeness, and misfortune cannot be exorcized by a plethora of sacrifices. If life could be protracted by repeated prayers and illness dispelled by expensive sacrifices, the rich could be certain to enjoy Fullness of Life and the noble could be free from illness. But gods do not delight in wrong-doers, and ghosts do not enjoy the sacrifices of the dissolute. The imperial coach cannot be turned in the servants' alleys, and six-horse teams cannot be operated by commoners. To be sure, we all belong to the human family, but we fall into high and low classes. And this distinction holds even more for the gods of heaven with their lightness, remoteness, purity, and eminence! The principles they observe are extraordinary; they themselves are the very pinnacle of nobility. It would seem to be quite *2b* clear that they are not to be brought down here by the wines and foods of putrid rats nor by the bowings and scrapings of the masses.

Disloyalty and unfilial action are the most heinous of crimes. If, when guilty of them, fair renown cannot be won from an enlightened overlord nor forgiveness of the misdeeds exacted from community and neighbors through bribes of thousands in gold or the most sumptuous dinners,

where man is dealing with man, you can be sure that longevity, under such conditions, will be harder to attain than
that fair renown, and serious illness will be harder to dispel
than those misdeeds. For the extraordinary principle observed by ghosts and gods includes also rectitude, and there
is no chance that they will bend or yield. Where the master
has a sense of his own inferiority and the servant tolerates
insult, it is still possible to reward good without payment or
punish wrong without personal considerations: One need
only prepare a chalk line and walk its mark without
prejudice or party feeling. And it is not far different from
this in the case of the ghosts and gods, who are not in-
fluenced by clever talk nor won by glossing bribe. Just
never forget that!

King Ling of Ch'u personally played the shaman and in
no way spared his sacrificial victims, but he could not prevent chastisement by the armies of Wu. The Prince of
Kuang-ling during the Han dynasty exhausted his treasuries
to show respect to the shamaness Li Hsü, but he could not
save himself from punishment for treason. Emperor Wu of
the Han had great faith in ghosts and gods, and honored
them indiscriminately, but he could not avoid dying in his
own palace Five Oaks. A sovereign surnamed Sun (San kuo,
Wu) respected Hua Hsiang to the point of enfeoffing him
3a   prince, but he could not put off the time when his own life
would end. It is not that the sacrifices were not most liberal,
nor that gems and silks were not abundant. Faith in the
procedures did not lack sincerity, and the respect shown did
not lack depth. When there are enormous losses and not the
slightest gains, is this not due to the fact that we have failed
in something close at hand while scheming for something
that is far distant?

Ti-wu Lün suppressed the demonists, yet he lived to an
old age in honor. Sung Chün abolished the sacrifices to the
mountain, but good luck attended him to the end. Wen
Tang destroyed the temple of the river god, but he himself

remained fortunate and his people at peace. Emperor Wu of the Wei forbade licentious religious practice among his subjects, but he received felicitations on many birthdays, and his great deeds were never forgotten, since they became a standard for the future. It is in the natural order of things that illustrious excellence is found fragrant, that the non-worrier lives long, that the man who uses his treasure carefully should not die prematurely, and that excessive grief consumes longevity. Externals can do nothing about these things.

If we lose our natural harmony in the cultivation of externals and let ourselves become irretrievably bound to them, illnesses will form through the blemishes that are in us; unnoticed, our blood and breaths will become exhausted. How can suovetaurilias help in such a situation? The things which the populace considers helpful are all monstrous and false. They transmit from one to another nothing but lies and confusions, and the longer these continue the farther they spread. Incompetent to exercise the healing arts and unable to turn from their great delusions, common people neglect the help that medicines can bring, and devote themselves solely to the deceptions of prayers and sacrifices. Their prayers rise incessantly; of divinations they never weary. Shamans and medicine men expound madly on maleficent influences, but the dangers and crises of illnesses are just the things they know nothing about. If they do, they insist on unlimited expenditures. The rich exhaust their wealth; the poor borrow and pay double in interest. Fields and homes are lost in the search for cures; boxes and chests are emptied until nothing is left. Then, if the patient happens to feel any better, they claim that this has been a gift from the gods; if he dies, it is claimed that his ghost was not pardoned. If through some accident the patient lives, his resources are exhausted, and then he dies of famine and cold. Sometimes this evokes open acts of violence; at other times, it comes like the thief and recognizes no bounds. The losing of one's

3b

life in knife battles and the suffering of ignominious punishments can have their origins in such practices. Sometimes all of one's possessions go to defray the costs of the sacrifices, or one's grain and cloth are lost to a greedy master of ceremonies who, on the day of death, does not return the costs of the burial apparatus and the full array of burial clothes. What is even more deplorable, the corpse is allowed to decay among insects. Such is the ignorance of our masses!

Evil ceremonies and wanton practices are forbidden by the rites and our laws, but it is utterly impossible to enlighten the crowd. The only thing rulers can do is to make the laws more strict. Let all violations, petty or major, be punished by death. Let those who will not stop enlisting the prayers of shamans be punished mercilessly and exposed in the markets and along the roads. Then in a short time all this malpractice will surely cease. In this way the people can be made to exclude the sources of cold and hunger and seal off the outcroppings of brigandage. A great favor would be thus accorded them.

In the past, persons like Chang Chio, Liu Ken, Wang Hsin, and Li Shen sometimes claimed to be a thousand years old, attributing their age to some insignificant recipe. By suddenly making themselves disappear or changing their appearances, they bewildered the crowd and enmeshed all the ignorant. They made no effort actually to protract years or augment longevity, nor did they do anything to diminish calamities or cure illness. Then, finding the mobilization of a party of wantons favorable to rebellion and disloyalty, they served as a cloak to such crimes. Sometimes they murdered even the best people or deceived the masses for the purpose of acquiring wealth. Their treasuries became mountain high; they were richer than princes and dukes, and wallowed in luxury and debauchery. Quantities of clothes, the rarest of foods and entertainers filled their homes; musicians formed there in ranks. Devoted daggermen were at their disposal. They inspired a fear that dethroned the sovereign; their in-

4a

fluence undermined officials. Refugees, fleeing for their lives, had to resort to the caves and marshes. All these things occurred because officialdom was afraid to check them; such a cause can only make us sigh. (These instances are drawn from the fall of the Second Han dynasty.)

Personally, I am a nobody. Although I see the logic in these things, there is nothing I can do, because I hold no position in government. Those in charge of our people hesitate to forbid the popular practices because they suspect that the gods exist. When a calamity occurs, officialdom may take it very much to heart, but it sees it without comprehension. This is not an important function of office, nor is it critical for placement on the merit list. Meanwhile these popular practices are sincerely trusted by the official's stupid wife and playful children, so the petty people attending him disapprove any action on his part: objectors are in the majority. Others who lack deep understanding of the problem but frighten by remonstrances speak differently but share in the outcry. The result is that the official is in doubt, and becomes lost in inaction, and this makes others wring their hands in their effort to do something.

4b

I myself have seen many knowledgeable persons pay no attention whatever to gods and make no sacrifices all their lives, and still they enjoyed long lives as well as high renown and position with an abundance of sons and grandsons and riches and honors. Even I pay no attention to these matters, merely offering sacrifice to my ancestors at each of the four seasons. In the course of the thousands upon thousands of miles I have traveled on land and water there were certainly more than a hundred temples along the roadside, but in both going and coming I did not visit a single one of them, yet I suffered no serious breakdowns in either vehicles or horses. In crossing streams I never had untoward experiences with the wind and waves. I frequently encountered epidemics and was obliged to have recourse to medicines, and many times was a target for arrows and stones, but I was never afraid of being wounded or cut. All this strengthened my conviction that ghosts and gods have no power.

The more than a hundred ways for dealing with demons all call for slaying living creatures so that their blood may
5a   be drunk. Only the doctrine of the Lis is slightly different. Yet, though it does no butchering, whenever its "good-luck food" is served, it includes varieties of mixtures without limit. In planning the meal one strives for sumptuousness, and the rarest things must be purchased. Several dozen may work in the kitchen, and costs for food can run high indeed. In turn, these are not completely disinterested affairs, and they might well be classed with things to be forbidden.

If asked when this doctrine arose, my reply would be that during the period A.D. 222–252 there was a certain Li Ah living in a cave in western China who never ate normal foods. He had been around for generations and was known as Sir Eight Hundred. People were ever going to consult him about their affairs, but he never uttered a word; he merely replied to their questions through looks and appearance. If he looked happy, all the matters in question would turn out well; if he looked unhappy, they would fail. If he smiled, there would be hearty congratulations. If he sighed ever the slightest, there would be profound grief. Never once was he wrong. One fine morning he suddenly left, and nobody knew what had become of him.

Later a man named Li K'uan came to south China but spoke with the accent of western China. He knew how to treat illnesses with holy water that produced many cures. Then the rumor spread both far and near that he was no other than Li Ah, so they called him Li The Eight Hundred, but in reality he was not Li Ah. From the nobility on down all flocked to his door in droves. Later he turned haughty
5b   and no longer permitted being called upon at all times. His visitors were so overawed by this that they merely bowed at the entrance and withdrew. Refugees from the govern-

mental labor force became his disciples, constantly amounting to almost a thousand individuals, but even those who were admitted to his presence for the most esoteric instruction got nothing more than holy water and *san-pu* amulets, calisthenics, and daily and monthly breathing exercises. There were none of the things really necessary to the proper ordering of our bodies: rules for immortality such as the taking of divine medicines and the protracting of the years to one's full life span. The swallowing of one's own breaths while eschewing the usual starches may continue, for almost a hundred days, but it cannot be tolerated for longer periods. This proves how very shallow his recipes were.

I am personally acquainted with many who visited Li K'uan, and they are unanimous in saying that he was weak with old age and emaciated, so that he panted for his breath whether moving about or sitting. His eyes were troubling him, and his hearing was bad; he had lost his teeth, and his hair was white. Little by little his mind began to deteriorate, so that he often did not recognize his own sons and grandsons. He was no different from the ordinary run of men. People kept saying, however, that he deliberately acted normally in order to deceive others, but that could hardly be so.

There was once a severe plague in south China with more than fifty percent mortality. Li K'uan too caught the illness and gave as a pretext that he was entering The Cabin to keep a fast (the place where he worshipped God being called The Cabin), and he died there. His followers, however, repeatedly claimed that he had become metamorphosed into a genie who had found release as a corpse and that his was not a true death. *6a*

Now the rule governing divinity and geniehood is different from that applicable to ordinary people simply in the value it places upon not growing old and not dying. In his day, however, Li K'uan was adjudged old, so he did become old; he was seen dead, so he did die. It is thus quite easy to see that he did not have the divine process. How can there be any doubt? If it is claimed that according to the rule for geniehood he should have attained release as a corpse, why did he not simply remain among men for a century or two, maintaining his present age without growing old, after which he could have departed? This does not mean that there is no divine process in the world leading to geniehood, but only that Li K'uan was not the right type of individual.

I have taken the trouble to discuss Li K'uan at length because his pupils are maintaining his tradition, their teachings filling the land south of the Yangtze. Normally, roughly a thousand persons, not realizing that Li K'uan's methods are too shallow to be followed, do accept and observe them in the hope of attaining geniehood. Accordingly, I merely wish people to be conscious of this and to be aware how stagnant and beguiling it is. There is really no limit to the number of doctrines in the world similar to that of Li K'uan, though they are not his. I shall now mention them briefly in order to inform future generations who may not see through them.

There was once in the prefecture of Ju-nan [Honan-Anhui border] a man who set up a net in a field to catch deer, and then left, thinking to catch one without any further effort. A peddler of salted fish, chancing to pass that 6b way, placed one of his fish in the net and departed. When the owner of the net returned, he was amazed to see the salted fish in the net, and, taking it for a god, did not dare bring it home. When his village heard what had transpired, all joined in erecting a shelter and a shrine called Lord Fish's. After much worshipping had occurred there, the shrine came to have columns lacquered red with capitals shaped like water plants, and the beating of the bell never ceased. Whenever any sick person got better, it was said that the god had done it. All passersby offered sacrifices at the shrine. Seven or eight years later the fishmonger again came that way and, on passing the shrine, stopped and asked the reason for it. When they told him the whole story, he remarked, "That was only my fish. What was there miraculous about it?" Thereupon, all the furor died down.

Chang Chu of Nan-tun [E. C. Honan] was sowing his summer crop, and being bothered by a plum tree that was in the way, he decided to take it home with him. He dug it up and, since he was not leaving immediately, put it with some mud around its roots in the hollow of a mulberry tree. Then he forgot to take it away with him. Later, he became engaged in duties far from home and had to leave the neighborhood, but a fellow villager noticed that a mulberry tree was suddenly sprouting a plum tree, and concluded it was divine. Someone suffering with eye trouble then rested in the shade of this tree and happened to utter in prayer that if Lord Plum could make his eyes better he would show his gratitude by sacrificing a suckling pig. Since his eyes did happen to get better, he immediately killed a young pig and offered it in worship. Rumormongers enlarged on the situation by saying that this tree could restore sight to the blind. *7a* Then with one accord people came from far and near seeking for good luck. The place was constantly overflowing with vehicles and horses. Wines and meats poured down upon the god. This had been going on for several years when Chang Chu finished his foreign duties and returned. On seeing all this he exclaimed, "This is only the plum tree I placed here long ago. There's no god!" Then he cut it down, and all the activity ceased.

The tomb of the P'engs of Ju-nan was near a main road and had the stone statue of a man at its entrance. An old farmer woman who had been to market to buy some biscuits happened to stop in the shade of the trees there, for the weather was hot. Her biscuits meanwhile were placed on the head of the stone statue. Then she suddenly left, but forgot to take her biscuits. A passerby noticed them and inquired about them with amazement. Someone then replied that the statue was divine and could cure illnesses, so a person

who had been cured had brought the biscuits as a thank
offering. Rumor then took hold and it became bruited
about that everyone with a headache who rubs the statue's
head and everyone with a bellyache who rubs its belly and
simultaneously does the same to himself becomes cured.
From a thousand miles around people then came to be
cured. At first it was chickens and dried meats they brought,
but later buffalos and sheep as well. A tent was erected for
the services and the sound of music never ceased. It went on
like this for several years when suddenly one day that woman
who had forgotten her biscuits heard of the doings. When
she explained what had happened, people stopped going to
7b   the place.

West of the Lo [Shensi] there are the remains of a large
tomb whose ruins contain much water, so that within the
tomb there is an abundance of lime water, especially good
for treating abscesses. One summer a traveler suffering from
them, being troubled by the heat, noticed the purity and
pleasantness of the water in this tomb, and bathed in it. His
abscesses happened to get better promptly. On learning of
this, all the sick went there to bathe. They even went so far
as to drink that water for stomach troubles. People living
near the tomb then erected a shrine on the site and sold the
water. Those who bought it also made offerings in the shrine
of wines and meats; it never ceased. But, since purchasers
arrived in ever increasing numbers, the water was becoming
exhausted. Thereupon, the sellers would steal other water at
night to augment their stock. Those living at a distance and
unable to go themselves sent credentials through travelers or
porters to buy it. Then the sellers became so rich that somebody let slip the remark that there was really nothing divine
about the water. Officialdom issued a proclamation halting
the traffic. Then the place was filled in and the activity
ceased.

While a Mr. Ma was prefect of Hsing-ku [W. Kueichou],
an old friend took refuge with him for help. Mr. Ma then

had him set himself up, away from the yamen, and started the rumor that this friend was a god-man or a processor who could cure illness at the drop of a hand. Mr. Ma also got some hawkers to travel about proclaiming his friend's renown as one who could make the blind see and the lame walk. Thereupon people came in large numbers as to a *8a* market and the money started to pile up. Instructions were given to those seeking cures that, even though they might not feel better immediately, they should tell others that they did, for in this way they would be sure to get better, whereas were they to admit that there was no improvement yet, they would never get better. Since God's methods by definition could not be wrong, they could not help but believe. So, when the later arrivals inquired of the earlier ones, they were always told about cures. Not a one dared say that he had not gotten better. Thus within a week great riches were accumulated.

The masses are prone to perspicacity in minor facts, but to stupidity in the major ones. On learning about the rules for protracting years and enjoying Fullness of Life, they unanimously dub the claims spurious, yet they delight in believing in the base and groundless, the ghosts and marvels that make people beat drums, dance, pray, and offer sacrifices. The things they call divine are of a class with the deception perpetrated upon others by Mr. Ma. I have recorded only a few such instances as a warning to the unsophisticated.

Interlocutor: Why are there people in the world who, although knowing nothing whatever about the divine process or prescriptions, enjoy serenity and longevity?

Ko: People of this type either have hidden qualities and good deeds that have attracted good fortune, or they have received a fundamentally long allotment of life, which makes it difficult for them to age and lets them approach death slowly. Or else they may be just lucky. Not meeting *8b* with disaster may be compared with the fate of birds and animals passed over by hunting parties, or of the grasses and trees that remain unburned when a big conflagration has passed their way.

Alone essential for the protection of our persons and the banishing of harm are the adherence to the prohibitions that protect our bodies and the wearing of the amulets and swords inscribed with heaven-writing. Sacrifices and prayers are of no help. We must assure our own invulnerability and not rely upon a hands-off policy on the part of ghosts and gods. It is possible to dispel a certain amount of evil and moderate bad luck by contemplating and holding fast to God (the Mystery, the One), by holding something brilliant in the mouth, or drawing a circle about one's person, but these things will not protract our lives nor cure constitutional illness. The man who just follows nature without any prescriptions or recipes may very well terminate the years assigned to him by heaven. But this is not the way to face the interference of violent ghosts and the spread of plagues; these require specific action. Those who provide themselves with loricas and helmets or with rain clothes of straw are likely to be thinking of warfare or rain. If they are lucky enough not to be involved in battle, or if the weather is not rainy, they find themselves on the same footing as those who did not take these precautions. When, however, arrows and stones gather like fog and flying javelins start crossing one another like smoke, they realize what agonies a naked body would be undergoing. When it rains in torrents so that rivers break their banks or when the pure white snow fills the sky, they realize the sufferings of those standing exposed. One is not to doubt the great vitality of yin and yang because the grains of shepherd's purse and wheat are so small (6.6b10), and in the same way one may not say that prescriptions and recipes are of no advantage because some useless fellow is deceiving students with such a charge.

10

Clarifying the Basic

Interlocutor: Which has the priority, Confucianism or Taoism?

Ko: Taoism is the very trunk of Confucianism, but Confucianism is only a branch of Taoism. My uncle felt that the arts of the prognosticators (Yin-Yang School) had so many taboos that they frightened people, whereas Confucianism, although encyclopedic, did not contain all the essentials, and caused much hard work with but few results. He felt that Mohism was hard to follow because it was so parsimonious; one should not practice it exclusively. He felt that the Legalists were too strict and lacking in graciousness; it harmed or destroyed the human ideal and propriety. He was convinced that only the teachings of Taoism made men's inner gods concentrate upon Unity (God: 18.1*a*) and enjoy a constant harmony with God (Form that is Perfect Freedom). Taoism includes all the good found in Confucianism and Mohism, embraces the essentials of the Logicians and Legalists, moves with the seasons, and adapts to all creation. Its directions are concise and its variations clear; its duties are few, but results abound. It struggles to preserve the simplicity of God (the Grand Ancestor) and defend the wellsprings of all that is true and correct.

Pan Ku says that Ssu-ma Ch'ien is in error when he prefers Taoism to the Six Classics. But, Ssu-ma Ch'ien's extensive learning, embracing as it does the subtleties, separates the good from the evil both in affairs and things; it authenticates both the perverted and the orthodox among the Ancients. In his critiques he really bases himself upon *1b* nature; his judgments are all modeled on strict logic. He neither praises without justification nor blames for concealed reasons; he does not repeat the sayings of others in order to conform with popular opinion. Liu Hsiang, calling him the most learned man of his day, has stated that while Ssu-ma Ch'ien's work is a record of facts, Pan Ku's discussions are unreliable. Pan Ku was a true Confucianist in that he did not thoroughly understand what is meant by "God," for as he wearied of his task he had difficulty in judging correctly.

Chinese use of the word Tao [God, etc.] is not restricted to the nurturing of life. *The Changes* (HYI, indexed ed., 49, Shuo 2) reads: "The terms *yin* and *yang* denote Process as establishing heaven; the terms *soft* and *hard*, as establishing earth; the terms *human ideal* and *propriety*, as establishing man." And again (42.9), "Here in *The Changes* there are four processes observed by the sages." — "If you are (48.7) the wrong sort of person, Process will not operate fruitlessly." Further, contemplating the prosperity and peace of a well-ordered age, we say that it possesses Process; contemplating the confused sovereignty in a state that is endangered, on the other hand, we say that it lacks Process. Those who sit and discuss Process are called the Three Dukes. When a state is following Process, the poor and lowly there become ashamed of themselves. All discussions of Tao begin with the two symbols (the whole and the broken lines) and come on down to all creation; there is nothing that does not have its source therein. It is merely that Taoism holds firmly to the trunk (the basic), while Confucianism governs the branches (petty details).

One might well say that our present generation recognizes only the following as possessing Process: those with a wide understanding of past and present, those able to observe the subtleties in the successive changes occurring in both heaven and earth and comprehending prosperities and failures of destiny and grasping the basic elements of order and disorder; those whose hearts and minds, having never entertained a doubt, reply to all questions. We are therefore asked why a man should cultivate the rule leading to Fullness of Life or emulate the examples of Ch'ih-sung tzu and Wang Ch'iao.

Peering at life through a tube, forming personal opinions, and expounding like blind men, people slander and poke fun on hearing of a man who dwells in the mountains and forests with the doings of Lao Tan (8.4*b*9—) as his ideal, and claim that this is only petty stuff not worth bothering with. This, alas, may be called holding a lighted torch within an enclosed space but not noticing the brilliance of the luminaries in heaven; or associating with little fish and crabs in shallow water and thus knowing nothing about the vast floods of the four seas; or esteeming the depths of the Yellow and the Yangtze but knowing nothing of the K'un-luns that bring them forth; or valuing the harvest of panicled millet but having no feeling for the rich earth that grew it; or happening to know today how to laud the arts of Confucianism but not realizing that their creator is God.

God is the power that fashions all individuals, forming the two symbols (the whole and the broken lines), enwombing all creation, and brewing all the rules and norms. But the shallow-minded in our world are legion while those of profound insight are few, and it has long been true that the few do not overcome the many. Therefore, Ssu-ma Ch'ien was talented but receives no praise; Pan Ku had little talent but he is not deprecated. Yet, when scarce, things are dear; when abundant, cheap. Why does this fail to hold only in the case of personalities? Since herbs and bean leaves grow

2*a*

2b everywhere but excrescences and brilliances are not everyday things; brambles and jujubes grow wild, but anything sought after flourishes only sporadically; sand and pebbles are immeasurably abundant, but pearls and jade are extremely rare; the wild goose flies in flocks, but the phoenix appears only rarely; snakes and lizards fill the marshes, but the horned dragon is seldom seen — therefore, it is highly (*ku*) fitting that Pan Ku have the largest following!

When our persons are ruled and the state is governed according to God, the planets maintain their courses and yin and yang their balance, the four seasons have their characteristic temperatures, and the winds and rains do not turn disastrous. Well-tempered seasons bear witness that a millennium approaches; if the wine fermented only once is clear, it is evidence of compliance with natural living. Hurricanes and rainbows, on the other hand, harbor ill omens from God; tornadoes and one-legged night birds indicate God's withdrawal. When everything sparkles, however, and there is light from on high, the crops mature, plagues do not spread, disasters do not arise, moats and ramparts need not be prepared, and there is no resort to arms.

It probably indicates that the world is being governed according to God if the proper thing is done without prior discussion, trust prevails without formal agreement, there is firmness without bonds, success without planning, zeal without rewards, obedience without punishments, acquiring without seeking, ceasing without prohibition, the sovereign is not found too heavy-handed, one leads without frightening, attitudes change before a cry is raised, and habits are reformed before the orders are issued.

Therefore, when God was flourishing, the Three Augusti and Five Emperors wore their long robes and kept their
3a hands joined, and the world enjoyed abundance. When God declined, bad times became rampant, and there were deficiencies. It is only during periods of abundance that

things get better naturally; it is only during deficiencies that depravities abound and punishments become severe. The populace turns restive; the imperial majesty evinces anger. Floods of water may inundate the land, excessive sun burn the land. Mountains and valleys interchange shapes; there is thunder in winter and snow in summer. Blood splashes against the battlements; piles of corpses immure the capital. Those entrapped devise innumerable stratagems; they split bones and sell their children. The walls become ever higher, the attacks cleverer. The moats are made ever deeper, scaling ladders more ingenious. The clearer the laws, the more numerous the thieves. The more numerous the treaties, the more frequent the revolts. As, when the wind and waves are violent, fish and soft-shelled turtles go pell-mell to the depths; when the nets are close-meshed, birds escape quickly to the marshes; when leopards and wolves are numerous, animals hasten into the woods; and when the cook's fire rages, the small pieces of flesh are reduced to a pulp in the cauldron. Also there are instances of lords and subjects changing places; of fathers and sons using knives against one another. After that, reputation for loyalty and propriety is won only by endangering the state; he who destroys the household is praised as filial. With illness and plague arising, witch doctors are held in high esteem. God and natural living being in a decline, Confucianism and Mohism are elevated. From a consideration of these facts you can decide for yourself whether Confucianism or Taoism has priority.

Interlocutor: Formerly, Ch'ih-sung tzu, Wang Ch'iao, *3b* Ch'in Kao, Lao Tan (8.1*b*1), Old P'eng, Wu-ch'eng tzu, and Yü-hua tzu were all God's Men, and they all held official positions in their day, with no urge to stray afar. Beginning with the era following them, however, all the gentlemen involved with God rushed to break with everyday life and lived as hermits. Why?

Ko: Antiquity was pure and unsophisticated; manipulations and counterfeitings had not yet sprouted. Those who in those days believed in God studied God assiduously, while the nonbelievers maintained silence. Slander of God never passed their lips; there were no sadistic hearts in the breasts of those days. That is the only reason God's Men moved sedately among the people in those days and did not hasten to mount into the empyrean. Then the farther the customs of the latter days deteriorated, the more deeply ingrained became the elaborate, empty conventions. With the decline in God's (the Mystery) impartial workings, cliques of depraved men flourished. With lack of faith, delight was taken in slandering God (the True and Correct) as being a mere deception. Branding gods and genii as false, some said that such doctrines confused the masses; others, that it engendered revolt in the crowd. The result was that gentlemen of the highest type were ashamed to dwell within such a society. The wise men of old were the type that dammed tricklings and confined evils while they were still tiny. So long as the hostile attitude was still insignificant, they departed without waiting for night to turn into dawn; observing the slightest signs, they got under way without waiting for the day to end. Therefore, when the prince of Chao slew Ming-tu, Confucius readied his carriage; when good wine was not served, Master Mu left under the stars. Saying, "They are many and I stand alone," Hua Yüan (*Tso*, Hsüan 2, Spring, end) dismissed his man. Think then how much more affection is needed to retain in society the intelligent (Taoists), whose work shows a preference for the fundamental and the strange!

4a

When the watery deep is exhausted and the pools have lost their water, the horned dragon can no longer find a place to swim. Where nests are destroyed and eggs stolen, the phoenix cannot perch. Where there is idle (*chü*) talk at home, the darting green gulls (*ch'ü*) do not descend (*Lieh* 2.17). Where the grass is cut in the spring, mushrooms do not flourish. In like manner, when it becomes characteristic of an age to insult uprightness, there will be disdain and shame for it. How can those who possess God help but leap to wend their wings out beyond the winds and clouds, and leave their mark, as they soar, in Paradise? God does not exist solely in the forests, but those wishing to cultivate God are obliged to enter mountains and forests because they must get far away from the fats and biles of society and enjoy the purity of these secluded places.

He who enters the *ming-t'ang* to give careful thought to duty and those who preserve Truth-Unity (18.2*b*3, 10) to summon the gods, do this because no pleasure is taken in shrill noises and association with the soiled and noisome. Similarly, those preparing the grand remedies of gold and cinnabar, or refining the sublimed essences of the Eight Minerals, must rigidly avoid the stupid and their chatter. Normally at the sight or hearing of the worldly the spirits would not descend, and the medicines producing geniehood would fail to form. This is no minor prohibition. So long as these operators remain among men, shallow-minded officials sometimes bring upon them the misfortune of punishment. At other times, old companions or family may interfere and drag them off to congratulate a friend or express con-dolences. Therefore, it is best to go into hiding and completely avoid such vermin. Would you not agree that those going far off into solitude to seek their satisfaction in the caves of Mount Sung have good reason for doing so?

It is sometimes said that gentlemen of the highest type achieve the divine process in the army (cf. 18.4*b*2); those of the intermediate type achieve it at the capital; but the lowest type must acquire it in the mountains and forests. All of these have successfully concocted the geniehood medicine, but they do not yet wish to mount to heaven. Even though they remain in the army, points and blades cannot harm them; even in the capital they are unaffected by misfortunes stemming from other persons. Those of the lowest class, however, not having achieved the proficiency of the others,

4b

best stay in the mountains and forests. This is not to say that those of the higher types need to be in the army or at the capital when they begin their study of the divine process in order to achieve it. Therefore, the doctrines of Yellow Emperor and Lao Tan are still with us to the present.

Interlocutor: You have certainly made it clear that Taoism is the source and trunk, and that Confucianism constitutes the branches and the stream. Today, then, what are the remaining differences between them?

Ko: Instruction regarding mounting and descending steps and bowing low and looking up; the three thousand ceremonials governing gyration; the arts of defense, offense, advance, and retreat; the regulations that make light of the person but stress propriety; matters of joy, grief, rituals, and music; plans for regulating the world and helping the people — these are the preoccupations of the Confucianists. The business of the Taoists, on the other hand, consists of these: to reject specialization in worldly matters; to wash away all trickeries; to forget wealth and neglect honors; to block repression and encourage free expression; not to be concerned about the loss of everything; not to glory in success; not to be saddened by denigration; and to take no delight in praise. Confucianists offer sacrifice to pray for good fortune; Taoists walk in rectitude to exorcize evil. Confucianists dote on the advantage of power; Taoists treasure freedom from covetousness. Confucianists thirst after the advantages of renown; Taoists embrace God (the One) to improve themselves individually. Confucianists teach written rules for mutual grinding; Taoists practice the teaching of prohibitions that banish worldly interests.

The active principle of Taoists is to be able to accomplish their interest through self-cultivation. Their inactive principle is to be adept at fostering nonbelligerence among men. For them, good order consists in being adroit in keeping misfortune away before it occurs. Their idea of charitable works is to help other creatures without thinking of their deed as being extraordinary. Their constant goal is skill in the use of heart and mind as they observe the people. Their repose consists in their ability to be free from worry as they take their repose in God (Truth). These are the reasons Taoism is lord over all the other schools of thought; the original progenitor of the human ideal and propriety. So much for the question of the differences between it and Confucianism. There can be no interchanging of head and tail; the one is exalted, the other soiled.

Interlocutor: Confucianism is synonymous with the teachings of Duke of Chou and Confucius. Its scriptures are the Six Classics; these may be said to be a means for keeping order in the world and preserving orthodoxy and a guideline for action that will establish a person. Their use is of long standing and the tasks they impose are honorable. Their doings are significant, and their language is beautiful. They constitute an undeviating system for governing a state or household. On the other hand, Taoists provide no scheme for teaching ceremony; they have no regard for the general arrangement of social relationships and duties. They associate with foxes and sloths in the bush and marshes; their companions are the monkeys and apes in the forests and on the slopes of mountains. Wandering about and playing the host, both on the grand scale, they have nothing but trees and stones for neighbors. These two groups are traveling in the same direction but for different reasons (HNT 16.17a4—), and they know only their respective specialties (*Erh-ya-i, shih ts'ao*).

Ko: The parading of fine phrases and the profuse use of ornament are not esteemed by those of us who are simple and direct, and I have had my fill of attacks upon my ignorance and of attempts to rescue me from confusion. I really never wish to compare the quality of principles with you again, or the aptness of what we may say. Observing a child fall into a well has nothing to do with the meaning of the human ideal, and seeing a blind man collide with a pillar is no definition of uniform love for all, for they are only convenient ways of raising one aspect of our topic.

Yellow Emperor and Lao Tan took God as fundamental to the creation of things and valued natural living as a means of enjoying Fullness of Life. Yellow Emperor so governed the world that a millennium resulted; and in addition he mounted to geniehood. We have no right to say that he was in any way inferior to Yao and Shun. Since Lao Tan embraced instruction in ceremony along with his doctrine and also enjoyed lasting vision, he cannot be said to have detracted from the Duke of Chou and Confucius. Thus Confucius himself sighed as he undertook to compare himself with Old P'eng (Ana. 7.1), and I have never heard that he ever used a word of adverse criticism, yet people of these latter days, who never attended his school, cultivate Confucianism and Mohism but malign Taoism. How does this differ from sons and grandsons cursing their own ancestors? This is tantamount to being completely and utterly ignorant of your origins!

The hands of a dwarf are not competent to overturn Mounts Sung and Hua, and the legs of pygmies are not competent to probe the azure seas. Every time I see common, stolid Confucianists buzzing about their ceremonies without any broad understanding of the principles involved, I charge them with stupidity and knavery, with promoting and dressing up vicious statements to bring false charges against Taoists. To hear them interpret the smears from their lees (*Chuang* 13.70) is like watching a fast steed pass by a crack. When they treat spiritual profundities, they become submerged in the topic. They are like the quail (*Chuang* 1.15) that would traverse Marquis Yang's waves on their short wings, or like greenhead flies exerting all their might to traverse the same peaks as the supple monkey. They do not have the strength; no sooner do they start than they are weary. Meanwhile, they warble away and take refuge in their narrow situation. Their hearing does not surpass

6a

Master K'uang's, and their eyesight is no better than Li-lou's, yet they pretend to stand on tip-toe to embrace sun, moon, and stars, or tap their bellies to simulate the thunder god. How stupid can they get!

One might express it this way: Once a man has mounted into the great distances of the celestial sphere, he realizes how shallow wells and valleys are. Once he has seen the brilliant sky lighted by the sun, he realizes how vile the yellow warbler and gold are. Personally, I was not born knowing   *6b* these things, nor did I believe them when young. In the beginning I was as ignorant as you. But when I had surveyed the vastness of the secrets, I regretted that I had become involved in these difficulties so late. In the case of the Five Classics, the explanations of the commentaries do offer some elucidation, but at early stages of one's study there are still times when they cannot be understood. This is still truer for the important utterances of the gold plaques, the jade tablets, and the classics provided by gods and genii. Furthermore, much is not written down; an altar is mounted, blood is drunk, and oral directions are transmitted. If one is not the right type of individual, these secrets will not be lightly transmitted, even though one had ravaged city after city and one's halls were filled with gold and jades. The meaning of these texts and communications is profound and comes from afar. Even though a man were to acquire the writings, he would not understand either head or tail of them without the help of a teacher.

You don't know the half of it! Those that have acquired geniehood often mount to Paradise; or soar in the purple firmament; or travel to Dark Isle; or nest a while in Pan-t'ung. They listen to God's (Creator Sky) music, and enjoy dishes of the nine sorts of excrescences. Or again, abroad, they join hands with Ch'ih-sung tzu and Hsien-men tzu out in space where the light shines upward; at home, they enjoy a constant potency. Why should they have to associate with foxes and sloths, and have monkeys and apes for companions? You have only been exhibiting your ignorance. The man occupied with God wanders freely on the rainbow and soars in the cinnabar firmament. He enlarges his boundaries to include all of space; goes where he wills. On the grand scale he moves about playing host; 7*a* he never knows sorrow.

At the assemblage point for the sacrificial pigs, even though the animals have been adorned with greenery and embroideries and we discuss their joy, how do they compare with the solitary unicorn who, quitting the herd to travel alone, abounds in prosperity as he basks in the light of peerless good fortune!

I I

The Genie's Pharmacopoeia

IN *Shen-nung's Classic* (cf. 14*a*6) we read: "Medicines of the highest type put the human body at ease and protract life so that people ascend and become gods in heaven, soar up and down in the air, and have all the spirits at their service. Their bodies grow feathers and wings, and the Traveling Canteen comes whenever they wish." — "The various (five) excrescences [mushrooms, lichens, etc.] may be nibbled, and cinnabar, jade flakes, laminar malachite, realgar, orpiment, mica, and brown hematite may be taken singly, and any of them can enable a man to fly and to enjoy Fullness of Life." — "Medium-grade medicines nurture life. Low-grade medicines banish illness and prevent poisonous insects from attacking and savage beasts from harming us. They immobilize bad vapors, and put evil influence to flight." *Hsiao-ching yüan-shen-ch'i* reads: "Pepper and ginger protect against the effects of dampness, sweet flag sharpens the hearing, sesame protracts the years, and resin puts weapons to flight."

The foregoing are words of the greatest import from the highest sages, a factual list of recipes. They are documented in the clearest of writing, but the people of our generation are lost in disbelief. This situation is pitiable.

At the top of the genie's pharmacopoeia stands cinnabar.

1b Second comes gold; third, silver; fourth, excrescences; fifth, the jades; sixth, mica; seventh, pearls; eighth, realgar; ninth, brown hematite; tenth, conglomerated brown hematite; eleventh, quartz; twelfth, rock crystal; thirteenth, geodes; fourteenth, sulphur; fifteenth, wild honey; and sixteenth, laminar malachite. After these come resins, truffles, yellow dock, *Liriope graminifolia,* "tree sesame," *Salomonia,* goldthread, fern, mulberries, and *hsiang-ch'ai.* This last is also known as *ch'un-lu.* Other names for it are genie staff (*Lycium*), western-queen staff, sky sperm, age dispeller, earth bone, and grass willow.

Asparagus (sometimes called *ti-men-tung, yen-men-tung, tien-chi, yin-yang-shih,* or *kuan-sung*) grows on high sites. It has short roots and a sweet taste. The fragrant type is best. The one growing beside waters and in low sites has thin leaves like algae and is yellowish. Its roots are long and its taste quite bitter. The type with a bad odor is ranked lowest, but it may still be eaten. It can be used as a sedative

2a but it is very slow in taking effect. When taken for a hundred days, asparagus will strengthen people and cause them to walk twice as fast as would thistle or knotgrass. Some can be steamed when one enters a mountain, and if enough of it is cooked and eaten it can displace the normal starches. Strong people may nibble at it. It may also be powdered or pressed for its juice, from which a wine is then made. It is best taken as a powder. The people of Ch'u call asparagus *pai-pu.*

For us, however, *pai-pu* (Stemona) is the name of another herb that has about a hundred roots. The two plants do look very much alike, but their sprouts are slightly different. The sprouts of Stemona resemble those of the sarsaparilla plant, but they are effective only in stopping coughs and killing lice. They are not to be taken internally; no mistake must be made in this regard. In the same way, knotgrass is sometimes called *pai-chi* (aconite), but it really is not the same as the aconite used to make glue. Very many medicines listed in *The Herbal* (*Pen ts'ao*) have the same names as other herbs of less efficacy. One must take care to distinguish between them.

Of knotgrass — also called hare bamboo, restorative, or pearl pendant — it is better to eat the flowers than the fruit, and better these than the root; but it is difficult to obtain a sufficient quantity of the flowers. One hundred pecks of its fresh flowers, when dried, shrink to only five or six pecks, and a daily ration may be as much as three hundredths of a peck. Handling knotgrass thus involves much hard work. To derive great benefit from taking it requires at least ten years. For taking the place of normal starchy foods it is inferior to thistle.

2b

Thistle makes men sleek and good carriers along cliffs, but it is not as pleasant and easy to take as knotgrass. During famine, it can be given to the old and young in place of grain. Those not knowing the difference think it is dried meat made of rice.

There are five types of excrescences: rock, wood, herb, flesh, and the tiny, and each of them has almost a hundred species.

Rock excrescences. The rock ones are semblances of mushroom in stone. They grow on the famous mountains by the sea. Along island streams there are formations of piled rocks resembling flesh. Those seeming to have head, tail, and four feet are the best. They look like something alive. They are attached to boulders, and prefer high, steep spots, which sometimes render them inaccessible. The red ones resemble coral; the white ones, a slice of fat; the black, wet varnish; the blue, kingfisher feathers; and the yellow, purplish gold. All of them glow in the darkness like ice, being easily visible at night from a distance of three hundred paces. Large ones weigh over ten pounds, the small ones three or four. This type cannot be seen, however, unless one has fasted long and meticulously and is wearing from the belt Lao Tan's Five Powers' Treasure Amulet for Entering Mountains. Whenever excrescences are encountered, an initiating and an exorcising amulet are placed over them, then they can no longer conceal or transform themselves. Then patiently await the lucky day (15b) on which you will offer a sacrifice of wine and dried meat, and

3a

then pluck them with a prayer on your lips, always approaching from the east using Yü's Pace (16*a*) and with your vital breaths well retained. When you gather a rock that resembles a mushroom, grind it with a pestle for 36,000 blows, and take three inch-square spoonfuls per day. After taking a pound, you will live to be a thousand; after ten pounds, to ten thousand. It may also be shared with others.

Jade-fat excrescences grow on jade-bearing mountains, always suspended from dangerous locations. They are formed from jade grease which flowed out thousands of years ago and congealed. Some are shaped like birds and animals and their coloring varies, though most of them resemble the blue jade from pure mountain waters. There are also some that are fresh and bright like rock crystal. When you get some of these, grind and mix them with cudweed juice, and they will immediately liquefy. Drink a quart, and live to be a thousand.

Seven-eyed and nine-eyed excrescences are both stones. They grow at the rocky base of high mountains overlooking streams and resemble flat bowls not more than a foot or thereabouts in diameter.

3b   They are connected by stems. Those three or four inches long and having seven hollows are called seven-eyed; those with nine, nine-eyed. These hollows are like stars, visible at night from more than a hundred paces, each eye showing separately. They may be powdered, but not mixed. They are always to be seen at the autumnal equinox, and when you gather them they are to be pestled and an inch-square spoonful taken. The moment it enters your mouth it will make your body very hot and sweet with the fragrance of the Five Savors. After taking a pound you will live to be a thousand. They give a man's body a glow, so that in no matter how dark a spot he may be, he will resemble the moon and be able to see at night.

The rock-honey variety grows in Rock House on Shao-shih (a portion of Mount Sung). This "house" happens to be over a chasm so deep that it cannot be crossed and that a stone thrown into it can be heard tumbling for half a day. Some ten rods below the house there is a stone pillar on whose top is a stone capital about ten feet in diameter. As one watches these excrescences it will be noticed that after a very long interval one drop falls from Rock House onto the capital. It reminds one of the drop of rain that will occasionally fall through the roof of a house after a shower. But the drops in this case never cease, while the capital itself never overflows. There is an inscription in tadpole writing on Rock House, reading "Anyone taking one peck of this rock-honey will live for ten thousand years." Pro-

4a   cessors all feel that this site is inaccessible and that this material is to

be caught only by fastening a bowl to the end of a strong pole of bamboo or wood. But no man has been able to make such an instrument. Yet, since the inscription there is known, someone in the past must have been able to get to them.

The rock-cinnamon type grows in the caves of famous mountains. It resembles a cinnamon tree, but is really a rock. It is about a foot high, and the large ones are a foot in diameter. It glistens and has an acrid taste. It is branched. Pestle and take a pound of it, and you will live to a thousand.

The Yellow-fellow-in-rock species is found everywhere, but it is most numerous on the mountains near streams. When they are found in large rocks, the latter are always damp and never dry. By breaking up the rocks, several dozen can be obtained. In a large rock the reddish yellow will ooze like a chick embryo in its shell. It must be drunk the moment you find it, otherwise it will congeal to stone and no longer be fit to take. The correct method is to drink it before it hardens. Once it hardens one is obliged to grind it and then take it. By opening one rock one can expect a maximum of one quart and a minimum of several gills which may be taken immediately. Though you may not get much at a time, keep taking it as you find it until the combined accumulation is three quarts. Then you will live to be a thousand. If you wish to take a larger amount, you may, but it will be difficult to obtain.

4b

The geode variety grows in soapstone and resembles the Yellow-fellow-in-rock, but it is not found in all soapstone. In breaking open about a thousand large pieces one may be found. The moment a rock that does contain one is broken, a multicolored light will appear, flashing automatically. Take a quart, and live to a thousand.

The sulphur type is found in all five revered mountains, but it is especially numerous in Mount Chi. There is a local legend to the effect that Hsü Yu came there and took some of them, thereby achieving Fullness of Life. That is why he no longer concerned himself with riches and honors and declined to succeed to Yao.

The red sulphur variety is the red sperm of rock, probably related to the yellow sulphur variety. Both abound on the banks of streams. While moist, they may be taken in the form of pills. After hardening they must be powdered and then taken.

There are 120 of the rock variety. The facts will be found in *T'ai-i yü ts'e* and *Ch'ang-yü nei chi*. I cannot list them all here.

Wood excrescences. Sap from evergreens soaks into the ground and after a thousand years changes into truffles. After ten thousand years,

5a small trees resembling water lilies start growing from the truffles; therefore we call them wood-resin mushrooms. They shine at night and are very moist to the touch. They will not burn. Worn at the waist, they protect against weapons. If a chicken is bound with them and placed in a crate with eleven others, and from a distance of twelve paces twelve arrows are shot at the crate, all the other chickens will be hit, but the one bound with the resin excrescence will go unharmed. Gather those that grow higher than your belly, and on the six days of the sexagenary cycle beginning with *chia* dry them in the shade for one hundred days. Powder, and then take three inch-square spoonfuls a day. After taking a whole branch of them, you will live to be three thousand.

A thousand-year-old dead tree will have a root under it resembling a seated man seven inches tall. When this is cut, blood will ooze forth; if the soles of your feet are smeared with this, you will be able to walk on streams without sinking. If your nose is smeared with it, a stream will open a passage for you so that you can stay at the bottom. If your whole body is smeared, you will be invisible; to become visible again, merely wipe it off. This blood can also cure illnesses. If the illness is in the abdomen, rub it with one spatula of the blood. For external swellings, rub the spot in question with one spatula of the blood, and no matter where it is, there will be immediate improvement. If for example the left foot hurts, rub it with this and Belam-
5b canda. If a torch is rubbed with a mixture of this and sesame and is shone at night wherever there is treasure in the ground, its beam will turn blue and shine only downward, so that you will be able to dig and get it. By taking somewhat less than ten pounds of this blood in powdered form, one can live for a thousand years.

Beneath the bark of the limb of a pine that is three thousand years old there will be found an accumulation of sap resembling a dragon. It is called Express Token Mushroom. Some larger ones weigh ten pounds, and by taking a full ten pounds, powdered, one will live to be five hundred.

The alum-peach variety looks like a rampant dragon, with flowers and leaves resembling a red net, and fruit resembling blue birds. It is not more than five feet high, and grows on the northern slope of the famous mountains on the banks of east-flowing springs. Gather it and grind it at Summer Begins [May]. Take the whole piece, and you will live for five thousand years.

The triple type is red and brilliant. When struck, its branches and leaves resound like metal or stone; when broken off, it regenerates and immediately becomes as before. The wood-shield species grows against large trees, like a water lily, and has nine stalks which form one mass. It tastes sweet and acrid. The fruit of the stabilizer variety grows in the fields of Tu-kuang. Its skin resembles a ribbon or a snake, and is marked like the male phoenix. By getting and taking   *6a* these three excrescences one will ascend to heaven in broad day-light.

The three types yellow-brazier, eight-foot-tree-flower, and primal-exudate-flower grow at Yao-hsiang and Feng-kao on Mount T'ai. All who gather and eat them will live for a thousand years.

The yellow-sucker *t'an-huan* variety: Among the roots of a thousand-year-old yellow-sucker tree there will be found something resembling a three-bushel container some ten or twenty feet from the main trunk, but connected with it by thin roots resembling a skein of thread. Find this, powder it, take it in its entirety, and you will become an earth genie and enjoy immortality.

Of this wood category there are also 120 species, all of which are illustrated in the books.

The herb type. The self-shaking variety of herb excrescence moves of itself even when there is no wind. Its stem is the size of a finger and red as cinnabar. Its leaves normally resemble Amaranthus. At its roots there is a large mass the size of a quart measure with twelve smaller globules the size of chicken eggs completely surrounding the main root like the twelve signs of the zodiac. Extending from these for a distance of about ten feet there are thin filaments like white hairs, all connecting with one another. It grows along the deep ravines of high mountains, where the surrounding areas have no other vegetation. Get the large mass, powder it, take it all, and you will live for a thousand years. One of the smaller globules, so treated, will bring you a hundred years and may be shared with others. The main root,   *6b* kept at the breast, will render you invisible. When you wish to be-come visible again, wheel to the left and remove it.

The buffalo-horn species grows in the Hu-shou mountains and along the slopes in Wu. It is shaped like an onion and noted for resembling a buffalo's horn three or four feet long. It is of a bluish hue. Powder and take an inch-square spoonful three times daily for one hundred days, and you will live for a thousand years.

The dragon genie type is shaped like rampant dragons placed back to back, its leaves representing the scales. Its roots are like a coiled dragon. By taking one of these you will live for a thousand years. The hemp-mother variety resembles hemp, its stalk is red, and its flowers, purple. Pearl-type excrescences have yellow flowers, red leaves, and its fruit, resembling plums, is purple in color. Twenty-four branchings hang connected with one another like a festoon of pearls.

The white-tally kind is four or five feet tall and resembles the flowering plum tree. It always flowers at Big Snows [December] and forms its fruit in winter. The vermilion species consists of nine bends, each of which has three leaves, with three fruits to a leaf.

The five-virtue one is shaped like a towering hall. Its stem is rectangular, and its leaves are of all colors, but not variegated. The top is like a capital. Within it there is always some nectar, and from a distance of several feet a purple vapor can be observed to rise.

Dragon-bit excrescences, in the second moon of spring, grow in pairs of three longitudinal sections and twelve branchings. The lower root resembles a seated person.

7*a*   All told, there are 120 species of the herb type, any of which, if dried in the shade and taken, will enable a man to last as long as all nature or live to be one or two thousand years old.

Flesh excrescences. The ten-thousand-year-old hoptoad is said to have horns on its head, while under its chin there is a double-tiered figure 8 written in red. It must be captured at noon on the fifth day of the fifth moon and dried in the shade for a hundred days. A line drawn on the ground with its left root will become a running stream. When its left foreleg is carried on the person, it will ward off all types of weapons. If an enemy shoots at you, the bow and arrow will both turn against the archer. The thousand-year-old bat is as white as snow. When perching, it hangs head down because its brain is heavy. If both of these creatures are obtained, dried in the shade, powdered, and taken, a body can live for forty thousand years.

The thousand-year-old power tortoise is variegated in color. Two bones like horns rise on the forehead of the male. After immersing this animal in sheep's blood, remove the shell and roast it in a fire. Then grind in a mortar and take an inch-square spoonful three times daily until a whole one has been consumed. You will then live for a thousand years.

If in the mountains you should come across a little man seven or eight inches tall riding in a palanquin or on a horse, it will be a flesh excrescence. By seizing and taking it you will immediately become a genie.

The wind-born animal, resembling a sable, blue in color and the size of a fox, is found in the huge forests of the southern seas and caught by means of nets. Several cartloads of faggots can be used to roast it, but after these faggots have been consumed, it will be found in the ashes unburned, its fur unscorched. Even an ax blade will not   *7b* pierce it. It will die only after being beaten over the head a thousand times with an iron mace as though it were a leather sack. After it is dead, if its mouth is opened toward the wind, it will promptly revive and walk off. It dies at once, however, if its nose is stuffed with reeds from the surface of a rock. Mix the brain with chrysanthemum flowers and take a full ten pounds, and you will live for five hundred years.

The thousand-year-old swallow nests on the north side. Its color is largely white, but the tail is —. Catch one of these, dry it in the shade, powder and take it, and you will live for five hundred years.

There are altogether 120 such species, all of them flesh excrescences.

Tiny excrescences. These grow deep in the mountains, at the base of large trees or beside springs. They may resemble buildings, palanquins and horses, dragons and tigers, human beings, or flying birds. They may be any of the five colors. They too number 120 for which there exist illustrations. All are to be sought and gathered while using Yü's Pace, and they are to be cut with a bone knife. When dried in the shade, powdered, and taken by the inch-square spoonful, they produce geniehood. Those of the intermediate class confer several thousands of years, and those of the lowest type a thousand years of life.

Entrance into the famous mountains in search of excrescences and herbs must be either during the third or ninth moons (17.1*a*11), these being the months when the mountains are open and produce the divine medicines. Refrain   *8a* from going on days when the mountains are hostile. The hour when heaven abets and the three lucky cyclical symbols are in conjunction (for heaven these are *i, ping, ting*; for earth, *chia, wu, keng*; for man, *hsin, jen, kuei*) must be deemed best for leaving via the Three-lucky-cyclical-symbols doorway of good fortune. Arrival at the mountain must be on a six-*yin* day (i.e., begin with a cyclical *ting*) at a *ming-t'ang* hour (i.e., begin with a cyclical *ping*) (cf. 15*b*). It is essential to wear the Powers' Treasure Amulets (cf. 3*a*), have a white dog on a leash, and carry a white chicken. If a peck of white salt and a tally opening up the mountain are placed on a large rock, and a bunch of Wu hops is held as the mountain is entered, the gods of the mountain will be pleased and you will be sure to find excrescences.

For gathering and taking them one should have lucky and thoroughly favorable days. It is best when the cyclical branches and trunks beget one another from top to bottom. In this connection, let me repeat that the excrescences listed in this chapter are found chiefly in the famous mountains. The ordinary processors, however, are not particularly intelligent. In them, character is low and high quality slight. They do not know the art of entering mountains. One may have pictures, but if the shapes are not known it is utterly impossible to find the excrescences. All mountains, whether large or small, contain ghosts and gods which withhold these things from people, so it would be possible to be walking right over them without seeing them.

There are five sorts of mica, between which people cannot usually distinguish. The only method is to examine them against the sun for color and look carefully at them like a diviner. When observed only in the shadows the various colors are not discernible. That which is iridescent but predominantly blue is called cloud sheen, and is to be taken *8b* medicinally in the spring. The iridescent but largely red one is called cloud pearl and must be taken in summer: The iridescent but primarily white one is called cloud exudate and is to be taken in autumn. The iridescent but largely black mica is called cloud mother (the usual term for mica). It is to be taken in winter. The one with only the two colors, blue and yellow, is called cloud sand, and is to be taken in the sixth moon. The pure white is called fish-scale stone. It may be taken at any time throughout the four seasons.

To take the micas, first liquefy them through the use of cinnamon-onion or *Pinellia tuberifera*, by cooking them in brine in an uncovered iron vessel or by burying them, mixed with saltpeter, in a tube. It may then be mixed to a paste with honey. After being steeped for one hundred days in black tea in a leather bag, they may be powdered. Or they may be nibbled dipped in aconite or ailanthus sap. If taken for one year, it will banish all illnesses. If taken for three years, it will restore youth to an old man. If taken steadily for five years, it will make possible the employment of ghosts and gods, entering fire without being burned, entering water without getting wet, walking on thorns without being hurt, and acquaintance with genii.

Other things decay when buried and burn when placed in fire, but when the micas are placed in a raging fire they do not burn at all even after a prolonged time, and they do not decay after long burial. Therefore they can confer Fullness of Life. It is also said that if you take mica for ten years a cloud will always hover above you; this is quite natural, for by taking the mother (*mu* of *yün-mu*, literally cloud mother, the common term for mica) one attracts her son.

9a

If the mica should gradually turn a deep black as one holds it against the sun, it is not fit to take, for it would make a person sick and break out in sores. Even when sipped in liquid form, it should first be soaked for a hundred days in water from the roof of a thatched hut, in an eastward-flowing stream, or in dew to wash away the earth and stones adhering to it. Only then is it to be used.

Wei Shu-ch'ing of Chung-shan took mica for a long time and could travel on clouds. After he had sealed his recipe in a jade casket and departed a genie, his son Ming-shih and a Han court emissary, Liang Po, got it. By mixing it according to the recipe and taking it, they were both able to depart as genii.

Realgar [*disulphide of arsenic*]. You should procure that found on Mount Wu-tu, which is pure and uncontaminated. Only that which is red as a chicken's comb and gleaming bright is to be used. That which is only pure yellow, resembling orpiment in color and lacking the red sheen, cannot be used as a medicine to produce geniehood. It is only *9b* good in medicines used for treating illness.

To nibble realgar, it may be cooked or sipped in wine; first liquefied in saltpeter and then congealed; it may be placed in a pig's intestine and roasted in a red clay oven; it may be mixed with resin; or it may be mixed with chicken, dog, or pork meat, stretched like cloth, and taken when it is white as ice. In each case it confers Fullness of Life; all illnesses are banished; the Three Corpses drop from the body; scars disappear; gray hair turns black; and lost teeth are regenerated. After a thousand days fairies will come to serve you and you can use them to summon the Traveling Canteen. Fairies are characterized by a piece of yellow jade the size of a grain of millet on their noses. Only such are the true fairies. When this distinguishing mark is missing, it shows that there is only a ghost testing human beings.

Jade too is a medicine leading to geniehood, but it is hard to find. *Jade Classic* reads: "The man taking gold will last as long as gold; the one taking jade will last as long as jade. . . . The life of the man taking Mysterious-and-True will never culminate." Mysterious-and-True is a synonym for jade. It will make a man's body light enough to fly; it will do more than make him an earth genie. It is slow, however, to take effect; the results can be known only after one or two hundred pounds have been taken.

Jade can be dissolved in black rice wine or Sanguisorba *10a* wine. It can also be crystallized with pigweed solution. It can be nibbled in the form of pills, or it can be heated and powdered. After you have taken it for a year or more you will not become wet when entering streams, nor will you burn when entering fire. Sharp things will not cut you, and nothing poisonous will harm you. However, jade that has been fashioned into articles may not be used, for it would produce only harm. You must get natural, unpolished jade, if you are to use it. It is best to get white jade from Khotan. The next best is jade from a section of Hsü-shan village in Nan-yang [C. Honan] and jade from the Lu-jung river in Annam.

Ch'ih-sung tzu took jade by dissolving it in the blood of cicadas, this enabled him to ride up and down on smoke. Whether taken in small fragments or liquefied and sipped, jade renders man immortal. It is inferior to gold, however, in that it frequently causes fever, for it resembles *han-shih-san*. When jade is taken in small fragments, a spatula of both realgar and cinnabar should be taken once every ten days. Then you will not run a fever when traveling against the wind after you have taken down your hair, washed it, and bathed.

Tung Feng once gave some dregs of jade to a blind man, and in ten days his vision had returned. On the other hand, a certain Wu Yen-chih made up his mind to take some jade and got an incomplete recipe from *Jade Classic*. But having no clear understanding of its rules and taboos, he assembled tablets, rings, and circular plaques of jade, as well as large quantities of sword ornaments, and was on the point of nibbling, preparing, or taking them. After I had explained to him that all those were useless, he sighed, "In all matters one must be careful about the essential details, for otherwise there is not only no benefit, but one can almost incur disaster."

rob

There is also silver, but it is inferior to gold and jade. It can make you an earth genie. Here are the directions for taking it: It may be made edible in barley water or sipped with Vermilion Grass wine. It can also be refined with raspberry juice. But since it is to be taken three times daily until a piece the size of a crossbow pellet has been consumed, it is not to be obtained by a poor, unsullied processor.

A genuine pearl an inch or more in diameter may be taken in order to endure long. For this purpose, it may be soaked for a long time in whey and thus become similar to mercury. It can be made edible with pumice water or "hive-crabs." Mixed with *Pao-t'ung* and serpents' bezoar, it can be stretched to a length of three or four feet and taken rolled into pills. If taken while starches are being avoided, it will impart immortality and Fullness of Life.

If pure, unadulterated lacquer is taken, it will put a man in communication with the gods and let him enjoy Fullness of Life. Directions: Mix it with ten pieces of crab. Take it with mica water, or mixed with jade water. The Nine Insects will then drop from you, and the bad blood will leave you through nose-bleeds. After a year, the six-*chia* gods and the Traveling Canteen will come to you.

Cinnamon can be liquefied by cooking with onion juice, and then sipped by mixing it with bamboo liquid. It may also be taken mixed with tortoise brains. After taking it for seven years you will be able to walk on water and enjoy Fullness of Life and immortality.

Sesame, also called *hu-ma*, can be nibbled to prevent senility, to protect against drafts and wettings, and to repair the ravages of old age.

When soaked in mulberry-ash juice and taken, peach-gum cures all illnesses. If taken for a long time, it makes the body light and shining; in dark places it will glow like moonlight. When it is taken in large quantities, starches should be dispensed with.

When the red fruit of the paper mulberry is nibbled for a whole year, it will rejuvenate the old and it will enable one to look through things and see their ghosts. In the early days, the processor Liang Hsü took some at the age of seventy and became younger. At the age of 140 he could write in columns in the dark and gallop his horse. Later he left for the Ch'ing-lung mountains.

Sophora seeds. Seal with clay in a new jar for twenty days or more, until the skin has fallen off. Then wash the seeds, and they will be like soy-beans. Taken daily, they will be especially good for repairing the brain. If one takes them for a long time, one's hair will not turn white, and one will enjoy Fullness of Life.

More than three hundred different things, among which are *hsüan-chung* turnips, *fang-ch'u*, thistle, water plantain, yellow dock, and goldthread can prolong life and may be taken uncompounded. *Ling-fei-san, wei-yang* pills, *chih-ming* pills, and sheep's-blood pills make a man hold his age and banish old age.

In the mountains of Li-hsien, in Nan-yang [Honan], is Sweet Valley River, whose water is sweet because the surrounding hillsides produce sweet chrysanthemums, and the petals, falling into the water for ages, have affected its taste. The inhabitants of this valley dig no wells but drink this water and live to a ripe old age. The maximum runs to hundred and forty or hundred and fifty years; the minimum to eighty or ninety. None die prematurely, and it is all due to the potency of this water. For this reason Chief Minister Wang Ch'ang, Minister of War Liu K'uan, and Grand Tutor Yüan Wei, having served as prefects of Nan-yang, ordered Li-hsien to furnish them forty vats of this Sweet Valley water monthly for drinking purposes wherever they held office. This was due to the fact that these men were much in fear of rheumatism and eye trouble, which were controlled by this water. They could not benefit from it, however, to the same extent as the inhabitants of the valley. Theirs were only minimal benefits from the drinking of this water.

12a

The blossoms of chrysanthemums and water lilies are similar and the two species are differentiated only by the sweetness and bitterness of taste, the former being sweet and the latter bitter, whence the popular saying, "Bitter as a water lily." Today, only few places have the true chrysanthemum, which generally grows beside streams. It is found in largest numbers in the Hou-shih mountains [SE of Loyang] and in Li-hsien. The terms Sun-sperm, Rebirth, Shade-formed, and Filled-everywhere, found in the recipes for geniehood, all refer to the chrysanthemum and are

names for its root, stem, flower, or fruit, respectively. These
descriptive epithets are all very fine, but those taking this
medicine these days find it practically ineffective, for they
simply cannot obtain the true chrysanthemum any more. It
cannot be overemphasized that all the people living on the
banks of Sweet Valley River with its chrysanthemum taste
enjoy protracted lives. How, then, could there be no benefit
were we to return to the good medicine?

My late grandfather (Ko Hsi), who became Assistant
Secretary in the Department of Foreign Affairs, was once
Prefect of Lin-yüan [N. Hunan], where there was a family
by the name of Liao whose members enjoyed great longevity, generation after generation. Some exceeded one
hundred, and others lived to eighty or ninety. After the
family moved from there, the younger members suffered
more and more from premature deaths, but the others who
were living in their old home were enjoying longevity
generation after generation. Accordingly, it was felt that the
house was causing it, but nobody knew why. Then, be-
12b   coming suspicious of the deep redness of the well water, they
did some digging around it and came upon several dozen
vats of cinnabar that had been buried there by men of old
only a few feet away from the well. Seepage from this
cinnabar had been entering the well via springs, and those
who drank of the well had, in consequence, enjoyed great
longevity. How much more effective it would be, then,
were one to nibble and take cinnabar that had been properly
prepared!

I have also heard of a certain Chao Ch'ü of Shang-tang
[SE Shansi]. He had suffered leprosy for many years without
deriving any benefits from a mass of treatments. When he
was on the point of death, someone remarked that he should
be abandoned, since he was now worth less than the living.
After consideration had been given to the sale of sons or
grandsons, the family provided funds for a suite to escort
him to a cave in the mountains. There he cursed his mis-

fortune and wept, bemoaning himself day and night. A
month later a genie happened to pass by and took pity on
him, as he inquired into all the details. Chao Ch'ü, realizing
that this man was different from all others, kowtowed, told
his story, and begged for mercy. The genie then gave him a
pouch of medicine and the directions for taking it. After
Chao Ch'ü had taken it for a hundred and some days, his
sores got better, his good complexion returned, and his skin
became like moist jade. When the genie again passed that
way, Chao Ch'ü thanked him for his kindness in returning
him to life. When asked for his prescription, the genie replied, "This is only pine resin, very abundant on this
mountain. Just refine this substance and take it, and you will   *13a*
enjoy Fullness of Life and immortality."

When Chao Ch'ü returned home, his family at first
thought him a ghost and was very much frightened. He
himself took the pine resin for a long time, with the result
that his body became ever lighter while his energy increased
a hundredfold. He mounted to precipitous heights and
passed over dangerous chasms, and was still going strong at
the end of the day. At 170 his teeth had not fallen out and
his hair had not turned gray. One night while in bed he observed a light the size of a mirror in his room, but when he
inquired of those about him they replied that they saw
nothing. After a time the light gradually grew larger until
the whole room was nothing but light, like the day. He also
observed — it was still night — two females clad in multicolored silks on his face, each two or three inches tall. They
both had faces and bodies, only on a miniature scale. They
played about between his mouth and his nose. This continued each night for a year as the females gradually got
taller and placed themselves at his sides. Further, he constantly heard the sound of lutes, so that all he did was smile
happily. He remained among men almost three hundred
years, his complexion always that of a young lad. Then he
left for the Pao-tu mountains [SE Shansi], undoubtedly to

become an earth genie. His contemporaries who heard of his success in taking pine resin then vied with one another in taking it. Those with many workers transported it in carts and by muleback to fill their homes with it. Having taken it disinterestedly, they felt no benefit in less than a month and then desisted. This is how difficult it is to find people with will power!

13b

Under Emperor Ch'eng of the Han, hunters in the Chungnan mountains [W of Ch'ang-an] saw a naked person whose body was covered with black hair. They wanted to capture this individual, but it passed over pits and valleys like a thoroughbred and could not be overtaken. Then they did some spying in the region, surrounded the place, and captured it. When they had established that it was a woman, she was questioned, and replied, "I was originally a Ch'in concubine. Learning that with the arrival of bandits from the East the King of Ch'in would surrender and the palace would be burned, I became frightened and ran away to the mountains where I famished for the lack of food. I was on the point of dying when an old man taught me how to eat the leaves and fruits of pines. At first it was bitter and unpleasant, but I gradually grew used to it until it produced lack of hunger and thirst. In the winter I suffered no cold, and in summer I felt no heat."

Calculation showed that this woman, having been the concubine of Prince Ying of Ch'in, was more than two hundred years old in the time of Emperor Ch'eng. When she was brought back to the court to be fed starches, the first odor from them nauseated her for several days, but then she became reconciled to them. After about two years of this new life, her body lost its hair, and she turned old and died. If she had not been caught, she would have become a genie.

A certain Wen of Nan-yang has described how his great-grandfather had fled to the mountains during the troubles at the end of the Han dynasty, where he suffered so intensely from hunger that he wanted to die. Thereupon, some person

taught him to eat thistle to alleviate his suffering. When he
returned home after several decades, his complexion was
that of a much younger man and his energy greater than
formerly. He claimed that while in the mountains his body
became so light that he wanted to dance. He mounted to
heights and passed precipitous places without being exhausted at the end of the day. He walked on ice and snow
without feeling cold. One day he noticed several men sitting
facing one another on a lofty peak playing backgammon.
One who was reading happened to look down and notice
Mr. Wen. Then he overheard them sizing him up. When
it was asked, "Is this man ready to be summoned on high?"
one of them replied, "Not yet."

Thistle is also known as Mountain Thistle or Mountain
Sperm, and we read in *The Pharmacopoeia of the Gods*, "Those
wishing Fullness of Life must always take Mountain Sperm."

Anciently, each of eight genii tried one substance to attain
earthly geniehood. After several centuries, each of them
compounded divine cinnabar or Potable Gold, and only
thus did they mount to Paradise. If men compound the
eight substances, refine them, and then take them, they will
not attain their potential because the potentials of these
medicines cancel one another. Han Chung took sweet flag
for thirteen years and his body developed hairs. He intoned
ten thousand words of text each day. He felt no cold in
winter, though his gown was open. To be effective, sweet
flag must have grown an inch above the surrounding stones
and have nine or more nodules. That with purple flowers is
best.

Chao T'o-tzu took cinnamon for twenty years, whereupon the soles of his feet became hairy and he could walk
500 miles a day; also he became strong enough to lift a
thousand pounds.

I-men tzu took Schisandra seeds for sixteen years, and his
complexion became like that of a fairy. He entered water
without getting wet, and fire without being burned.

Prince Wen of Ch'u took yellow dock for eight years and in the end had an apparition of something shining with a repeater crossbow in its hand.

Lin Tzu-ming took thistle for eleven years with the result that his ears became five inches long and his body light enough to fly. He could jump across an abyss almost twenty feet wide.

Tu Tzu-wei took asparagus, with the result that he had eighty concubines, sired 130 sons, and walked three hundred miles a day.

Jen Tzu-chi took truffles for eighteen years, then genii and fairies consorted with him; he could make himself invisible or visible, and he no longer ate starches. All his cautery scars disappeared, and he had a brilliance like jade.

Tzu-chung of Ling-yang took bitter milkwort for twenty years and begat 37 sons. He never forgot anything that he had read, and he could disappear at will.

The Genii Classics state that although several centuries of life may be acquired by taking the leaves of certain plants and trees, it is quite impossible to attain geniehood while ignorant of divine cinnabar. On the basis of this statement we can realize that plants and trees only protract life but they are not medicines producing Fullness of Life. They may only be taken to keep oneself whole until the elixir has been successfully prepared.

Someone then inquired whether medicine should be taken before or after meals. *Ko:* Chung-huang tzu's *Regulations for Taking Medicines* says that medicines intended for the curing of illness should be taken before meals, but those intended as tonics should be taken after meals. When I asked Cheng Yin the reason for this, he replied that the explanation was quite simple: If you want to attack illness with your medicine, it will be easier for the potency of the medicine to operate before meals while the interior is empty. If taken after meals its potency would be consumed in attacks against the starches. If you desire the tonic effects of medicine and

15a

take it before meals, it would be driven down by starches before its potency can take effect and therefore would prove not to be beneficial.

Interlocutor: When a man takes medicine as a tonic, it is said that certain conditions are requisite. Is that true?

Ko: ★*Yü ts'e chi* and *K'ai ming ching* both consider that the situation of a man's age-fate can be learned from the Five Notes and the Six Regulators of the denary cycle.[1] Those born in the years (or on the months, days, or hours) *keng-tzu, keng-wu, chi-mao, chi-yu, wu-yin, wu-shen, hsin-ch'ou, hsin-wei, ping-ch'en, ping-hsü, ting-ssu,* and *ting-hai* are "ones," belonging to the note *kung* and the agent earth. The "threes" are those born under another series of twelve and belong to the note *chih* and the agent fire. The "fives" were born under still another series of twelve and belong to the note *yü* and the agent water. The "sevens" were born under yet another series of twelve and belong to the note *shang* and the agent metal. The "nines" were born under the remaining series of twelve and belong to the note *chüeh* and the agent wood.

15b

When your fate is classified under the agent earth you should not take green [=blue] (wood) medicine; under metal, no red (fire) medicine; under wood, no white (metal) medicine; under water, no yellow (earth) medicine; under fire, no black (water) medicine; for in the case of the elements, wood subdues earth, earth subdues water, water

---

[1] In *Monumenta Serica*, Vol. 11 (1946), pp. 28–30, Father Feifel has described this system. The Six Regulators are numbers 7,8,5,6,3, and 4 of the denary cycle in that order. Used twice, they form a series of pairs with the duodenary cycle, namely, *keng-tzu, hsin-ch'ou, wu-yin, chi-mao, ping-ch'en, ting-ssu,* and also *keng-wu, hsin-wei, wu-shen, chi-yu, ping-hsü,* and *ting-hai.*

This is used as a table of reference by which a given binary from the sexagenary cycle can be altered to a binary consisting solely of elements from the denary cycle. For example, *chi-ch'ou* becomes *chi-hsin* because the above table pairs *ch'ou* with *hsin. Hsin* is number 8 in the denary cycle and *chi* is number 6. Then by counting the number of places in the denary cycle from *hsin* to *chi* one obtains the number 9, which equates with the musical note *chüeh.* Thus the client's sexagenary number will classify him as a one, three, five, seven, or nine, all of which is highly useful to the fortune-teller.

subdues fire, fire subdues metal, and metal subdues wood.
Only in the case of the great medicines gold and cinnabar is
16a there no need for all this talk about requisites.

Yü's Pace: Advance left foot, then pass it with the right.
Bring the left up to the right foot. Advance right foot, then
pass it with the left. Bring the right up to the left foot.
Advance left foot, then pass it with the right. Bring the left
up to the right foot. In this way three paces are made, a
total of 21 linear feet, and nine footprints will be made
(17.5*a*3).

(*Translator's note:* The following seems to be out of place; it appears
logically in 4.17*b*6—; but Ko Hung may have repeated it here for the
convenience of his readers.) *The Lesser Divine Elixir.* Take three pounds of
real cinnabar, one pound of white honey, stir together, expose to the sun,
and cook until it can be shaped into pills. Every morning take ten pills
about the size of a hemp seed. In less than a year, whitened hair will be-
16b come black, lost teeth will regrow, and the skin of your whole body will
shine. Those who take it will not age, and old men will regain their
youthfulness. If it is taken constantly, one will enjoy Fullness of Life, and
immortality.

The Lesser Recipe for Nibbling Gold (4.18*a*2). Dip melted gold in and out
of clear wine about two hundred times until the wine bubbles. Knead it
until it comes through the fingers like mud. If the wine will not bubble
and the gold will not come through the fingers when you squeeze it, remelt
it and dip it in wine innumerable times. When ready, take one piece the
size of one or two crossbow pellets, dividing them into smaller pills, over
thirty days. You will then be immune to cold and heat, and gods and
fairies come down to you. Silver too may be nibbled in the same way as
gold. If those who take these two substances can dwell in a cave on a
famous mountain, they will levitate to become celestial genii within one
year. If they take them while living among other men, they will become
earth genii. Don't transmit these recipes heedlessly.

Liang-i tzu's Recipe for Nibbling Melted Gold (4.18*a*8). Prepare three
pounds of the skin and fat from the back of a hog and one quart of strong
vinegar. Place five ounces of yellow gold in a container and cook over an
earthen stove. Dip the gold in and out the fat one hundred times; likewise
in the vinegar. Take a pound of this gold, and you will outlast all nature.
17a Take a half pound, and you will live to 2000; five ounces, to 1200 years.
It may be taken in any amount, but it must be made on lucky days to be
miraculously effective. Let this recipe not be given to others, for the
medicine they make would be ineffective. If you wish to take medicine
that will banish the Corpses from your body, you must take cinnabar.

Directions for Nibbling the Elixir (4.17b9). Take one pound of cinnabar, pestled and sifted, three quarts of strong vinegar, and two quarts of clear lacquer. Mix these three thoroughly and cook over a slow fire until the compound can be shaped into pills. Take three the size of a hempseed twice daily for forty days, and all abdominal illnesses will be cured, and the Three Corpses that are in your body will depart. Take for one hundred days, and your flesh and bones will become strong and sturdy. Take for one thousand days, and the Governor of Fates will strike your name from the Book of Death; you will last as long as all nature, and the sun and moon will always shine on you. You can change shape continuously. You will cast no shadow in the sun, for you will radiate your own light.

12

The Discussion Period

Interlocutor: If it were definitely established that geniehood could be achieved, the sages would have cultivated it, but the fact that neither the Duke of Chou nor Confucius did so proves that there can be no such process (8.9*a*8).

Ko: A sage does not necessarily become a genie, just as a genie does not necessarily become a sage. When their destinies were ordained, the sages you mention did not meet with a potential that would bring Fullness of Life; they merely desired spontaneously to remove oppressors, exterminate bandits, overcome dangers, pacify the violent, regulate rituals, compose music, formulate standards, and confer instruction; to modify unorthodox behavior, change depraving customs, restrain dangerous princes, uphold tottering states; publish *The Poems* and *The Writings of Old*, compose the books known as *Ho-t'u* and *Lo-shu*, prepare basic decrees, and harmonize elegant panegyrics and instruct the young. They replied to the various states sending ambassadors to the court, and presented them with gifts. Their chimneys ever belching smoke and their mats for sitting ever warm, their burdens never reached a culmination and bad harvests knew no cease. How then could they ever close the door to reports, cover their vision, do their seeing and listening inwardly, engage in formal breathing exercises and calisthenics, undertake long fasts and periods of purification, stay at home to refine their bodies, climb mountains to gather herbs, count respirations in order to keep their inner gods in mind, and dispense with starches to clear the intestines!

The genii, on the other hand, need only be of firm resolution and high sincerity. If they are zealous and do not slacken; if they can be calm and quiet, their goal is easily achieved without awaiting an increase in their resources. However, for the man involved in popular high estate there will be heavy embarrassment if he wishes to perform the divine process.

1b

Once the candidate for geniehood has succeeded in compounding one great medicine or in learning one vital thing for the nourishing of his internal gods, he will enjoy Fullness of Life and lasting vision. This bears no comparison with the endless things pursued by the sages, this, that, and I know not what! Further, those popularly known as sages were all sages in the art of government, not sages in the art of obtaining the divine process. Those of the latter sort were Yellow Emperor and Lao Tan; those of the former, the Duke of Chou and Confucius.

Yellow Emperor did not mount to geniehood until he had first restored order to his generation. This means he was a man who uniquely had the capacity to combine these two opposing activities. Of all the emperors and kings of old there are only seventy-two whose names we can read cut into the rock of Mount T'ai; the others whose names have become obliterated are legion, but it is only of Yellow Emperor that there is any record that geniehood was attained. This fact is supported by all the evidence.

The people of our world, feeling that some one individual's ability is unachievable by the mass, call him the "sage" of that particular activity. Therefore, those who have been without peers at backgammon are known as

Sages of Backgammon, and in our day Yen Tzu-ch'ing and
Ma Sui-ming do have that title. Those surpassing their con-
2a temporaries in the writing of history become known as
Sages of History, and such is the title we give today to
Huang Hsiang and Hu Chao. Those who exceed others in
the ability to paint are called Sages of Painting, such being
the titles we give to Wei Hsieh and Chang Mo. Chang
Heng and Ma Chün we call Sages in Woodworking because
they were the most clever at carving. By the same reasoning,
Mencius calls Po-i Sage of the Puritans (5B.1); Chan Huo,
Sage of the Amiable; I-yin, Sage of the Abiders-in-office.

Accordingly, in the expanded meaning that I would im-
part to the word, the title *sage* is not restricted to political
activity alone. Pan Shu and Mo Ti are the Sages of
Mechanization. Yü Fu, Ch'in Yüeh-jen, Ho, and Huan are
Sages of Healers. Tzu-wei and Kan Te are Sages of Astro-
logy. Astrologer Su and Hsin Liao are Sages of Divination
by Tortoise and Milfoil. Hsia Yü and Tu Hui are Sages of
Muscle-work. Ching K'o and Nieh Cheng are Sages of
Courage. Flying Lien and K'ua-fu are Sages of Footracing.
Maestros K'uang and Yen-chou are Sages of Singing. Sun
Wu, Wu Ch'i, Han Hsin, and Pai Ch'i are Sages of Military
Strategy. In other words, *sage* is a designation for the out-
2b standing person in any human endeavor. It is not to be
restricted solely to political and civil activities.

Chuang Chou (10.11—) has said, "Among thieves you
will also find five of the sage's procedures: They know
intuitively where people's treasures are hidden: this is intelligence. They do not hesitate to enter the homes of others:
this is bravery. After leaving those homes they are not afraid:
this is propriety. They differentiate between the possible and
the impossible: this is wisdom. They divide the booty fairly
among themselves: this is the human ideal in action. Nobody has ever become a great robber without following
these procedures."

If someone argues that the process followed by the sage

is indivisible and must be seen as a whole, for only then is it sagehood, my reply would remind him that seventy-two of Confucius's followers understood him, and each of them acquired one portion of his sagehood. This proves that sagehood *is* divisible. And when we are told that Yen Hui embodied the whole of Confucius, but in miniature, it means that sagehood can be characterized by size.

We read in *The Changes* (*Hsi tz'u* A9), "The procedures of sagehood are four: In speaking it values the right words; in action it values results; in producing things it values conformity to model; in divining by tortoise and milfoil it values correct prognostication." Therefore, it is clear that sagehood is divisible. Why then should only those who are sufficiently expert in relation to God and natural living to be able to summon the gods and genii be denied the title of Sages-who-have-attained-God? If there are no sages in the attainment of God, neither can the Duke of Chou and Confucius be considered sages in the art of government. Granting, however, that there is more than one type of sage, why should a man be required to combine his own specialty with that of government?

3a

The genii classics hold that all who attain geniehood were so predestined; they merely happened to be granted the potential for divinity and geniehood; it was spontaneously conferred upon them. Therefore, already in the womb they possessed a nature that believed in God. When they had acquired some knowledge, their hearts and minds were drawn toward such matters as these, so all they needed was to encounter an enlightened teacher and acquire his method. Otherwise, they would not have believed and they would not have sought, and if they had sought they would not have found.

The *Chu-ming-yüan* section of *Yü ch'ien ching* reads, "A man's good and bad fortunes take form on the day that the fetus is formed and receives its potential (8.7a7). All receive sperm from the asterisms above. If the fetus meets with the sage asterism it will become a sage; with the highest-caliber asterism, a man of the highest caliber; with the civil asterism, a man of the civil arts; with the military asterism, a military man; with the honors asterism, an honored man; with the riches asterism, a rich man; with the low-estate asterism, a man of low estate; with the poverty asterism, a poor man; with the longevity asterism, a man of long life; with the geniehood asterism, a genie. There is also a god-genie-sage asterism; a sage-giving-order-to-his-generation asterism; an asterism combining these two types of sagehood; an asterism for being honored but not rich; an asterism for being rich but not honored; an asterism combining riches and honors; an asterism for being first rich but later poor;

3b　　an asterism for being first honored but later of low estate; an asterism combining poverty and low estate; an asterism for unending riches and honors; an asterism for loyalty and filial piety; an asterism for evil; etc. I cannot give the complete list. Generally, however, a man's life is rooted in a predetermined fate. Chang Ch'e-tzu's exposition of this problem is correct.

If you are not fated to become either a god or genie, you will certainly not have your heart and mind drawn toward geniehood. No man has yet sought for such things without having a heart and mind fond of them; none has yet found them without seeking. From antiquity down to the present there have been highly talented and intelligent persons who did not believe in the existence of geniehood; there have also been many very ordinary persons who attained geniehood by study. The former knew many things but in some way were blind to geniehood; the latter were ignorant of much, but they had a special understanding of the logic governing geniehood. Wouldn't you say that this was caused by heaven's command?

Taoists prize and keep secret the recipes leading to geniehood. They take pains in selecting the very best pupils, and only after a very long time do they give them the all-important oral directions. As for the rest of the world, happy in its natural disbelief and failure to seek, why should the Taoists compel themselves to talk with them? Since it is impossible to transform them and make them believers, one would only evoke ridicule and bring speedy denigration. Therefore, those with the divine process travel paths different from those of the rest of mankind and live in different places. They do not wish to talk with them, and *4a* they want no bodily contact with them. Though separated from them by a thousand miles, they fear that this is not enough to avoid the shocks of annoyance. Though they follow other roads and paths, they fear that even this is not sufficient to avoid the stench of slander. Taoists cannot be seduced by honors, nor will they shift residence for riches. How could they willingly peddle themselves to ordinary students, saying, "I have a method for acquiring geniehood?" This is possibly why the Duke of Chou and Confucius were never fortunate enough to learn of the divine process leading to geniehood.

It might well be said that the Duke of Chou and Confucius were the profoundest in eminent talent and in study on a broad scale. They were not accustomed to make any use whatever of the minor arts: juggling balls, playing with swords, crossing over weapon points, throwing things into narrow places, rope-walking, drape-climbing, discus-throwing, acrobatics with tables or hanging by the heels over a fathomless chasm, swimming the unplumbed depths of a Lü-liang, weight-lifting, fire-walking, tiger and leopard taming, or catching arrows on the fly. These are the type of thing that ordinary people do but the Duke of Chou and Confucius could not. How much less could they then do things that surpass the foregoing list: Know what other people are thinking or which way a flea will turn; distinguish between vermilion and purple through a barrier; find a particular straw in a great pile; tell what books are in a box; find hidden treasures in the earth. As for the birds and beasts nesting in the deep forests and the fish and tortoises abounding deep in the waters, if you would ask the Duke of Chou and Confucius to detail their colorings, distinguish their names, determine their numbers, and verify their presence or absence, it is not at all certain that they would be able to inform you completely. So, how much less could they do it for things farther removed than these?

When sages do not eat, they get hungry; when they do not drink, they get thirsty. If burned, they feel the heat; when it is freezing they feel cold. When struck they feel pain; when knifed they are wounded. After many years they grow old; when harmed they become ill. When their breaths are exhausted, they die. This means that there are many things in which they do not differ from people in general, even though there are a few things in which they do differ from others. They surpass others solely in talent, depth of thought, facility of speech, lofty literary style, wholeness of excellence, purity of conduct, good advice, and broad learning. How indeed can they embrace all these and other things equally? After they had provided security for rulers and order to the people by composing codified advice, it would be going too far to chide them for failure to know an additional huge field: the practices leading to geniehood, Fullness of Life, and immortality.

I have been taught that speech of the highest type grinds upon the ears of the masses, and truth is sure to evoke contradiction in the crowd. When the Confucianists have finished perusing this book of mine they are sure to conclude that I oppose the sages. But do I? My only desire is to treat the logic in things exhaustively. When this logic has been thoroughly examined and all the facts are in, *they* may seem to calumniate the Duke of Chou and Confucius.

People say that the sages came down from heaven; that they are divine creatures who know everything and can do anything. People so revere the reputations of the sages that they dare not reexamine them in the light of the facts. They say that if there is anything the sages could not do, then nobody can ever do it; if there is anything they did not know, then nobody can ever know it. How ridiculous can they get! But bringing our knowledge of today to bear against these opinions, I feel that enlightenment is possible.

Confucius did not understand the appropriateness of the cry of the bird on Mount Wan and the cry of those who were selling the living to bury the dead (cf. *Shuo yüan* 18.19*a*6; KTCY 5.1*a*12—),[1] so he replied promptly that only Yen Hui had that special understanding! When he heard the good wife on Mount T'ai weep (*Li chi, T'an kung* 2: Couvreur 243), he learned only by asking that a tiger had eaten three men from her home, but he did not know why she had not quit the place until she had enlightened him. When he saw that a sparrowcatcher had only fledglings (*Shuo yüan* 10.14*b*7), he could not explain; he had to ask and be told. When he wished to bury his mother, he did not even know where his father's grave was; someone had to tell him. After she had been buried with his father the tomb collapsed (*Li chi*; Couvreur 1.113), but his pupils had to tell him, for he did not know; then he wept torrents. Suspecting that Yen Hui was stealing food (LSCC 17.10*b*9—), Confucius pretended that he wished to sacrifice it to his ancestors and divine regarding the vanity of accumulating possessions. When the stable burned (Ana. 10.11) he did not know whether any person or horse had been harmed, and Yen Hui had to tell him that some were already dead. He wandered everywhere throughout more than seventy states but could not foresee that anybody who knew him would certainly not employ him; that as he stopped without duties here and

5*b*

---

[1] KTCY: Confucius heard some weeping which he did not understand. He asked Yen Hui whether he knew the reason for it. The reply came that it could only be for somebody dead and also for separation from somebody living, because it reminded him of the cry of a bird on Mount Wan which had seen its four fledglings fly away, never to return again. When inquiry was made of the weeping person, he replied that his father had died and out of poverty it was necessary to sell one of the sons in order to bury him.

there, his mat would never have time to get warm. Not knowing that the men of K'uang would ambush him (Ana. 9.5; *Chuang* 17.60), he traveled through their country. The fact that he asked Lao Tan about the ceremonies of antiquity (SC 63.1*b*1) indicates that there was something he did not understand about them. Since he had to ask the Lord of T'an about official offices that had the names of birds (KTCY 4.4*a*9), there was something he did not know about officialdom. While traveling, he did not know where the ford was (Ana. 18.6), and he sent someone to inquire, but he did not know that the man of whom he inquired would be sure to upbraid him and refuse to tell him the right road, because a person like Confucius should know it without asking. When he descended from his carriage to pursue a man who was singing about the phoenix (Ana. 18.5), he did not know that the man would not stop. When he visited Nan-tzu (Ana. 6.28) he did not know that she would be of no benefit to him. I cannot continue with a complete listing of such evidence. But now why wonder that he was unacquainted with the methods leading to geniehood?

Ordinary Confucianists claim that no others can do anything that the sages could not do as well. Yet, the people of Tang dwell in the water; Liang Mu transformed himself in fire; Lou Kuei withstood extreme heat, and Wang Chung-tu the bitter cold; Tso Tz'u was split by a weapon but he did not die; Kan Shih spent a year without starches; Fan Yi was struck with an ax but it did not pierce him; a man continued to live by turning tortoises into floating corpses (HHS 115.2*a*10) and using them to cross a stream and thus escape hostile pursuers; Shao-kan seized a hundred ghosts; Fei Ch'ang-fang shortened distances; Li Chung-fu assumed the appearance of a wild duck; Chang K'ai's exhalations raised a mist. I have never heard, however, that the Duke of Chou or Confucius could do any such things.

6a

If an ordinary person then argues that the Duke of Chou and Confucius could very well have done these various things but it so happens that they did not, my reply is that when you cease seeking for facts in the texts and use your imagination, I can just as well claim that they were able to fly back and forth, soar to the limits of the universe, raise clouds and produce rain, move mountains and snatch off wells — only they did not. What limits are there, once you no longer restrict yourself to the facts in the texts? Why, I could even claim that the Duke of Chou and Confucius became genii? But I feel that this is no way to instruct the world, and I suspect that if everyone knew that immortality was achievable, they would all most certainly stop providing for their families and the state, abandon entrance into official life and, mounting to dangerous peaks or swimming in the depths, devote themselves to the divine process, so that families would no longer have sons and grandsons, and the state would no longer have ministers and officials. Loyalty and filial piety would both disappear; the great system of social relationships would certainly be thrown into disorder. If I were to claim that the Duke of Chou and Confucius followed these procedures surreptitiously but kept it secret and, saying nothing to others, pretended to die, while they really became genii, what could you say to contradict me? In fact, that is exactly what may have happened!

Ling pao ching contains three booklets *Cheng chi, P'ing heng*, and *Fei kuei shou* all consisting of recipes leading to geniehood. The story is that while stone was being cut to build the King of Wu's palace, some writings consisting of gold plaques with purple characters were found within a double stone, but they could not be deciphered. He had messengers take them to Confucius for clarification. To Confucius, however, the messengers told a different tale: "The King of Wu was sitting idly by when a red bird with some writing in its beak settled on the palace. Not knowing what this meant, we have come a great distance to report to Confucius that he might enlighten us." Confucius replied, "This is a Ling-pao prescription, the method for attaining

6b

Fullness of Life followed by Yü the Great, who lived as a hermit in a place noted for its streams. When his years were equal to those of all nature, he became a courtier in Purple Palace. When about to attain geniehood, Yü sealed this text in a stone casket on a famous mountain. That a red bird now carries it in its beak probably means that heaven is conferring it upon you." According to this story, Yü the Great never died, and Confucius knew it. How do we know, therefore, that Confucius did not practice this divine process in utter secrecy? If we return, therefore, to your first statement that the sages did none of these things, we are not yet in a position to say definitely that they were unaffected by them.

Among men, likes and dislikes vary from individual to individual. How can we disbelieve this when it shows in their faces? If something agrees with a man's ideas, he is sure to do it no matter how minor it is. But if it disagrees with his inner gods, he will not pursue it no matter how big and important it may be. There are even people that like the bitter and dislike the sweet. Incalculable is the number of those that would abandon propriety out of thirst for profit. In the eyes of the sages the big prize is position, but wealth is the way to win the crowd. It has been said that *7a* riches and honors are what men most desire (Ana. 4.5), but in antiquity there were men who would not accept the position of Emperor or King; who did not wish for the riches of the whole world. Probably it would be impossible to count those disdaining office in the official hierarchy, refusing gifts of jewels and silks, and instead resorting to the pure heights in mountains and forests or finding the lowly occupation of fisherman sweet.

It is also said that man's great desires being directed to male, female, food, and drink, fondness for sex is not to be deprecated, and we should forget to worry about the sweet and pleasant. It would be difficult, however, to give a complete account of all individuals who have abandoned starches and fine foods; who did not maintain wives and concubines and, going off suddenly alone, took satisfaction in their overwhelming vitality, found joy in caring for themselves, and forgot savors as they sipped from streams.

In their sexual relationships all men like the seductiveness of the rouged face and the soft flesh in a slim frame, yet Yellow Emperor took for his wife Mu-mu who was truly ugly, and the Marquis of Ch'en had compassion on the detestable Tun-hsia. Since all human noses like perfumes, loosestrife, turmeric, boneset, storax, *yüan-tan*, *su-chiao*, Gracilaria, *chieh-ch'e*, the spring orchid, and the autumn orchid are valued like gems. Nevertheless, women living by the seashore pursue acrid smelly husbands and never fail to stay with them.

King Wen of the Chou craved unpleasant pickled foods, and would not exchange them for the tempting tastes of pork, mutton, or beef. Emperor Ming of the Wei preferred the sound of mallet and chisel and would not exchange them for the harmonies of strings and bamboos. Since everyone has his own preferences, how can you ask *A* to be like *B*? The Duke of Chou and Confucius automatically happened not to believe in the divine process leading to geniehood. Remember, however, that just as there are places not lighted by the sun and moon, so there are things that the sages did not know. Do you think it admissible to declare that there are no genii in the world just because of something the sages did not do? This would be like blaming the sun, moon, and stars for not lighting the interior of an overturned basin!

7b

13

The Ultimate in Speech

Interlocutor: Did all the genii of antiquity achieve their state through study or through a special endowment of breaths for that goal?

Ko: What sort of question is that? Not a single one of them failed to carry his package of books and resort to a teacher to perform many acts of labor. They underwent frost and dangers and were combed by the wind and bathed by the rain, as they personally did sprinkling and sweeping and worked away at the art in widely separated places. They revealed themselves first in acts of faith, and in the end they were tried by perils and hardships.

If found to be sincere and steadfast, their hearts and minds free from rancor and doubts, they were allowed to ascend into the hall and enter the home of their masters. Some grew weary and stopped in midcourse; others withdrew out of resentment and dissatisfaction. Some, enticed by worldly glory and advantages, returned to engage in lay pursuits; others, won over by perverse argument, lost their will to tranquillity. Some became active in the morning and wished the task completed that same evening; others worked at their ease and expected immediate results. It would be an overstatement to claim that there is even one man in ten thousand whose heart and mind are unmoved by the sight of wealth or beauty, and whose will is not weakened by the talk of the common herd. Therefore, those wishing to enter the path to geniehood are as numerous as the hairs on a buffalo, while the successful are as rare as the horn of the unicorn.

1b

The shooter of a stiff crossbow shows his strength when he releases the arrow; those wading mighty rivers preserve themselves whole by reaching the farther bank. A well is not dug until a spring has been reached; one step from the goal is the same as not starting at all. A path is not made by watching the clock; anything as high as shimmering heaven requires more than one basket of material. It is with all this in mind that those who scale towering heights fear that their strength will fail as they approach the point of attainment, and those working the divine process worry that their resolution may not carry through when the prescription is succeeding. A thousand barns and ten thousand coffers are not the result of one season, and a sky-touching tree did not grow that high in a week. The unfathomable pool begins in muck and mire, and the great wealth of Fan Li was accumulated by hundreds and thousands. Thus it was that Yin Ch'ang-sheng effected the highest type of divine process by personally advancing while others withdrew. By respecting the end as much as he did the beginning, Hsien-men tzu was able to summon the cloud-dragon. Why concern ourselves, however, with the others when our own determination is really firm!

Having no power over life, the masses devote their energies to its destruction. Nothing perishable can provide an iota of eternity, any more than the streams of our great rivers can fill a bottomless jar. Expending more than they receive, ordinary people are like non-providers. How much the more so when there are thousands or hundreds in outgo without a farthing of income!

All men, both young and old, are subject to illness; the

2a

difference is only a question of degree. Everyone, similarly, has received a variable quantity of breath. Those with much of it are extinguished slowly; those with little come to a quick end. Those knowing a process make repairs to their breaths by coming to their rescue, in the course of which they must first revert to their original state of breathing like a fetus. After that they seek to augment its quantity in themselves.

If the flesh would fly and the body prance after breath and medicine had been taken for a full day, and if a month's calisthenics produced that differential of flying on wings, nobody in the world would fail to believe in the divine process. I fear, however, that before a spoonful of benefit can be crystallized, there is a succession of expense measurable in vats. Before something secure can be attained, the poisons of ice and frost must be combatted. Not realizing that the fault lies in themselves, men turn to opposition, declaring that the divine process is profitless, and they abandon the pills and powders and stop the breathing exercises.

It has been said, "It is not difficult to enjoy Fullness of Life; the difficulty lies in learning the divine process. It is not difficult to learn the divine process; the difficulty lies in carrying it out. It is not difficult to carry it out; the difficulty lies in persisting to the end." The master carpenter can give a man his compass and square, but he cannot guarantee dexterity. An intelligent teacher can give a man a written prescription, but he cannot warrant that he will compound it. Cultivation of the divine process is like the sowing of grain; success in it may be compared with the harvest. The field may be fertile and the water conditions perfect, yet if the right weather is not at hand or the hoe is not applied, *2b*   the grain you have sown will merely form little mounds, but you will reap nothing. No matter how large your farm, there will be no crop.

The ordinary man not only does not realize that profit begets profit; he does not even realize that loss begets loss.

To be sure, loss is more easily and more readily recognized; profit is hard to recognize and reveals itself more slowly. If, however, facility is not realized, how can one recognize difficulties? Losses may be compared with the flame of the lamp melting the grease; nobody notices what is transpiring until suddenly the light dies. Profit is to be compared with the sowing and cultivating of plants. Before anyone realizes it, the shoots begin to appear. Therefore, when regulating the body and nurturing its life, give care to the little things. Even a slight profit is not to be considered unimportant and left uncultivated, nor is a slight loss to be considered harmless and left unblocked. Greatness is always the result of an accumulation of little things; a million results from an accumulation of units. If you can appreciate it when it is only a promise and perfect it when it becomes evident, you are close to knowing the divine process.

Interlocutor: Did anyone in antiquity ever suddenly enjoy Fullness of Life without having done anything about it?

Ko: No. Some worked long and diligently with an intelligent teacher and then were presented with the medicine ready-made; others received a secret prescription and made it themselves. This all took place away from the everyday world with no involvement in lay activity, but the historians *3a* have merely preserved their names without providing details about how they achieved geniehood. It is just as though they had never existed.

Of old, Yellow Emperor was born with the ability to speak and had all the divinities at his command. We might say that heaven had conferred divine spontaneity upon him. Yet he was unable to acquire the divine process by merely sitting upright and doing nothing. Therefore, on ascending Mount Royal Abode, he was given the Cinnabar Classic (see above, 4.5*a*7). At Tripod Lake he distilled mercury. Climbing Mount K'ung-t'ung he asked questions of Kuang-ch'eng; reaching Chü-tz'u Peak he studied under Ta-wei.

Going to Mount T'ai in the east he received commands
from Chung-huang. He entered Gold Valley to consult with
Chüan tzu. To discuss calisthenics and diet, he had the help
of Heaven-fairy and Simplicity-fairy. To refine his progress,
he consulted Shan Chi and Li Mu. To prognosticate situations, he had information from Lord Winds. To diagnose
through the pulse, he studied under Lei kung and Ch'i po.
To master the art of war, he acquired booklets on the Five
Notes. To learn all the vile tricks of the gods, he noted what
the animal Pai-tse had to say. To become a good judge of
distances, he recorded the explanations of Bluebird. To
succor those who are hurt and wounded, he received the
arts of Metal-smelter. Therefore, he knew all secrets, had a
thorough knowledge of the processes, knew all about God
(Truth), and then he rode a dragon to mount on high and
be with Nature at Pinnacleless. Accordingly, the gods and
genii classics are unanimous in their account that both

3b Yellow Emperor and Lao Tan studied under T'ai-i-yüan-
chün in order to receive his secrets. How then could those
inferior to them ever attain geniehood automatically?
Impossible!

Interlocutor: If Yellow Emperor mastered geniehood perfectly, why is his tomb on Mount Ch'iao?

Ko: *Ching-shan ching* and *Lung-shou chi* both report that
after Yellow Emperor had taken the divine cinnabar, a
dragon came to meet him. The mass of state officials continued to feel affection for him; he was never out of their
thoughts. Some, therefore, built a shrine to house his
tabouret and his staff, and there they made offerings. Others
preserved his hat and gown by burying them. *Lieh-hsien
chuan* reports that Yellow Emperor chose his own day of
departure. After having departed for seventy days, he returned for another seventy days, to be buried ultimately on
Mount Ch'iao. Later, when, that mountain crashed, the
tomb was found devoid of the corpse. It contained nothing
but a sword and shoes. Despite certain differences in details,

all sources agree that he became a genie. This statement is widely documented in the Taoist writings and the philosophers, yet the Confucianists are unwilling to circulate marvels and blaze unorthodox paths. With their stress on ceremony, they feel that matters relative to gods and genii cannot be instructive to the people. Therefore, they say that he died merely in order to close the people's hearts and minds.

In return for the kindnesses shown them, the people erected shrines to Chu Yi, Luan Pa, and Yü kung while they were still alive. In antiquity, after the death of a man of outstanding merit, his retainers and sons carved a record of his deeds on an imperishable vessel, and to this day there are many examples of laudatory steles being erected by lower officials and people out of affectionate remembrance for high officials who had served a term in their districts. This is the sort of thing that occurred in the case of Yellow Emperor. But is that any proof that he certainly died?

Interlocutor: The 800 years of Old P'eng and the 3000 of An-ch'i constitute longevities surpassing the human norm. If there really is a divine process leading to immortality, why didn't those two men achieve immortality? It can only be that, having a natural predestined life span with the appropriate potential, they happened to acquire a large amount which, in the logic of the situation, could not be extended, but in the end they did not escape death.

Ko: ★*P'eng-tsu Classic* reads, "Beginning with the period of Emperor K'u, when he was an aide to Yao, Old P'eng was a grand officer throughout the Hsia dynasty down to the Yin. The King of Yin sent a geisha to get from him his recipe for sexual intercourse, and tried it effectively. Then he wished to murder Old P'eng in order to terminate his disseminating the procedure further, but, suspecting this would happen, Old P'eng had disappeared. He was some 700 or 800 years old at the time." This does not say that he died. *Huang-shih kung chi* records, "Seventy some years after

4a

4b

P'eng's departure, one of his pupils met him west of the Gobi." It is clear, therefore, that he did not die. Further, how would Old P'eng have been willing to die when seven or eight of his disciples — Ch'ing-i-wu kung, Hei-hsüeh kung, Hsiu-mei kung, Pai-t'u kung-tzu, Li-lou kung, T'ai-tsu chün, Kao-ch'iu tzu, and Pu-i-lai — lived for several centuries and departed as genii under the Yin. In addition, Liu Hsiang's *Lieh-hsien chuan* calls Old P'eng a genie.

Master An-ch'i used to sell medicines along the coast. The people of Lang-yeh had seen him for generations and reckoned that he was already a thousand years old. Ch'in Shih huang-ti asked to talk with him for three days and nights during which his discourse was of the higher things, deep with meaning, broad and substantiated. The emperor was so astonished that he conferred upon him gold and circular jades to a value of many, many thousands. An-ch'i accepted these things and placed them in the alms shelters of the cities and towns, for he felt that a pair of red shoes ornamented with jade was sufficient reward. He left a letter which read, "After another thousand years look for me in the P'eng-lai mountains." This is evidence that at the time of his interview with Ch'in Shih huang-ti he was already a thousand years old. It contradicts stories of his death.

Remember further that Ch'in Shih huang-ti was a skeptical and arrogant man, very much the type that is unlikely to have faith in gods and genii. He was untouched by those who did not answer him truthfully. When he asked

5a

An-ch'i about enjoying life in all fullness and he was satisfied with the answers, the emperor came to the conviction that the world must certainly contain a divine process leading to geniehood. Since he rewarded An-ch'i so richly, he must have been quite willing to study immortality. Lacking, however, an enlightened teacher, he was only deceived by such people as Lu Ao and Hsü Fu. That is the only reason he did not achieve geniehood (cf. 2.6*a*2—). If, earlier,

An-ch'i's words had been unreliable, the period of three days and three nights would have been sufficient to determine their inexactness, and the emperor would certainly have had him boiled or slain, and An-ch'i would not have escaped the terror of the cooking pot. Then, how would he have been so richly rewarded?

Interlocutor: Why do some people who take medicines, circulate their breaths, and do the calisthenics, still die?

Ko: Those not acquiring gold or cinnabar but taking only herbal medicines and practicing the lesser arts, can only protract their years or retard death. They do not attain geniehood. If they only know how to take herbal medicines but do not know the essential recipes for reverting their years, they completely lack the method for lengthening their existence. Also, if they do not know how to wear divine amulets, observe the prohibitions, give thought to their internal gods, and preserve God (Truth–Unity: 18.2*b*3, 10), they can only prevent internal illnesses from arising and drafts and dampness from harming them. If, finally, some malicious ghost, strong evil, mountain power, or liquid poison should harm them, they will die immediately. If they do not acquire the method for entering mountains, then the mountain deities will harm them, destructive ghosts will test them, wild beasts will wound them, poisons from pools will attack them, serpents will bite them, or they themselves will cause many death situations of various sorts.

5b

In some cases the divine process is undertaken too late in life, when deep harm has already been done to the person and it is difficult to make the necessary amends. And if, before the benefit of repairs takes effect, a man should suddenly again do something which can harm himself, what means is there for that man to attain Fullness of Life? Some can carry out the divine process late in life and still attain geniehood; others undertake it while young but do not succeed. Why? The former may be old, but their original allotment of breath (potential) was abundant. In this case, the harm

they suffer is slight, and it is easy for them to nourish themselves, with the result that they achieve geniehood. In the
case of the younger ones the original allotment of breath was
limited. The harm they suffered went so deep that it became
difficult for them to be saved, with the result that they did
not attain geniehood.

Cuttings from wax-myrtles and willows grow again when
planted, whether you bend them upside down or parallel to
the ground. Nothing surpasses these trees for ease of growth.
Cover them, however, no matter how thinly, and before
long there will be splits, and loss of foliage; they will shake
and fall. Even though they are treated with rich soil and
sprinkled with springtime water, they are bound to die, because they were not firmly rooted. Since there was no
opportunity for them to produce sap for their shoots, they
could not organize a life potential.

Constitutionally, man is easily wounded and is nurtured
only with difficulty. He is far inferior to the two types of
trees just mentioned, and the means for his destruction are
greater than splittings and loss of foliage, graver than
shakings, and uprootings. Few things aid him, but many are
harmful; it is quite fitting that he should die. Those spitting
out the old breaths and letting in the new are increasing
breath through breath, but once breath has been greatly
weakened it is difficult to increase it again. Those taking
medicines are increasing their blood supply through more
blood, but when the blood has become worn out it is
difficult to replace it.

If you find yourself panting when you rush, your breath
coming and going in gasps, and if you always become
breathless when you exert yourself physically, you are in a
state of breath deficiency. If your face lacks luster, your skin
is dry, your lips parched, your blood vessels gray, and your
features drawn, it is a sign of blood deficiency. These two
types of symptoms being external signs of decline, you can
be sure that the roots of your inner powers are also faded

within you. In these cases, only the most potent type of medicine is helpful. When the pursuit of the divine process is unsuccessful and death occurs while life was in the planning, there was no lack of inner breaths and blood, but the roots and sources for the making of breaths and blood were gone, and there remained only the flow in the smaller branches. It resembles the situation where submersion into water terminates a fire; there is an extinguishing, but the smoke does not cease immediately. Or we might compare it *6b* with the growth of branches and twigs after a tree has been cut down. In these cases it cannot be denied that smoke and leaves are present, but it is still a fact that their source has already perished. People think that an illness begins the day they feel sick, just as they think a body is dead when its breathing ceases. They are afraid of cold drafts and humidity, not realizing that such things do not hurt a healthy person. The only thing to fear is that he whose constitution is hollow while his inner breaths are few will not be able to stand cold drafts and humidity, and will therefore be harmed by them.

What shall I use for an analogy? Let us assume several men alike in age and good health and with the same food and clothing. Let them all go to the wilderness and undergo nights of severe cold, when pure snow falls upon them from above and ice forms below them. The cold wind howls in the night as it breaks the little branches. Ice forms on the men's lips. There will be among them one who alone feels the cold, although he may not necessarily become severely ill. This does not mean that the cold was more intense where he was, but only that that man's constitution probably could not withstand it. By the same token, when all eat of one particular thing but only one falls sick, it does not mean that there was a prejudiced poison in the food. All can drink the same quantity of wine, and some will become wider awake *7a* while others get tipsy, but this does not mean that there was any variation in the potency of the wine. We all share the same spells of extremely hot weather, but there are only isolated cases of death from the heat. Again this does not mean that the hot weather is prejudiced. All can take one particular medicine, but only some become dizzy or are depressed. This does not mean that the poison in its intensity likes some people but dislikes others.

Notice that when a gust of wind strikes a forest the dead trees are the first to fall. When a flood hits the banks, breaks and crevices are the first to crumble. When a raging fire burns a plain, the dry grasses are the first to burn. When baskets and bowls fall, it is only the weak ones that break. Accordingly, the man who is not following a process will normally be of a sickly constitution, which is only revealed through exposure to drafts, cold, heat, and dampness. If he can be made to rectify his breaths so that they do not fail, his body and its inner gods will prove a mutual protection for one another, and nothing will be able to harm him. Those following a process always become fearful if they started old, but not if they started young. Secure in the vigor of their youth and the firmness of their physical strength they overtax themselves. All sorts of illnesses form in them and the threat to their lives soon reveals itself. If they do not get the great medicine but only the herbal ones, they may become different from ordinary people, but they cannot protract the general limit of life. The genii classics tell us, therefore, that in nurturing life the vital thing is not to get wounded. This is the critical statement. It is nothing but the truth when God Farmer says, "How are you to acquire life in all its fullness if the various ills are not cured?"

Interlocutor: Wouldn't you say that that which inflicts wounds are the moments of licentiousness?

Ko: Why only these? The vital item in the enjoyment of Fullness of Life is the process for reverting one's years. Knowing that process, processors of the highest type can protract their years and banish illness, but afterward they do not boast of the accomplishment. If a man in the vigor

7b

of youth learns how to revert his years, repairs his brain with his sperm, and gathers mucus from his nose, he will live not less than three hundred years without taking any medicines, but this will not bring him geniehood. For the Ancients, the man who did not have this recipe was comparable to a cup made of ice filled with a hot liquid or a bundle of feathers filled with fire.

Further, wounding occurs when our thought is troubled with things for which we lack talent; also, when we force ourselves to do lifting without the requisite strength. Sadness, decrepitude, uneasiness, and torment are wounds, as is also excessive joy. Constant covetousness wounds, as do long conversations and the telling of pointless stories. Wasting time abed, archery contests, drunkenness and its vomitings, lying down after a heavy meal, getting breathless from running, shouts of joy and weepings, abstention from sexual intercourse — all these are wounds. When wounds have been accumulated to the point of exhaustion, death soon ensues, and this is a denial of God.

Therefore, the prescription for nurturing life is this: Do not spit for distance [too much breath would be lost]. Do not walk too fast. Do not listen too intently. Do not look too long. Do not sit too long. Do not stay in bed until you *8a* get too weak. Dress before you get chilled. Lighten your dress before you get overheated. Do not overeat when you have been starving. Eat only to satiety. Do not overdrink when you have been parched. Do not overdrink. Overeating begets congestions, and overdrinking produces accumulations of mucus. Don't overwork or take too much ease. Don't get up too early or too late. Don't perspire. Don't sleep too much. Don't race your carriage or your horse. Don't strain your eyes to see too far. Don't chew your food so long that it gets cold. Don't drink wine when you are going out into the wind. Don't bathe your body and hair too frequently. Don't overextend your will or desires. Don't scheme to achieve something ingenious. Don't seek too much warmth in winter or too much cold in summer. Don't lie without covers under the stars. Don't expose your shoulders while sleeping. Don't undergo severe cold, severe heat, strong winds, or heavy fogs. Don't overemphasize any one of the Five Savors when eating, for too much acidity harms the spleen; too much bitterness harms the lungs; too much acridity harms the liver; too much salt harms the heart; too much sugar harms the kidneys. These are merely laws of nature and the Five Agents.

All these things called wounds are indeed not immediately noticed as such, but in time one's longevity is lessened by them. Therefore those knowing how to care for the life that is theirs regulate the times of their sleeping and rising according to the season of the year. Their activity and repose *8b* follow the constant rule of perfect accommodation. To invigorate the tendons and bones there are prescriptions for bending exercises. To combat illness and noxious influences there are arts of swallowing and spitting. To circulate the blood and breaths there are rules for preventing waste. To act with or without restraint and to work hard or take repose it is vital that there be compensations. Repress anger to preserve your yin breaths; restrain your joy to nurture your yang breaths. After that, take first some herbs to relieve your defects; only then take gold or cinnabar to assure that you will never become exhausted. This constitutes the whole system for enjoying Fullness of Life.

If anyone preferring to cling stubbornly to his own opinions — claiming to be a learned and wise man who refuses to embroil himself in strange doctrines; a man devoting all energies to facts of top priority who will do nothing about lengthening life — if such a man should hear these words, he is not worthy of them, even though he should blow a gale across our ears or flash lightning before our eyes. Though he be ever so willing, as his body wastes away in depravities and indulgences and his breaths become exhausted in luxurious living, how can such a one be informed about the nurturing of life? When there is no careful forethought and there are no initial offerings, we speak of flattery and deception. To expect such a person to believe is the same as giving mirrors to the blind or diverting the deaf with music.

14

Seek Diligently

THE GREATEST of nature's [Heaven and Earth] acts is the begetting of life: It embodies love for creation. Therefore, of all that the Taoists revere in highest secrecy, nothing is more important than the prescriptions for attaining Fullness of Life. They transmit them only under an oath sealed with blood, and it is a crime punishable by heaven itself to communicate them to the wrong type of person. Earlier teachers dared not disclose these prescriptions to others in return for some slight good action. Those interested were obliged to seek for them with supreme diligence, and only then the best of the candidates were selected and taught. There was never any question of huckstering to those with no heart for such things or to those who either did not seek them at all or sought them halfheartedly. Even though persons not destined for geniehood were to see crowds of genii every day, they would still consider them eccentrics or think of them as a special class. Some would call them demoniacal phenomena; others would call them freaks of nature. It would never be acknowledged that geniehood is attained by persistent action; fickle minds would never believe it. Even if Ch'ih-sung tzu and Wang Ch'iao were to attract their attention, they would still consider the claim false.

On the other hand, I fear that if there were many believers in our day they would be unable, despite their diligence, to find enlightened teachers, for those knowing the highest essentials and possessing the true divine process are indeed, in the nature of things, extremely rare. They are not to be met at a moment's notice. In the very nature of things, however, only a few persons ought to know the process. Those who seek it deliberately without ever breaking with wordly business have no broad knowledge of things and are insincere. Those fated for geniehood must of course meet with a teacher, but there are those who have sought without encountering one. Nobody has ever found one without seeking.

In the natural order of things, there are crafty persons in the world scheming for money and laying false claims to the title of processor. Their number is legion. I do not claim that they are utterly devoid of knowledge, they all exhibit some rough acquaintance with our topic. Sometimes they falsely vaunt renown to conceal their depravity and gloss over their deceit, and curiosity-seekers, not knowing whether they are true or false, attract deception and fascination by the many questions they idly put to them. Such preachers do not have their adherents travel widely in search of the best processes and extraordinary individuals but claim that the divine process is contained wholly in their own teaching. Thus they lead astray many who were determined to search, and this is very much to be pitied and deplored. If they happen to hear that someone knows how to melt the five sorts of mica, sublime the Eight Minerals, cycle the Nine Cinnabars, smelt gold and silver, liquefy agate, transform red jasper, and congeal frost and snow in a "divine furnace," and also knows how to gather potent excrescences on Mount Sung, they generally malign him by saying that these methods were known only to Ch'ih-sung tzu and Wang Ch'iao, and that anyone today claiming to know them is an impostor. Thereupon those with little learning, not realizing that such statements are false, put aside all thought of seeking far and wide. Sad, isn't it? These people are to be pitied.

Like the passing of the pointer's shadow on a sundial or like a gust of wind, in one moment one is young and then suddenly old. All happens so quickly that one could almost say there never was such a creature. A life of one hundred years is only a little more than 30,000 days. In childhood we do not yet know anything, and when the decline sets in, both contentment and joy cease. Childhood and dotage thus subtract several decades, and difficulties, worries, and illnesses follow one another in a steady succession. They take roughly half the time we spend alive. A man may think he will live to be a hundred and be happy and contented, but then, alas, he perishes without getting beyond fifty or sixty. Given grief and dotage, after merely six or seven thousand days, he has perished in the twinkling of an eye, for not one person in ten thousand lives a full hundred years! The very thought of it leaves us no reason to mock insects lasting only one summer and the morning-long mushroom. One might say that those ignorant of God find grief everywhere.

The villager would say that in this world man loses one day every day, and like the buffalo or sheep being led away to the slaughter, every step forward brings him nearer to departure in death. This may be an unpleasant analogy, but it is factual and logical. The successful man, however, does not worry about death, not because he would not like to find a recipe for avoiding death, but because he knows that to give himself fruitless worry is no help to his affairs. He says, "Let us rejoice in heaven and accept our fates"; and this is his only reason for not worrying. It is not because he does not wish to live long. The Duke of Chou asked to die in place of King Wu (SC 4.6*b*11), and Confucius dragged his staff in grief,[1] so we know that the sages themselves found no pleasure in sudden death. When ordinary men see

2b

---

[1] *Li ki*, S. Couvreur (1913), Vol. 1, p. 144.

Chuang Chou comparing life to a long dream (2.82), they vie with one another to talk of the equating of death and life. Confucius, I suggest, felt that the teaching of vigorous studies of dangerous ways and the failure to suppress pretense were contraventions of our regulations, leading to the death penalty.

These days I notice that people who talk this way rush off for acupuncture and moxa when sick, and are quite afraid of death when confronted by danger. But of course the lowly crowd is only conversant with the vile and does not exalt the true and credible. Turning away from the pronouncements of the Classics, it runs after the various philosophers. If the teacher or writer is not uttering clever and eloquent inanities, he is considered a rustic and in opposition to Lao Tan and Chuang Chou. Therefore, those lacking a solid frame of reference and drawing upon every passer-by get lost in teaching that is false, and cannot get back to truth.

Lao Tan set as his life's goal the achievement of Fullness of Life and lasting vision (59), while Chuang Chou stresses the dragging of one's tail in the mud (17.84), and not being *3a* like a tortoise caught in a net (26.28) or a buffalo dressed in embroideries for the sacrifice (32.47). When he was hungry, however, he asked for grain of the Marquis of Chieh-ho (26.6); from this we know that he was unable to equate death and life. How misleading it is when those coming late to their studies cannot separate fancy from fact and biasedly place reliance upon one isolated phrase. Further, the endless night deep beneath the Nine Springs — first becoming food for the ants, and ultimately becoming one with the dust and dirt — makes men shiver out of grief and groan out of ignorance. If they had the will to seek life, how could they fail to set aside non-vital things and cultivate work leading to God (the Mysterious and Marvelous). For disbelievers there is nothing to do. When, however, they do believe, then they worry lest their worldly affairs go to ruin. Being unable to devote themselves wholly to the nurturing of life, they give it only the time remaining from their devotion to lay duties. Therefore, some of these persons are constantly concerned about the lateness of their start and are generally unsuccessful.

On the whole, what men persistently covet is power, preferment, and satisfaction of appetites. Yet, if our bodies are not whole, even the massive power of high office, mountains of gold and jewels, and beauties by the thousands will not be our firm possessions. Therefore, the superior gentleman first makes plans for life in all its fullness, after which he can do as he pleases. Before he mounts to God (the Mystery) and leaves this world, he can be an earth genie for a time, just as Old P'eng and Lao Tan remained among men for several centuries without foregoing the joys of mankind. Afterward they serenely mounted afar, having enjoyed a full life.

3b

It is absolutely necessary to treat your teacher right.

> *If teacher you can't remunerate,*
> *No way will you have to operate.*

Anciently, the Han empress was taught *The Writings of Old* by Hsia-hou Sheng, and conferred upon him one hundred pounds of gold as well as other things without number. When he died, two million were conferred upon his household, and the empress wore mourning for one hundred days. While still crown prince, Emperor Ch'eng studied the *Analects* under Chang Yü, and on mounting the throne made him a Marquis of Kuan-nei with an income from one thousand households of the city, named him High Excellency, and presented him with one hundred pounds of gold. Later he was promoted to Vice-premier and his title raised to that of Marquis of An-ch'ang. When he became old and asked to retire, a comfortable carriage and a team of four were conferred upon him as well as a hundred pounds of gold and several thousands of cash. When he fell ill, the emperor paid him a personal visit and bowed at the foot of his bed.

Emperor Chang, while crown prince, studied *Filial Piety* under Huan Jung, and on coming to the throne made him President of the Bureau of Imperial Religious Services. The emperor on one occasion honored his establishment, had him sit facing the east and lay aside his staff and tabouret. Then in the presence of his suite and Huan Jung's aspirants and pupils to the number of several hundred, the emperor personally assumed the task of lecturing. He conferred upon his former teacher the title of Marquis of Kuan-nei, with the income from five thousand households of the city. When *4a* Huan Jung fell ill, the emperor honored his home, and on entering the street he descended from his vehicle, and rushed to his former teacher with a bundle of books, like any ordinary pupil. When Huan Jung died, the emperor wore mourning for him.

These various gentlemen were heaped with honors, but not because they could breach walls or fight in the fields, break through an enemy's lines and extend frontiers, fall ill and resign office, pray for a plan of confederation and give the credit to others, or possess a zeal transcending all bounds. Merely because they expounded an interpretation of one solitary classic, such were the honors lavished upon them. And they were only lecturing upon words bequeathed by the dead. Despite their own high positions, emperors and kings deigned to serve these teachers.

In our present world people sometimes wish to try cultivating the divine process for enjoying Fullness of Life but are unwilling to humble themselves before a competent teacher. They go directly to him and ask for things of the highest importance. But how can they get them in that fashion? What do obedience and discipline in the case of study add to the stature of the teaching? Without them, hearts and minds would not be completely devoted to the task at hand, and this in turn means that instruction would not proceed vigorously. In that case, how could all the secret directions possibly be acquired? In spite of himself, the teacher would then impart to the student only the superficial aspects of the topic, and these would not permit him to learn the lesson on immortality.

There are cases where the student looks with joy at the prospect but his faith in the divine process is not rooted in his heart-god. He is seeking and desiring something and the respect he shows is positive, but as the days go by he turns lax. If he has an intelligent teacher who wishes to observe the changes in new-comers carefully, he will be given the time test and deliberately told nothing in order that his will-power may be probed. In this way, students of this type have the falsity of their situation revealed and cannot be instructed at all. If they are instructed, they cannot be told the whole truth, and there is no benefit to them if everything is not told.

At the age of thirteen Ch'en An-shih seems to have been only the son of a guest at the home of Kuan Shu-pen. Since, however, he had been first to acquire the process leading to geniehood, Kuan Shu-pen, despite his seventy years and gray hairs, would bow morning and evening to young Ch'en, saying, "God is to be honored and excellence esteemed. Being the first of us to obtain the divine process, you are the teacher, and I cannot let myself fail to observe the etiquette required of a pupil." Because of this attitude Ch'en gave him an important prescription, and he in his turn departed a genie.

Men first receive their internal spirits and gods from nature (heaven and earth) and later they are endowed with breaths and blood from their parents, but if they do not acquire an intelligent teacher to inform them about the divine process leading to geniehood they will have no way to escape dying. If any flame is left in the hollowed stone, the stone's endurance is as good as gone. Therefore, with all these things in mind, we can say that the favors of an intelligent teacher far surpass those of nature itself; they are much more important than those you have from your parents. How can you help but exalt him? How can you fail to seek him out?

5a

The Ancients were substantial and orthodox; they valued good conduct, but belittled talk. Therefore, governors did not honor ornament or rhetoric; while cultivating God, articulated exposition was kept in the background. As these good customs declined, external ornaments grew apace. Written schemes having piled up mountain-high among the Confucianists, and private writings also being carried about by the specialists, neophytes could not easily be given the essence of all this in outline. Further it became the fashion to have the accounts of human affairs rich and full, so that those who later understood God — writers like Yü Chi, Kung Ch'ung, and Kuei Po — each wrote thousands of chapters, all of them, however, largely ethical and not acceptable for revealing to the uninitiated guides back to God (Maximal).

The secret directions dealing with the highest truths were often transmitted by word of mouth; at other times they were inscribed on a piece of silk eight feet by one, worn around the neck or at the waist, which was not to be obtained without passing a long probationary time with a teacher to test one's diligence. Out of the heterogeneous mass of students each one was given something depending upon the aptitude with which he used his heart and mind, the length of the hardships he underwent, the depth of his intelligence, and the discrimination of his willpower. In the course of centuries and millennia it was only rarely that mastery was acquired over the secret essentials found in bags or under pillows, or kept at an elbow or rump. Some-times these were used merely to compound medicines, which were then distributed and were only able to keep the par-takers alive. At the possessor's death, however, the text of the prescription was not passed on. The result is that not one

5b

processor in thousands knows about gold and cinnabar. This does not prevent those who look at things through a tube from saying that the rules for geniehood are all contained in that mass of writing, in the sacrifices to heaven and earth, and in prostrations. But Fullness of Life depends on the great medicine; it is not to be attained by thanksgivings and libations.

Under the Ch'in and Han dynasties [221 B.C.–A.D. 220] there was widespread use of petitions to the gods, and in the sacrifices to T'ai-i with the Five Gods and to Ch'en-pao with the Eight Gods there was constant use of buffaloes, sheep, grain and silk. The cost was in the millions, but the benefits nil, especially for the nobodies who, deficient in excellence and unnurtured in body, wished to seek a prolongation of years through suovetaurilia, libations, and imprecations directed toward ghosts and gods. It was utter bewilderment.

In many cases curiosity-seekers (4.3*a*1) sincerely wished to pursue the divine process but were unable to devote themselves to finding an intelligent teacher and compounding the extraordinary medicine. Day and night they merely read and interpreted thousands of volumes of unimportant writings and arrived at old age without acquiring any benefits. Therefore they concluded that of course there was no method anywhere for acquiring geniehood. In some cases a whole group kowtowed to a vacant spot, a chef offered a victim of one color or a suovetaurilia, or incense was burned to ask for good fortune, but the sick got no better. Deaths and mournings came one after another, production and capital were exhausted, but there was not the slightest trace of a miracle. Never realizing the futility of their action, they said that they themselves had not been sufficiently sincere. If they had sought diligently with equal ardor for a teacher with prescriptions, or spent as much to purchase medicines, they would certainly have acquired Fullness of Life or geniehood like the gods and other genii. How can it be considered strange that a goal is not achieved

6a

when a life-time is spent giving all one's energies to farming a field of stones in the hope of reaping enough to fill a thousand barns. It is like going to Ch'u (=south) via Yen (=north). Your horse may be of the best, but you do not arrive. You didn't travel too slowly; you went the wrong way!

Others were natural believers and happy in belief, but their intelligence was not competent to distinguish between the true and the false or probe the depths and the shallows. Their experience being normally quite restricted, they could do nothing for creatures. The stupid of a later generation were then attracted to the son of some such sole, self-lauding man, who claimed to have a secret which he was guarding and following. Many ordinary people and children openly claimed to possess the divine process, the claim having no foundation in reality, since they were acting out of pure effrontery. Meanwhile, they cherished avarice in their hearts, their only goal being profit. When asked to do something with the secret, they indulged in sighs and bowed from the waist as though the precious secret entrusted to them was so deep that it could not be fathomed. When everything they requested had been done, they would nod and smile, sometimes promising the miracle shortly. They deliberately tried to make their ignorant clients desist, but they would not, for they felt that they had not yet worked hard enough, and that the presents offered were insufficient. *6b*

Thereupon, trusting hearts became still more respectful and gave the impostors extraordinary trinkets for presents. They acted as their servants. They did not refuse to carry heavy burdens for them on long journeys. Dangers and risks were incurred, for it was thought that one could win merit for oneself through the accumulation of tasks. They underwent suffering and grief in the hope of learning something extraordinary, but the months and years went by with nothing gained. They fruitlessly neglected to care for their parents, and they did not worry about abandoning wife and children. Undergoing frosts and cold, they followed the impostors for years, but, funds diminished and efforts lost, they ended with nothing accomplished. In some instances, the original deceivers themselves became ashamed. They felt confused within, empty, and impoverished because, lacking all means of instructing themselves, how were they to perfect others?

With my own eyes I have seen several of this type, probably a dozen or so. They sometimes give themselves high-sounding titles, claim to have been alive for generations, sometimes three or four hundred years, but of course under different names. They impose upon others by claiming to be sages, and many people follow them. I do not wish to name names, but they are well known among the masses. Without knowing whether these preachers are good or bad, people compound the confusion by vaunting and lauding them, thus creating groundless praise for the clever and deceitful, so that practices that were already on the decline went to the point where nobody could reform them. The result then is that our illustrious people no longer give them any attention, or they listen to them only with their ears. Erroneous doctrine among our students always comes from people of this type, and it never fails to give me concern. I always notice, however, that those deceiving the world and leading it into error with a view to power and profit sooner or later get their punishment. Heaven's net may have wide meshes, but they do not let everyone escape. Those willfully leading others astray might well bear this in mind.

For the most part, people will follow those with a reputation, but few have the capability to compare facts. The moment they hear that Mr. *A* has a hundred or so followers they conclude that he must possess something marvelous and immediately rush off in their vehicles or on horseback to join the pupils grouped about him. But they only waste their working energies in honoring those stupid people, and give up searching for the best. Thanks to the efforts of their

7a

disciples, such impostors occasionally become wealthy, but despite the length of the pursuit they still lack a process for perfecting others. Stupid persons may not recognize that this man is not worth cultivating, but why do they never awaken to the situation? They are a pitiable lot! When search is made on a tiny hill for a sky-scraping tree and a buffalo's tracks are drained in search for a ship-swallowing fish, how can there be success, even though days be spent in the search? How distressing it all is! Though students in the future will be obliged to spend their energy in the search for a teacher, they cannot help but consider careless selection 7b as inimical. Among the low classes, action is shallow, natural excellence scarce, accomplishment minute, and resources few, the result being that they are incompetent in processes for the perfection of others and have no projects to retain the respect and favor of others. Give deep thought to such tendencies so that you may not trouble yourself for nothing.

Since they are clever at lying in order to deceive students, processors of hollow renown are generally denigrated, and try to conceal their stupidity. Ashamed of their ignorance and pretending that their acquaintance with things is sufficiently broad, they end by becoming unwilling to seek instruction from their betters. They ignorantly preserve their intellectual poverty and stand facing a wall. Also, they will not merely maintain silence but turn spiteful toward those who really possess the divine process and malign them, because they fear that their own renown is being overshadowed. I wonder if such people are giving any thought at all to genuine methods producing life in all its fullness? Or are they acting solely from the wish to gather pupils in order to acquire resources for the satisfaction of their own appetites? If so, they are forgetting that heaven may be high but its hearing reaches low, and sooner or later they will certainly suffer disaster from on high. It is improper for the poor to claim to be rich, and those of low estate should not claim to be exalted. How much the more is it improper to maintain aspirants and pupils fruitlessly because one knows nothing about God and excellence! If it is unfitting for the mass of men to be jealous of expertness, how much more should a processor devote himself to the joys of loyalty and sincerity.

8a

Interlocutor: What sort of vivid imaginings are these? Since man himself cannot hear or see the gods and spirits, how can it be so easy for them to hear and see?

Ko: How does this differ from being on the outside of the curtains and unable to see within the palanquin and then proceeding to display insolence in the belief that nobody is looking? It is like the bonging that occurred when a certain man stole a bell's beam and then disliked the fact that others heard it when his own ears had been covered! Only persons whose inner spirits and gods are deaf and blind wish to have a monopoly of fair renown, to be the only ones with a crowd of students. Externally they seek renown as their price, but inwardly they scheme for wealth and power. Overcome by insecurity, they struggle for power more intensely than the ordinary man. Then making swords and spears of their lips and allies of praise and blame, they are friendly of speech while their hearts and minds are indifferent. They look co-operative but their actions are divisive; openly they speak of concert of wills, but secretly they have in their grasp the poison of wasps and scorpions. These are the persons disliked equally by heaven and man; they are the harbingers of disaster.

When studying the Five Classics it is accepted that no shame attaches to inquiring of those beneath us in order that our progress and study may be daily greater and more notable. In such ordinary arts as archery and driving, the lowly tasks of writing and calculation, the revealing work of farming and arboriculture, and skill in the use of the carpenter's compass and square, a master must instruct us if we are to learn the various systems. This holds even still more for the rules to be followed in planning life in all its

8b

fullness. The wish to extend years and become a genie is nothing less than freeing a man from worry about death. How can a man devote his energies to not being known as one who seeks information, so that he may persist long in the torment of ignorance, never changing even in old age, and still be without regrets when on the brink of death? Such a man is the perfect ignoramus among heaven-begotten folk; he makes others blush and fear for him. Men like this simply have no regard for substance versus shadow.

Among Confucianists it is necessary that a student preserve constant simplicity and avoid showing affectation. While knowing a thing, he acts as though he did not; while possessing something, he acts as though he did not. Thus no ordinary person can know just how much he is to be esteemed. When respect is shown for him, he replies only to the questions asked, and in replying he will speak only after some expression of refusal. Why then should those processors boldly treat their ignorance as knowledge and their nothings as something? They are people who, possessing nothing, promote their own renown with a view to dishonest profit! Since those who are confused to the point of not knowing their own way back only grow worse under pursuit, let any who are in such a situation reflect that no disgrace attaches to change. I am not uttering these words in jest; I have reasons for acting as I do. When one is deeply concerned, silence becomes impossible. I am merely sympathizing with the stupid, and cannot stand the sight of a child falling into a well. Understanding by viewing is one plant in the pharmacopoeia of the genii. I act because it is extremely *9a* dangerous not to do something about suffering when it first appears, and because this is a thing that need not await a taking of the pulse before being understood.

If a person were guilty of a capital offense and someone were in a position to save him, he certainly would not be sparing in hard work or self-abasement, and he would not hesitate to humiliate himself, for to be sure of preserving life is the very task of life. Today, we can be certain that the miscellaneous group of processors who have failed to obtain the important method of preparing gold and cinnabar will not obtain Fullness of Life. They may cure illness, raise people from the dead, go years without hunger by abstaining from starches, command ghosts and gods, disappear at will, see what is occurring a thousand miles away, foretell the prosperity and decline of others, reveal pitfalls and rises for hidden things, and know misfortune and good fortune for things that have not yet occurred, but none of these things benefits their longevity.

To prefer requesting a disgraceful deed or early success in a shameful business is to regret one day of discomfort but find endless pain sweet! Such a man has not noticed the inter-relationships of things. The Ancients used to say that our greatest asset was life. If it is quality that you would discuss, then even the rank of emperor or king is not comparable with the method for attaining life in all its fullness. If it is quantity that you would discuss, all the riches in the world are not to be exchanged for this art. That is why we have the story of the dead king who would have been glad to be a living rat.

9b   The peace enjoyed by a well-ordered state and the life in a well-ordered body have not occurred by themselves; both have been induced. If you were to tell me that the man who bemoans a short-lived, empty renown or who is ashamed of the brief moment of hard work necessary to study under a teacher is not stupid, I would disagree with you. Today, if a man were to avoid certain death by submitting to mutilation, he would be delighted to trade something serious for something lighter. If a man escapes the flames and preserves his vision and respiration, he will much prefer his suffering to a departure from life. But since no man knows the day he will die, death is not a momentary worry. If he really did know and by a cutting off of the nose could protract his life, he would be sure to do it. Still more logically, how could a student who personally sprinkles, sweeps, and holds the towel as he devotes all his energies to self-discipline think of the divine process for immortality which he is being taught as painful, and recoil from it in his ignorance? If a man, ashamed to run away quickly, stood waiting for a prairie fire to consume him, or, ashamed to flee a typhoon, let himself drown in the deep, everyone would certainly call him stupid. And yet, while all know how to mock his failure to flee danger, nobody is surprised that he does not fear the genuine disaster of certain death that awaits him. Why?

None of the Taoist books written by the Ancients fails to devote much energy to publishing impractical, clever talk to exalt the significance of God (the Mystery and the Undifferentiated). None of them, however, has studied and discussed the steps leading to Fullness of Life. Taoists complain about the lack of such a book, and if it has become the goal of my constant endeavors, it is because I truly wish to let those who are confused know how to return to their true bearings. What is lost at sunrise can be recouped by sunset. It is better to extend a rope to the man who has fallen into a well than to follow him into it. My only regret is that nothing can be done about those who reject a bitter medicine when in a fever. All men have their faults, but faults can lead to reformation. Even the sun and moon suffer eclipses, and consider for a moment the pupil Yen Hui, who never committed the same fault twice (Ana. 6.3).

10a

I also wish to make future students of the life process examine carefully in whom they place their confidence. To this end it is with all sincerity that I give them my best advice without indulging in seductive elegance of language, for when speaking I am a man who does much writing with a finger, and when writing, the phrasings give me pain. It is too bad that only in the Fullness of Life shall I be able to correct these faults. And where shall I seek that?

I am deeply mindful that if students of the Taoist arts and the nurturing of life do not find the right man as they resort to the teachers, they will accomplish nothing whatever. Then later, like-minded students, noting this failure to attain Fullness of Life, will declare the only logical conclusion to be that there is no method anywhere leading to geniehood. Generally speaking, the self-taught are quite unable to drive themselves hard and discipline themselves to cultivate God (the Mysterious and the Marvelous); all they do is lose positions where they would be paid and still fail in the accomplishments that would banish old age. They lead themselves into error, and set up barriers for those to come.

10b

Geniehood can be induced by study just as the two sorts of millet can be made to prosper only by sowing seed. But no man ever got fine grain without tilling it, and no man has ever attained Fullness of Life and geniehood without diligence.

15

Miscellanea

Interlocutor: I should like to inquire whether a man can attain Fullness of Life by merely dispensing with starches. How many methods for this are there altogether, and which is the best?

Ko: By dispensing with starches a man can only stop spending money on grains, but by that alone he cannot attain Fullness of Life. When I inquired of people who had been doing without starches for a long time, they replied that they were in better health than when they were eating starches. When they took thistle and nibbled mercury and when they also took pills of brown hematite twice a day, this triple medication produced an increase in breaths, so that they gained the strength to carry loads on long trips, for their bodies became extremely light in weight. One such full treatment protected the patients' inner organs for five to ten years, but when they swallowed their breaths, took amulets (2*b*4), or drank brine, only loss of appetite resulted, and they did not have the strength for hard work.

The Taoist writings may say that if one wishes Fullness of Life the intestines must be clean, and if immortality is desired the intestines must be without feces; but they also say that those eating greens will be good walkers, but at the same time stupid; that those eating meat will be very strong, and

1b   also brave. Those eating starches will be wise, but they will
not live to an old age, while those eating breath will have
gods and spirits within them that never die. This last, however, is only a biased claim advanced by the school that
teaches the circulation of breaths. One has no right to claim
to use this method exclusively. If you wish to take the great
medicines of gold or cinnabar, they will act more quickly if
you fast for the preceding hundred days or so. If you cannot
fast that long, take them straightway; this will do no great
harm, but it will take more time to acquire geniehood.

Should you take to the mountains and forests during
political troubles, you will avoid dying of starvation by
observing the rule about starches. Otherwise, do not rush
into this practice, for rushing cannot be very beneficial. If
you dispense with meat while living among others, you will
find it impossible not to desire it deep in your heart when
you smell its fat or freshness. If you consider it inconvenient
to break with the world, abandon your household, and live
high on a peak, you will certainly not succeed in abandoning
the Five Savors.

If you would not distress yourself, it is best not to dispense
with starches but merely to regulate the diet, for which there
are about a hundred methods. Sometimes, after a few dozen
pills of interior-protecting medicines have been taken, it is
claimed that appetite is lost for forty or fifty days. (Other
times, one or two hundred days are claimed, or the pills
must be taken for days or months.) Refined pine and cypress
as well as thistle can also protect the interior, but they are
inferior to the great medicines (1*b*2), and last only ten years
or less. At other times, fine foods are first prepared and con-

2a   sumed to utter satiation, and then medicines are taken to
nurture the things that have been eaten, so that they may
not be digested. This is claimed to remain valid for three
years. If you then wish to revert to the eating of starches, it
is necessary to start by swallowing mallows and lard, so that
the fine food you prepared will pass from you undigested.

There was a processor at Lo-yang by the name of Tung Ching, who normally stayed at Pai-she and ate absolutely nothing. Ch'en Tzu-hsü provided him with protection and service, and in return acquired his recipe after studying the process under him for a very long time. Pestle to a powder about ten substances, such as licorice, Bidens, and amaranthus seeds. After taking an inch-square spoonful of this, swallow twelve pebbles the size of a sparrow's egg. This will allow a claim of a hundred days without hunger, after which the dose is repeated, and your energies and complexion will become normal. If you wish to revert to the eating of starches, you may do so only after taking a mallow infusion to pass the pebbles. He also produced Red-dragon blood and Blue-dragon ointment, which were made by placing pebbles in cinnabar or malachite solution. After a short time the pebbles soften and become edible, but if you do not remove them immediately they will dissolve completely. Eat these stones to satiety and you will become a strong young man. He also had a powder for dilating stones. A square-inch spoonful of this is placed in a bushel of white pebbles and the mixture cooked in water, whereupon the pebbles become like taro tubers and can be eaten instead of starches. Chang T'ai-yüan and his household, together with several dozen pupils, lived in retirement in Mount Lin-lü, and following the first method, subsisted on stones for some ten years, all of them becoming sleek and strong. Since, however, it calls for white pebbles, this recipe is inferior to either Red-dragon blood or Blue-dragon ointment, in which, ostensibly, any pebbles may be used, and only the bother remains of cooking them over a faggot fire.

2b

Some recipes call for amulets, others for liquids, still others for the joint use of holy water. Others call for nine dried jujubes per day and one or two quarts of wine. Sometimes the breaths of the twelve double hours are eaten, beginning with midnight, and going from nine times nine respirations (*Y* 61.16*a*—) to eight times eight, seven times

seven, six times six, and five times five, at which point one
stops. In the spring one may face east to eat the blue breath
of the planet Jupiter, making it enter the liver (the fours here
are correspondences); in summer, the red breath of Mars,
which enters the heart; in the last month of each season, the
yellow breath of Saturn for the spleen; in autumn, the white
breath of Venus for the lungs; and in winter, the black breath
of Mercury for the kidneys (15.11*a*10).

A processor of Mount Sung, by the name of Ch'ih Yüan-
chieh got excellent results from eating the spirits of the Six
Wu [the six combinations in the sexagenary cycle containing
the sign *wu* as first element]. Assume a ten-day cycle
beginning with *chia-tzu* (No. 1), which will contain a
wu-ch'en (No. 5) spirit, and throughout that ten-day period
constantly face the *ch'en* site [SE] and swallow breath. Proceed thus to the last (the sixth) period of ten days, during
which you must face the *wu* site [center].

Kan Shih had a method [for replacing starches] whereby
the Six Chia and the Six Ting fairies were summoned, each
3a   by her proper name, and holy water was then drunk. Cattle
and horses too could be rendered hungerless by this method.
Others think of the name of the god in the spleen, Yellow-
clad. Then, by merely keeping the lips together, the inner
breaths are eaten. All these different methods produce
positive effects.

I have personally observed for two or three years men
who were foregoing starches, and in general their bodies
were slight and their complexions good. They could withstand wind, cold, heat, or dampness, but there was not a fat
one among them. I admit that I have not yet met any who
had not eaten starches in several decades, but if some people
cut off from starches for only a couple of weeks die while
these others look as well as they do after years, why should
we doubt that the (deliberate) fasting could be prolonged
still further? If those cut off from starches grow progressively
weaker to death, one would normally fear that such a diet

simply cannot be prolonged, but inquiry of those pursuing this practice reveals that at first all of them notice a lessening of strength, but that later they gradually get stronger month by month and year by year. Thus there is no impediment to the possibility of prolongation.

All those who have found the divine process for attaining Fullness of Life succeeded by taking medicines and swallowing breath; on this they are all in perfect agreement. A moment of crisis, however, generally occurs at an early stage when medicines are being taken and starches abandoned, and it is only after forty days of progressive weakening, as one uses only holy water and feeds solely on breath, that one regains strength.

My teacher, Cheng Yin, once remarked, "Originally my constitution could not stand much wine. A long time ago, however, while I was being cut off from starches for a couple of years or so on Mount T'ung, I could drink several demijohns of wine without getting drunk." It may be deduced from this that fasting makes a man more tolerant of poisons, and this is the requisite condition for preventing illnesses. When I asked him where he had obtained wine there in the mountains, he replied, "First ferment rainwater, and don't strain it. Then pulverize and form into pills some five or six things, including cinnamon, aconite, and licorice. After drying the pills in full sun, put one pill about the size of a chicken's egg into a gallon of the liquid and it will immediately turn it into excellent wine."

There is also Yellow Emperor's method for producing rain-spring. Rice malt is combined with seven or eight ingredients and a quart of it added to one quart of water. It is like adding thousand-year-old strong vinegar to water. In no time at all it is ready and always tastes good, never varying. Drinking this can be very beneficial to a person.

Holy water and dispensing with starches may weaken a man at first, but they should be used jointly. When famine suddenly strikes and there is no time to compound medi-

3b

cines, holy water will be found the best substitute. A certain
Feng Sheng had been giving himself to swallowing only
breath and dispensing with starches for three years, and I
noticed that when climbing into the mountains with a load
of several bushels on his back he went all day without
becoming weary. Further, he constantly stretched his bow,
4a   but hardly spoke at all; if he did, it was only in a low voice.
When I inquired about this, he replied that when dispensing
with starches one must be very careful not to lose sperm or
waste breath.

I have also frequently seen ignorant processors who,
wishing to boast and amaze and acquire a reputation for not
eating when they really knew nothing about such procedures, merely claimed not to eat gruel. Meanwhile, they
would drink more than a gallon of wine daily, and dried
meats, puddings, jujubes, chestnuts, or eggs were never out
of their mouths. Sometimes they would eat large quantities
of meat — several dozen pounds daily — swallowing its
juices and spitting out anything that was unpleasant. This,
however, is actually feasting. Wine drinkers will eat dried
meats with their wine but not starches, and they can keep
this up for six months to a year without stumbling or falling.
Never yet, however, have they claimed that this was "cut
off from starches!"

During the Wu (A.D. 222–280) there was a processor
named Shih Ch'un, who would not eat in order to hasten the
cure when he was treating a sick person by circulating his
own breaths. It would sometimes be a hundred days or only
a month before he ate again. When Emperor Ching heard
of this he exclaimed, "In a short time this man is going to
starve to death." Then he had him locked up and guarded,
and all that Shih Ch'un requested was two or three quarts of
water for making holy water. It went on like this for more
than a year, while his complexion became ever fresher and
his strength remained normal. The emperor then asked him
how much longer he could continue like this, and Shih

Ch'un replied that there was no limit; possibly several dozen years, his only fear being that he might die of old age, but it would not be of hunger. The emperor then discontinued the experiment and sent him away. Note that Shih Ch'un's statement shows that giving up starches cannot protract one's years. Some today possess Shih Ch'un's method. 4*b*

Interlocutor: What is to be done about the cold?

Ko: From Arrival of Winter [early November] some take Six Ping and Six Ting amulets; others close their mouths and circulate the breaths of the Five Fires. After doing this 1200 times they do not feel any cold during the twelfth moon. Still others take sun wine. Others take amethyst and vermilion lacquer powder. Some persons, by taking one "male" pill followed by two "female" pills can be free from any sensation of cold for one day and one night. A "female" pill consists of orpiment, laminar malachite, alum, and magnetite; a "male" pill consists of realgar, cinnabar, and copper sulphate. None of these methods, however, help to prolong the years.

Interlocutor: What is to be done about the heat?

Ko: Beginning with Arrival of Summer [early May] some wear Six Jen and Six Kuei amulets; others circulate the breaths of the Six Kuei. Some take mercury pills; others, fei-shuang powder. Since, however, the latter requires bark from a tree on Wormwood Hill and blood from a black snake traveling north at noon on the fifth day of the fifth moon, few have succeeded in compounding it. Probably because they used these recipes, Yu-po tzu and Wang Chung-tu 5*a* never mentioned heat, nor did they sweat as they wore layers of fur-lined clothing in the full sun on a summer's day, surrounded by fires from twelve furnaces.

Interlocutor: What protection is there against the five different weapons?

Ko: I understand that Emperor Ta of the Wu once received an effective process for this purpose from Chieh Hsiang. Merely by writing in red the words Great Dipper and Sun and Moon (on one's own weapons: 5*b*5) it was claimed that one need have no fear of bare blades. The emperor tried this with several dozen of his followers who were always in the van of an attack, and they remained unharmed all their lives. My teacher, Cheng Yin, said that good results could also be obtained by merely intoning the names of the five different weapons. A knife is called Ta-fang and is controlled by the asterism Aquarius. A bow is called Ch'ü-chang and is controlled by the asterism Librae. Arrows are called P'ang-huang and are controlled by Mars. A sword is called Shih-shang and is controlled by Virgo. A crossbow is called Yüan-wang and is controlled by Hydra. A lance is called Generalissimo and is controlled by Orion. Before going into battle always pray carefully to them. Some, on the fifth day of the fifth moon prepare a Red Power Amulet, which is worn over the heart. Others, at noon on a *ping-wu* day will prepare the three sack-amulets Yen-chün, Dragon, and Tiger. (Year amulets are to be changed yearly; the month ones, monthly; and the day ones, daily.) Some wear a Hsi-wang-mu Weapon-Passport amulet, others a Mars Vermilion-Bird amulet, or a Southern-Pinnacle Mine-Gold amulet at their belts and a Banish-Blade amulet and a Pray-Harmony amulet on their heads. Some dust themselves with jade plaque powder; others take an onion bath that dispels evils. Some make a Six-Yin Gods-Commander amulet of Vitex which they point at the enemy. Others, at the very instant when the moon is eclipsed, will write (5*a*4) on their knives and swords with the blood from a three-year-old hoptoad that has a figure eight on its throat. Some carry with them Military-Prestige amulets and fire-sparkling pills. Others also get positive results by leaping and strutting at the moment that swords are to be crossed and shouting that they are lords over all. Some people of our day — you will find them here and there — have processes for counteracting the processes that protect from the five sorts of weapons (the anti-process process!).

Interlocutor: How does one vanish?

Ko: There are five divine processes for this purpose, the fastest of which makes it possible to disappear at will, but they are of no benefit to our longevity. Nevertheless, they are not to be used heedlessly, such as for example to produce outbursts of amazement when employed without reason in company. They may be used only in dire necessity against military reversals and dangerous crises, for in that way no harm will be incurred. My teacher, Cheng Yin, remarked that after Grand-Concealment amulets have been taken for ten days, one may disappear by wheeling to the left, and reappear by wheeling to the right. Some produce this effect by coating their interiors with pills of jade pudding or with snake-foot powder. Some hold Gastrodyia grass to their bosoms; others make mats of Blue-Dragon grass on which to prostrate themselves at the feet of the Six Ting. Some, entering a field of bamboo, hold some Heaven-Pivot soil; others build a River-Dragon cave to conceal themselves in the shadow of Cloud Cover. Some prostrate themselves to a pure, clear depth of water to cross via Dark-Gateway path; others mount a Heaven-One horse to wander in Purple House. Some mount to the Heaven-One hall of enlightenment; others enter the gold coffer of the fairies. Some, with their backs to the side supports and their faces to the office, stand beneath Three Covers; others, removing kerchief and shoes. . . . By taking *liu-chia-fu-mu, p'i-ts'e* gum, dappled-horse-mud-pills, Vitex, or gold-merchant-Artemisia some can turn into little boys, old men, birds, wild animals, grass, trees, or a domestic animal. They resort to a tree and become a tree, to a stone and become a stone, or water or fire to become water or fire. All these are changes in form and shape; they do not result in complete concealment.

6a

6b

Interlocutor: Emperor Wu of the Wei once arrested Tso Tz'u and placed him in stocks, but he succeeded in freeing himself. What method did he use?

Ko: I cannot tell exactly what Master Tso did. There are,

however, recipes for this in the literature. For example, one may take Job's-Tears combined with Three-Five sperm, or doublespiked Yang-pao three times a month. Some use a grasshopper caught while traveling east on the seventh day of the seventh moon; others use a frog's skin left on a rock on the fifth day of the fifth moon. Some use a cherry tree struck by lightning at the summer solstice; others use an amulet with twenty-one characters in heaven-writing. Some use snake blood; others, Solomon's-Seal. Some escape by daubing themselves with a combination of Tiger Eyes, Yellow-River-Count hematite, and mica. Nevertheless, Master Tso's prescription for becoming invisible was not necessarily one of these. Having the Six Chia gods in his personal employ for transformation, his regular body could not be seized.

Interlocutor: Can the processor avoid illness?

Ko: If you are going to do everything possible to nurture your life, you will take the divine medicines. In addition, you will never weary of circulating your breaths; morning and night you will do calisthenics to circulate your blood and breaths and see that they do not stagnate. In addition to these things, you will practice sexual intercourse in the 7a right fashion; you will eat and drink moderately; you will avoid drafts and dampness; you will not trouble about things that are not within your competence. Do all these things, and you will not fall sick. On the other hand, you are sure to become ill if you are afraid of not always having your own way in society and of instability in your affairs; also, if laxity and lack of diligence trouble you. If all you have is a heart faithful to God and yet do nothing for your own benefit — your predestined life span being defective and your body threatened with harm — the Three Corpses will take advantage of your weak months and perilous days, the hours when your longevity could be interrupted or sickness incurred, to summon vicious breaths and bring in any demons they might be able to find to do you injury. The danger is certainly great for any person for whom these six obstacles are grouped and the Three Destructives (from duodenary cycle) united in the same quarter. And when this situation intensifies, it produces the various illnesses. But all of this was set in motion by the anxiety that was present in the first place.

Accordingly, those who first did something about God in antiquity exercised all the medical arts at the same time to save themselves from misfortunes that are ever present, but this principle is unknown to ordinary processors who, not understanding what they have been taught, pay no attention to the prescriptions for treating illness. Further, being unable to break with worldly life and live as hermits, and using only personal remedies to drive away illness, they lack all means for combating it and curing themselves. They are by no means as well off as the people in general who use various infusions. They are people to whom we may apply this adage: One may go to Han-tan and fail to acquire the gait used there, and then forget what was known in one's native Shou-ling (*Chuang* 17.79).

7*b*

I have personally seen the *Chin k'uei* and the *Lü nang* compiled by Tai Pa and Hua T'o, Ts'ui Chung's writings, Huang Su's prescriptions, and prescriptions from various writers — some 500 scrolls in all. Kan Hu, Lü Po-wang, Kan Shih, T'ang T'ung, and Juan Ping have all compiled prescriptions against violent attacks and prescriptions that fortify against crises, each containing anywhere from 110 to 94, 85, or 46 recipes. Everyone considers these collections excellent and utterly complete. I, however, have examined them and found them very incomplete, lacking treatment for many critical illnesses. Further, they are confused, disordered and lacking logical arrangement. When one searches for something in them it cannot be found in time for the proper handling of a crisis. They also all employ several dozen kinds of expensive medicines, and unless one is rich and living at the capital they cannot usually be pro-

vided or secured promptly. Further, they frequently recom-
mend treatment by acupuncture, and their rules for moxa
are not clear regarding the precise extent of the spots to be
stimulated. They merely expatiate upon the names of the
body's hollows and blood and breath conveyances. Unless
one is an experienced physician and has made an exhaustive
study of *Ming-t'ang liu-chu* and *Yen-ts'e t'u*, how are these
things to be understood? In the hundred scrolls which I have
compiled, *Yü han fang*, the names of illnesses have been
differentiated and placed in a sequence by categories to avoid

8a confusion. Ninety-three of my scrolls circulate inde-
pendently and are explicit; they are concise and easy to consult. In the whole mass of one hundred scrolls you will find
mention of all medicines and a full treatment of all serious
illnesses. Any household possessing this book can dispense
with the services of a physician, for physicians generally
transmit a tradition in which there may be renown but there
is no substance. All they do is cultivate empty fame with a
view to wealth; they are not to be employed by poor
gentlemen living a nonofficial life. When consulted, they
generally lead people astray. It is best to master the essentials
yourself; then you will be better than the unknown
physician whom you may meet. Further, it is not always
possible to find a physician at a moment's notice, and when
you do find one, he will not wish to be engaged immediately.
If the lines of the face have smoothed out, the illness has
formed deep in the diaphragm and the patient is beyond
help. In a crisis, if you must travel far in your search, a need-
less death will generally occur.

Interlocutor: Are there any procedures for determining the
good and bad fortunes that lie ahead, the risks, the failures
and successes, so that we can keep ourselves whole?

Ko: Astrology, geomancy, austromancy, arithmancy,
deductions from The Three Marvels, movements on a
design representing the nine divisions of space, comparison
of the eight trigrams, study of the places where birds and

animals gather, judging misfortune from creature types, and prognosticating through the tortoise and milfoil — all these are common, low-class arts, troublesome and untrustworthy. On the other hand, if you wish to get a view of the world from the privacy of your study, you can become one of the gods.

8b

Some persons use the book *San-huang t'ien-wen* to summon the Director of Fates, the Director of Dangers, the lords of the five revered mountains, the headmen of the paths, or the Six Ting powers, who permit themselves to be seen of men and to make replies. Ask them about anything, and good and evil fortune will become as evident as though lying in the palm of your hand, so that everything will be known in advance — whether distant, near, obscure, or profound. Others summon the Six Yin fairies. This method takes sixty days to complete but, if successful, makes it possible to retain them in your employ for a long time. Still others offer sacrifices to earth in order to summon the Eight Recorders, who are the spirits of the eight trigrams; through them it is possible to know in advance about things that have not yet formed.

Some take a spatula or an inch-square spoonful of the narcotics Kudzu flowers and absinthe, and experience a sudden urge to lie down. Then they hear a voice talking to them about matters that have not yet been decided, and at once the good and bad prospects are laid bare.

At other times a bright mirror nine inches or more in diameter is used for looking at oneself with something on the mind. After seven days and nights a god or genie will appear, either male, female, old, or young, and a single declaration on its part discloses automatically what is occurring at that moment a thousand miles away. Sometimes two mirrors are used and designated sun and moon respectively. Or four are used and designated as the four circumferences, by which is meant the front, rear, left, and right, to which each points when one looks into them. When four mirrors

9a   are used, a large number of gods are seen to appear: sometimes pell-mell, other times riding dragons or tigers and wearing hats and clothes of many colors, different from those seen in ordinary life. There are books and illustrations to document all this. If you wish to follow this procedure, you must first learn secretly the names and titles of the gods you wish to summon and also know what clothes and hats they wear. Otherwise, when they suddenly arrive you will forget which gods they are, or they could harm you through fright. Most of those wishing to hold this ceremony will seek peace and silence in the woods and mountain forests where no external shapes will pass before their eyes and no extraneous sounds will enter their ears. There this procedure is sure to be successful. Three lads, nine maids, the Lord Reckoner of Longevity, the nine-headed serpent body, and the 120 officials may arrive, but you must not look at them familiarly. If they put questions or scold, do not answer them. If they are attended by mighty, shining, armored warriors riding dragons and tigers to the accompanying beats of ornamented drums, give them neither a glance nor a word. Keep your mind solely on the true likeness of Lord Lao, and when this appears, rise and bow deeply to him. When you see his true likeness, bear in mind that his family name is Li, his personal name Tan, his courtesy name Po-yang. His body is nine feet tall, of a yellow color, bird-mouthed, with an arched nose, bushy eyebrows five inches long, ears seven inches long, and three vertical wrinkles on his forehead, his feet are marked with the eight trigrams,

9b   and he lies on a god-tortoise. He lives in a storied abode of gold where the rooms are lined with jade and the steps are of silver. His clothing is a cloud of many colors; his hat is tiered, and his sword is a pointed lance. He is attended by 120 yellow lads. To his left there are twelve blue dragons, and to his right thirty-six white tigers. Before him go twenty-four vermilion sparrows; to the rear, seventy-two *hsüan-wu*. His vanguard consists of twelve *ch'iung-ch'i*; his rearguard, of thirty-six evil-chasers. Above him there hover thunder and lightning with their flashes and brilliances. (All these details are taken from the genii classics.) If you see Lord Lao, your years will be extended, your heart and mind will become as clear as the sun and moon, and there will be nothing that you do not know.

Someone asked how to anchor teeth. *Ko:* They are to be nurtured with vinegar and soaked in exudate of new wine. After three hundred such treatments, shining, strong teeth will remain firm for a long time. The next best thing is to hold in the mouth some yellow dock extract or some mica broth, pills of snake fat, pills of alum, and Nine-Jujube powder, then any that were loose will be returned to their sockets and the wormy ones will be cured. The taking of *ling-fei* powder can make lost teeth regenerate.

The question of hearing was raised. *Ko:* Ability to writhe like a dragon, stretch like a tiger, waddle like a bear, swallow like a tortoise, fly like a swallow, twist like a snake, dilate like a bird, look heavenward and earthward — all these will prevent the orange-colored wax from leaving the portion of the head called *tung-fang*. Then when you have climbed like a monkey and jumped like a hare 1200 times, your hearing will not deteriorate. The deaf may steam their ears with lizard. Or they may form a packet of jujubes, sheep-turd cinnamon and plumed-sparrow cinnamon, and seal their ears with it. Or they may use wolfsbane and poison sumac. Some combine aconite with onion juice and place it in the ears; others sprinkle the ears with steamed carp brains. All of these procedures produce cures.

Eyesight. *Ko:* Since they knew how to draw bright sheen from the Three Cookers [esophagus, lining of stomach, and urethra] in the body, muster the great fire from the south, wash their eyes with mica, soothe them with sunlight, and burned *ping-ting* (fire) and *tung-shih* (profound vision) amulets (4.6*a*7) mixed with wine, the Ancients used to write in the dark. Or else turnips are cooked in strong vinegar until

10a

done, then dried in the sun and powdered. When an inch-square spoonful of this is taken three times daily until a little more than a peck has been consumed, it becomes possible to see any object at night. Another method is to use dog-gall extract and lucerne, abalone, motherwort, and Pai-hua powders. If the milk, juice, or extract of Aquilaria or yellow lotus are put into the eyes, any and all eye disease will be cured and one's vision will be twice as good as before.

Climbing peaks, crossing dangerous ledges, and under-taking endless journeys without exhaustion. *Ko:* If you will just partake of the great medicines (cinnabar or gold), your body will become light and your strength will remain unabated. You will be able to work hard without becoming *10b* weary. If you enter mountains and forests before your body is fully ready, you should wash your feet in a solution of powdered mica, honey, and brine. If you take tiger-gall pills, summer wine, heaven-male-crane-fat pills, thistle ex-tract, absinthe, plantain, or water-plantain powder for ten days, you will not only go far without exhaustion, but you will travel three times faster than usual.

If you can ride the arches of your feet, you will be able to wander anywhere in the world without hindrance from mountains or rivers. There are three methods for this type of riding: Dragon, Tiger, and Deer-hound. Whoever takes the correct amulet and gives serious thought to the process may travel a thousand miles by concentrating his thoughts for one double hour. If he thinks similarly for a full period of twelve double hours, he will be able to travel 12,000 miles within one day and one night, but no further. If he wishes to go beyond this, the thinking must be repeated as before.

Some build a flying vehicle from the pith of the jujube tree and have it drawn by a sword with a thong of buffalo hide at the end of its grip. Others let their thoughts dwell on the preparation of a joint rectangle from five serpents, six dragons, and three buffaloes, and mount in this for forty miles to the region known as Paradise. Here the air is very strong and capable of supporting people. My teacher told me that the kite, as it flies ever higher and higher, merely relaxes its two wings and does not flap them again at all, but advances automatically by agitation, because it gradually comes to ride upon stronger air. Similarly, as soon as the dragon mounts above the clouds to forty miles, it travels automatically. This is a statement coming from genii, but its transmission not having continued among the laity, the fact is not known to ordinary folk.

11a

Further, if you wish to ride the arches of your feet, you must fast for a long time and give up shallots and bloody things; only after one year of this can you use one of the three arch methods (10*b*5). Even though you again take the proper amulet and do the required thinking, after five trips by the dragon method, the maximum distance will have been traveled, and any other trips will net you only a thousand miles (10*b*7). For the risings, dippings, goings, and stoppings there are special methods; you cannot do just as you please. If you do not get the charms, you should not heedlessly travel by arches, for you might fall.

Interlocutor: Lao Tan's *P'ien-chung chi* and *★Kuei-wen-ching* both say that in the metal or wood years after large-scale warfare there is sure to be plague in which only one out of thousands will survive. How can one escape its effects?

Ko: According to the Genii-enter-plague-secret-charm-method one is to think that the body is composed of five jades varying in color according to the season of the year (15.2*b*6—). In spring the color is green; in summer, red; in the last months of the four seasons, yellow; in autumn, white; in winter, black. The method also provides that one think that a kerchief of gold is being worn; that the heart is like a gleaming fire as large as a bushel measure. In this way there will be nothing to fear. Another method is to think that the hair falls down your back sufficiently to cover your whole body, each strand having one large star at the end.

11b

Think also that the seven stars in the Great Dipper have come to cover your head with the four stars constituting the bowl, and point firmly at whatever confronts you. Think also that the breaths of your five inner organs are darting from your two eyes and surrounding your body like a mist, and that the blue breath of your liver, the white of your lungs, the yellow of your spleen, the black of your kidneys, and the red of your heart have all intermingled. Then you will even be able to sleep with those sick with the plague.

Some, while walking with Yü's Pace, shout for the fairy on duty that particular day; others close their breaths within themselves and think that they are being protected by 120 mighty warriors wielding metal hammers that weigh a thousand pounds each. Still others use Shoot-ghost pellets, Red-vehicle-messenger pellets, Cap-army pellets, Chief-minister-Hsü powder, Jade-coffer-spirit powder, Blue-buffalo-processor-smoke-body pellets, Ts'ui-Wen-yellow powder, Plant-jade wine, Huang-t'ing pellets, Three-Augusti amulet, Lao-tzu-control-center amulet, or Ch'ih-hsü tzu's Peach-flower amulet, all of which are highly effective.

16

The Yellow and The White

IN THE GODS-AND-GENII classics we find more than a thousand prescriptions in twenty-five scrolls dealing with the Yellow and White. Yellow means gold; white silver. Keeping their procedures secret and treasuring them, the Ancients refrained from speaking openly and resorted to language known only to the initiates. For example, some chapters have the term *keng-hsin* [originally designations of the seventh and eighth days of the Chinese ten-day "week," which were assigned to the agent or element Metal] in their titles. Well, *keng-hsin* too means gold. Much of what they say is so esoteric that only a small portion can be given clear explication. The laity largely suspects these prescriptions to be groundless inventions; in this they agree with the atheists.

Personally, I formerly received from my teacher, Cheng Yin (4.2*a*2—) both *Chiu tan ching* and *Chin yin i ching*; after this I sought further and was taught *Huang pai chung ching*, in five scrolls. Cheng Yin told me that he had been successful with these recipes when he tried them on Mount T'ung, in Lu-chiang, together with Tso Tz'u. The rigor of the rituals of purification and the taboos (4.5*b*3) required by these processes, however, is identical with that required when pre-paring the god-genie medicines of gold and cinnabar. People are largely critical of my devotion to these strange matters; they claim that I am being drawn by a desire to force comprehension of things in this world which are not comprehensible. Why do I do it? Certainly not because I desire through such things as these to attain literary fame in the future. My *Wai p'ien* and miscellaneous compositions, amounting to over 200 scrolls, are amply sufficient to transmit my ideas without need of this present material (A 9*a*10—). Further, this *Nei p'ien* consists of only straightforward speech; there is no ornamentation.

I am also aware that the type of thing I am discussing here is generally considered far-fetched and of no urgency, and that I would be better off discussing things closer to people's concerns if I wanted popular support. But I cannot let these matters be because I know that, even though it has not come to the ears of the uninitiated, still its expounders have actually seen its effects and evidences. Moreover, the teachers who taught me these things were not liars.

I suffer from poverty and lack of resources and strength; I have met with much misfortune. There is nobody at all to whom I can turn for help. The lanes of travel being cut, the ingredients of the medicines are unobtainable. The result is that I have never been able to compound these medicines I am recommending. When I tell people today that I know how to make gold and silver, while I personally remain cold and hungry, how do I differ from the seller of medicine for lameness who is himself unable to walk? It is simply impossible to get people to believe you. Nevertheless, even though the situation may contain some unsatisfactory elements, it is not to be rejected in its entirety. Accordingly, I am carefully committing these things to writing because I wish to enable future lovers of the extraordinary and esteemers of truth, through reading my writings, to consummate their desires to investigate God.

What is it that the arts of transformation cannot do? May I remind my readers that the human body, which is normally visible, can be made to disappear. Ghosts and gods are normally invisible, but there are ways and means to make them visible. Those capable of operating these methods and prescriptions will be found to abound wherever you go. Water and fire are present in the sky, but they may be brought down with specula and burning-mirrors; lead is naturally white, but it can be reddened and mistaken for cinnabar. Cinnabar is naturally red, but it can be whitened to look like lead. Clouds, rain, frost, and snow are all breaths belonging to heaven and earth, but those produced by art differ in no way from the natural phenomena. Flying things and those that creep and crawl have been created in specific shapes, but it would be impossible ever to finish listing the thousands upon thousands of sudden metamorphoses which they can undergo.

Man himself is the most highly honored member of creation and the most highly endowed, yet there are just as many instances of men and women changing into cranes, stones, tigers, monkeys, sand, or lizards. The cases of high mountains becoming deep abysses and of profound valleys changing into peaks are metamorphoses on an immense scale. It is clear, therefore, that transformation is something spontaneous in nature. Why should we doubt the possibility of making gold and silver from something different? Compare, if you will, the fire obtained with a burning-mirror and the water which condenses at night on the surface of a metal speculum. Do they differ from ordinary water and fire? *2b*

When a snake turns into a dragon and sundew produces fat, the transformations do not differ in any way from those which occur in nature, for the basic cause in both cases is a natural stimulus. Only a man who has thoroughly studied the underlying principle can understand the significance of such phenomena. Only one whose range of vision is universal can grasp their circumstances. The narrow view and myopic common sense are like fetters and burrows; they dismiss the profound and marvelous as unfathomable and conclude that the divine transformations are empty boasts. How petty to declare anything false that was not expounded by the Duke of Chou and Confucius and is not contained in ancient books!

Learning that Liu Hsiang was unsuccessful in his effort to make gold, the man in the street declares that it is quite evident that no such process exists. This is like farmers whose crops were ruined by flood or drought declaring that the various grains will not grow if sown. Let me remind you of Secretary Wu Ta-wen of Ch'eng-tu, a man of broad understanding and wide knowledge. He tells us that he once studied under the processor Li Ken and saw him throw a few pieces of medicine the size of a large pea into some lead and tin that he was cooking, and stir the mixture with a ladle. Upon cooling, it had turned to silver. Wu Ta-wen obtained the secret prescription from him and intended to carry it out. But the work had to be preceded by one hundred days' ritual of purification and he could not get away from his office, so he was unable personally to succeed in making the silver. He was always sighing that it was not worth while to remain among men.

3a

Huan T'an tells us of the Han courtier Ch'eng Wei who was fond of the art of yellow and white. He married a girl from a family which possessed prescriptions. He used to take part in state processions without wearing the clothes proper to the season. When this worried his wife, she said, "Let two pieces of taffeta appear." And immediately, without any clear reason, they appeared. Ch'eng Wei had been unsuccessful in his effort to make gold by following the *Chen-chung* and the *Hung-pao* directions (2.11a2), until one day his wife went to watch him. At that moment he was fanning coals to heat mercury that was in a tube. His wife then said, "Let me try something," took some medicine from her pouch, and put the slightest bit of it into the tube. Then, after taking time for a meal, they opened the tube and found that the contents had changed to silver. Much amazed, Ch'eng Wei cried out "Why didn't you tell me sooner that you had such a process?" — "To possess this," his wife replied, "one must be fated." Then he kept pleading with her day and night for the recipe. He sold lands and buildings to provide her with the best of food and clothing, but she still did not find it proper to tell him. Then he schemed with a friend to extract it from her by force, but she became aware of this plan and told him that the process was to be transmitted only to the right person. If the right person was found, even if they met on the road, she would teach it to him. If, however, it was not the right man — one whose words were right but whose heart was not — the process would not be forthcoming even though she were to be cut into bits and the members torn from her body. Ch'eng Wei kept up the pressure, however, until finally his wife went mad and, running away naked, smeared herself with mud and later died.

3b

More recently, the former Governor of Lu-chiang, Hua T'an, a man of exceptional talent, deep study, and wide knowledge, was largely skeptical regarding matters not attested in the Classics. Later, a processor was expounding a prescription dealing with yellow and white, and he got Hua T'an to try it out, saying, "Melt some lead in an iron vessel, put some powdered medicine in it, and it will immediately turn to silver. Then melt this silver, put another ingredient into it, and it will become gold without delay." He also studied a method for penetrating vision with this same processor. Before one hundred days had passed, while abed one night, he suddenly saw the constellations and all his neighbors' places. Then, before he realized it, his house with all its hedges and walls were there once more. He also saw and talked with one of his concubines, Yao-hua, who had died some time before, just as he did when she was still alive. On another occasion when Hua T'an was offering sacrifice in the temple he heard its god answer his bows; the bench seemed to move, making a sound. As a result of all this, Hua T'an finally exclaimed, "Without doubt the world is full of all manner of things. Even though the Five Classics may not mention some thing, we should not arbitrarily conclude that it does not exist." Therefore, when someone who has never listened to the wonder-workers hears of things like this, how can he help but be amazed?

Just as for compounding divine cinnabar, it is necessary for the art of yellow and white to fast and purify oneself for at least a hundred days. It is also requisite to find a like-minded person familiar with the literature of alchemy before the prescription can be compounded. This is not something *4a* to be undertaken by the impure and unintelligent or those with but little experience in the occult arts. Certain matters can only be transmitted orally, and must be learned from a teacher. Also, you must go to a pure spot deep in the mountains, so that the unlearned crowd will not know what you are undertaking. Liu Hsiang, however, remained in the palace when he undertook this art, and in letting the palace people attend to his wants he obviously did not maintain the requisite purity. Also, he continued to maintain his involvement in human affairs so that there were constant comings and goings. Under such circumstances, how could he ever expect to succeed?

Huan T'an's *Hsin lun* reads: "On being named Premier's Secretary, Shih Tzu-hsin built a shed and mobilized those under him as well as government slaves to furnish the labor necessary to make gold. When this project was unsuccessful, the Premier decided that he himself lacked sufficient labor for the undertaking, and reported accordingly to Empress Fu, who however saw no advantage in the making of gold. But as soon as she was informed that such gold could be used as a medicine for prolonging one's years, she became willing. Shih Tzu-hsin was then named Courtier and lodged in the northern palace where palace messengers attended him." As though a divine prescription of this sort could be effected in a palace with all sorts of ordinary people in attendance! It is common knowledge that even dyers of silks do not wish to have all kinds of people watching them for fear their work will be spoiled. How much truer is this for the transforming of yellow and white!

4b

In all matters, whether important or unimportant, one must learn the essentials. If the proper methods are not followed and one proceeds heedlessly, even wines, preserves, vinegar, sauces, and bouillons cannot be made successfully. How much truer is this for important undertakings! I once inquired of my teacher Cheng Yin: "Lao Tan (T 64) says to place no value on things that are hard to get, and that in a well-ordered generation all gold (cf. T 9) will be thrown back to the mountains and all jade to the valleys. It is not clear to me, therefore, why the Ancients valued gold and silver and left us these recipes." This was his reply: "Lao Tan means that people sift sand, split rocks, crumble mountains, drain depths, and go anywhere, giving no thought to the danger of being crushed or drowned in their search for jewels and baubles. Thereby they interfere with the proper use of the people's time, and observe no measure in their efforts to bedeck themselves with useless things.

"When those desiring to effect the divine process and purposely seeking Fullness of Life concomitantly engage in trading, they are not sincere in their faith and humility. Floating upon the deep and passing through dangers, they pursue profits on land and sea. They are not careful of their lives, and they do not work to diminish their desires. However, when God's Men make gold, they wish to take it in order to bring divinity or geniehood upon themselves, not wealth. It is for this reason that the classic says, 'Gold can be created, and geniehood attained.' Silver too can be taken, but it is inferior to gold."

I then countered, "Why produce it by transformation instead of nibbling mundane gold and silver? If you make it, it will not be genuine, and if it is not genuine, it is

5a   counterfeit." His reply was this: "Mundane gold and silver are acceptable, but as a rule processors are poor. As the adage has it, 'There are no fat genii and no rich processors.' A group consisting of a teacher and his pupils may amount to five or ten persons. How could so many be supplied with gold and silver? Further, since they cannot travel far and wide to gather them, it is fitting that they create them themselves. In addition, gold created by transformation, being the very essence of a variety of ingredients, is superior to natural gold."

The genii classics tell us that cinnabar sperm produces gold; this is another way of saying that gold can be made from cinnabar. That is why gold is generally found beneath deposits of cinnabar in the mountains. If you have been successful in creating gold, it will react as the real thing; it will be alike inside and out, and a hundred refinings will not diminish it. Accordingly, when the prescription reads, "money ingots can be made of it," it is evidence of its strength. Thus you will know that you have acquired the natural process. And given its potential, why should it be called counterfeit? "Counterfeit" describes iron that has been coated with laminar malachite, so that it assumes a reddish color like copper, or silver that has been transformed by white of egg, which renders the silver yellow like gold. These are instances where the surface has been affected but the interior remains unchanged.

Mushrooms grow naturally, but some genii classics speak of five sorts of "stone" and five sorts of "wood" excrescences (11.2b4), which are gathered and taken after they appear, and are no different from the mushrooms which occur in nature, for all of them will bring a man to Fullness of Life. This belongs to the same category of things as the
5b   creation of gold.

When the pheasant turns into a *shen* bivalve and the sparrow a clam (3.8a3) they become exactly like the natural ones. Accordingly, we read in the genii classics:

Mercury being cycled nine times,
Father not speak to sons.
When there is transforming to yellow or white,
Natural agencies at work.

They also say that those who make gold from cinnabar and achieve geniehood by taking it are first class. Those enjoying Fullness of Life through roots, mushrooms, calisthenics, and breathing disciplines are second class. Those who subsist on herbs and live for less than a thousand years, are third class. They also tell us that it is in the nature of gold and silver that one can make them, whereas, Fullness of Life is something that can be obtained through study.

Yü tieh chi reads: "Everywhere, throughout the world, everyone could enjoy Fullness of Life. The only reason they do not is that doubt makes them hesitate . . .. Congeal mercury into gold fit to be a money ingot." *T'ung chu ching* reads:

> *Cinnabar can become gold and mercury silver.*
> *Quickly they're made, the genuine article.*
> *Get this procedure; a genie you'll become.*

Huang-shan tzu has said, "Since heaven and earth contain gold, I can also create it. With two parts of yellow to one part of red, there is no doubt that it can be formed readily." *Kuei chia wen* reads:

> *The span of life is up to me, not heaven.*
> *The reverted cinnabar becomes gold, and millions of years are mine.*

Do you think the Ancients would have lied to us? My only concern is that those who know these processes are generally poor, and the ingredients required, though sometimes extremely cheap, are native to distant places and cannot be obtained in our troubled times. Things like Turkestan salt *6a* and native lake salt are both inexpensive commodities, worth nothing in times of peace. Today, however, they are unobtainable regardless of price. Though thousands be offered for one pound of copper sulphate from the villages

to our northwest, it cannot be had. Knowing the prescription in vain is exactly the same as not knowing it at all.
All we can do is sigh.

Those who possess a recipe are often so poor that they
lack the means to do the compounding; the rich, in turn, do
not know the recipe, and when informed, not a one of them
believes it. Further, supposing they entertain some degree of
belief in it, they are already well provided with gold and
silver and have no incentive to spend present wealth to
purchase the ingredients. None of them finds it reasonable
to do so, for they fear that they would be releasing the one
in their hand for the two on the wing. They further
calculate that even though the product obtained would yield
a huge profit over expenditures for materials, it would still
not be worth the inconveniences of the requisite fasts and
prohibitions. Consequently, they cannot bring themselves
to undertake the work. Also, the task is not to be undertaken
lightly, without secret oral directions obtained from an
enlightened teacher.

Medicines commonly used by physicians are quite humble
things known to all, but even the effective prescriptions in
ordinary use are kept secret. Thus such ingredients of prescriptions as wandering ladies of the rear palace [lightning
bugs], sideways gum, Lord Seal's *nirvana* [?clay pills],
wooden ghost [?Vitex], gold merchant's mushroom [?cat-
alpa, Jew's-ear], flying lord's root [bee-sage], vanquished
dragon's liver [old cinders], white horse's sweat [raspberry
juice], floating-cloud lees [mica], dragon's offspring elixir
6b   [frog's skin], night-clothing luminous bones [torch ashes],
white-flower wine [honey], and Mr. Tsou's winter fast are
all familiar materials, but without the secret oral directions
one would never know them. How much truer is this, then,
in the art of yellow and white! Today those competent in
this art keep it secret not only because of the high price of
the products but also because the success of this process
makes it possible to enjoy Fullness of Life, which is the

pinnacle of all processes. That is why the Ancients valued it so highly.

The medicines and ingredients listed in the prescriptions sometimes bear the same names as things in common use, but in reality they are different. For example, Young-woman-along-the-river [mercury] is not a female; Peak-male-brightness[mercury] is not a male; Yü's-left-over-grain [brown hematite] is not rice; Yao's fluid (?) is not a liquid. However, when the uninitiated read that the prescription calls for Dragon Gall [gentian], Tiger's Paws [jack-in-the-pulpit], Chicken Heads [Euryale], Duck Soles [Commelina], Horse's Hooves [water shield], Dog Blood (?), Rat Tail [sage], or Ox Knee [marjoram], they are unanimous in declaring that these things are animals with blood and breath. When they read that the things to be used are Broken Cup [raspberry], Covered Basin [raspberry], Crucible (?), Big Lance [spurge], Ghost Arrow [Euonymous], and Sky Dog [ginseng], they call them iron or pottery utensils. On reading. of Barbarian King's Messenger [anemone], New-wife-who-leans-on-mother-in-law (?), Wild man [anemone], Field Defender [Pinellia], Tai Wen's Bath (?), and Head Minister Hsü [Pycnostelma], they think that they are persons. If we can be so confounded by common plants, how can we expect to comprehend arcane, *7a* recondite prescriptions? Is it any wonder that Liu Hsiang was unsuccessful in his efforts to create gold? Once these essentials have been secured, anyone can effect this process without concerning himself any further with the great talents of the sages and worthies. Was Liu Hsiang stupid? Certainly not! He is merely guilty of failing to obtain the secret oral directions.

At present I am making a rough sketch of the things toward which energy is to be directed, in order that I may bequeath something to like-minded persons of the future. You must first get Mount Wu-tu [Kansu] realgar, cinnabar in color like a chicken's comb and bright, free of impurities, any quantity you wish, but not less than five pounds. Pestle it to a powder, mix with oxgall and roast until dry. Take a red clay crucible large enough to hold a bushel, and first line its interior with powdered salt from Turkestan and copper sulphate to a thickness of three tenths of an inch. Then insert the realgar powder to a depth of one half inch, adding on top of that a layer of Turkestan salt. Repeat this stratification until your supply is exhausted. Add a two-inch bed of hot charcoal, the pieces being broken to the size of jujube pits. Prepare a cement of earthworm excreta and Turkestan salt to cement the exterior of the crucible. Cover it with another crucible and cement the whole to a thickness of three inches so that there will be no leaks. Then dry this in the shade for one month, after which it is to be heated in a fire of horse dung for three days and nights. After it becomes cold, bring out the contents. Apply a bellows to run off the mixture, which will flow like newly smelted copper or iron. Then have a tube cast of this mixture and fill it with cinnabar solution (see below). Heat this in a horse-dung fire for thirty days. At this point, prepare a furnace and apply a bellows to get the metal and make a tube of it to be filled in turn with cinnabar solvent. This is to be heated in a horse-dung fire for thirty days, opened, and the contents pestled. To prepare the gold you are seeking, take two parts of what you have just pestled, one part of crude cinnabar, and some mercury. The mixture will immediately congeal to gold. It will be brilliant and of excellent color, fit for a monetary ingot.

Method for preparing cinnabar solution. Prepare and insert one pound of cinnabar into a green bamboo tube. Add two ounces each of copper sulphate and saltpeter above and below the cinnabar. Close the tube openings and seal them with a globule of hard lacquer, which must be allowed time to dry. Place the whole in strong vinegar and bury three feet deep in the earth. After thirty days it will have liquefied and become red in color and bitter to the taste.

In the recipe for making gold received from Ch'ing-lin
tzu and followed by Master Chin-lou, one first casts ingots
of tin six inches square and 1.2 inches thick. These ingots are   *8a*
then covered everywhere to a thickness of 0.1 inch with a
paste made from red crystal salt and lime water and placed
one after another in a red clay crucible. For each ten pounds
of tin one uses four pounds of red crystal salt. Close the
crucible and seal all cracks well. Heat in a fire of horse dung
for thirty days. Remove from the fire and examine the
contents. The whole interior of the tin will look like lime
with clusters of beans, as it were, which are gold. Work these
nuggets together and insert them into an earthen crucible
where you will refine them ten times in a charcoal fire under
forced draft, after which the product will be ready. In all,
ten pounds of tin will provide twenty ounces of gold. Use
only a clay crucible from Ch'ang-sha, Kuei-yang, Yü-
chang, or Nan-hai. The people of these places are very
proud of the clay pots they make for cooking.

Method for the preparation of red crystal salt. Use one pound
of amethyst; get one pound of calcareous spar, one pound
of alum shale, and one pound of pure alum. Combine these
in an iron crucible and heat in a charcoal fire until the whole
melts and becomes reddish in color. At this point it is usable.

According to the method for transforming materials into
gold transmitted by Chi-ch'iu tzu and followed by Lu-li tzu,
two parts of kalinite solution are placed in an iron crucible   *8b*
and brought to a boil over a charcoal fire. Then add a convenient amount of mercury and stir until thoroughly mixed.
After six or seven boilings, pour upon the ground where it
will form silver. Then, placing one part each of cinnabar
solution and malachite solution and two parts of realgar
solution into a crucible, put this over a slow fire until it
boils, stir frequently to make a thorough mixture, and then
boil over a charcoal fire. Thereupon, place as much as
convenient of the silver you just made into this boiling
crucible. Bring to a boil six or seven times; pour upon the

earth. On congealing it will have formed purple, powdered gold of superior hue.

Method for preparing realgar solution. Prepare and place one pound of realgar in a tube of green bamboo, placing two ounces of saltpeter as a bed, and cover. Seal the tube with a globule of hard lacquer. Immerse the whole in strong vinegar and bury three feet deep in the earth. After twenty days it will have liquefied. Malachite solution and kalinite solution are made in this same way, but separate tubes must be used for each.

9a

Small boy's method for producing gold. Prepare an iron cylinder twelve inches in diameter and twelve inches deep; also a smaller one six inches in diameter polished to a shine. Pestle together and put through a fine sieve pure powdered red bole (one pound), saltpeter (one pound), mica (one pound), red hematite (one pound), sulphur (one half pound), laminar malachite (four ounces), and calcareous spar (one pound), and make a paste of it with vinegar. Coat the interior of the small cylinder with it to a thickness of 0.2 inch.

Procure one pound of mercury, a half pound of cinnabar, and a half pound of amalgam (*liang fei*). (To prepare the amalgam, place ten pounds of lead in an iron crucible on a stove and heat it without covering. When it is melted, add three ounces of mercury. A scum will soon appear which you can remove with an iron ladle; it is called amalgam.) Mix these together thoroughly until the mercury is no longer visible. Place in the small cylinder and cover with mica. Then place an iron lid on the small cylinder. Place the large cylinder on a stove and pour into it enough molten lead to cover the small cylinder and reach to within a half inch of the top of the large cylinder. Cook this over a raging fire for three days and nights, at which point it will have become what is called "purple powder" [litharge].

9b

Melt twenty pounds of lead in an iron vessel for about twenty days, then place it in a copper vessel (the lead must be molten), and add seven inch-square spoonfuls of the litharge. Stir, and it will immediately turn into gold.

To make silver. Put mercury in an iron vessel and insert three inch-square spoonfuls of litharge. Fire to fusion. Pour into water, and it will become silver at once.

Wu-ch'eng tzu's method. Use an iron cylinder nine inches deep and five inches in diameter. Three pounds of realgar and the same amount of earthworm excreta are pestled together to form a paste with which the interior of the cylinder is coated, reducing the diameter to three inches and leaving the opening with a diameter of four inches. After two gills of cinnabar solution have been added, the vessel is surrounded and its contents dried thoroughly over a horse-dung fire. The contents are then placed in a copper cylinder and a copper lid tightly fitted. Prop the cylinder in place with yellow sand. The cover is plastered with several layers of earthworm excreta to prevent leaks. Place in a furnace on a three-inch bed of charcoal. When the mouth gets red, the tube may be cooled and opened. All the realgar will have adhered to the copper tube. Remove this, and repeat the process. When the essence of all three pounds of realgar have adhered to the copper tube and been removed, mix it with equal parts of yellow sand and use it to make a crucible of any desired size.

When you wish to use such a crucible, place it in a charcoal fire, and when it becomes red add some mercury. As soon as the mercury moves, add lead. When the yellow coloration which begins at the sides has met at the center, pour the contents on the ground, and it will immediately become gold. After 1500 pounds of gold have been thus *10a* prepared, the crucible will be no longer usable.

After soaking for a hundred days in Vitex or red panicled-millet wine, this gold softens sufficiently to be miscible with other things. If one pill of it the size of a gram is taken three times daily until one pound has been consumed, the Three Worms will cry for mercy and all illnesses will quit the body. The blind will see; the deaf, hear; the aged will become like thirty; those entering fire will not be burned; all evils, all poisons, cold, wind, heat, and dampness — none of these will be able to attack such a man. If he continues the dosage until three pounds have been consumed, he will be able to walk on rivers and all the gods of the mountains and streams will come to serve and protect him. His lot of longevity will last as long as all nature.

If one of these pills is boiled with orange juice or vermilion grass and then used to rub the corners of the eyes, it will enable one to see ghosts and the things that reside in the earth and also to write in the dark. If one of the pills is smeared with ram's blood and thrown into a stream, the fish and the dragons will come out immediately, and it will be easy to catch them. A pill smeared with chamois blood or cinnabar-colored fowl's blood and suspended in the top of the gateways to the capital will keep plague a mile away. If such a pill is used to smear the foreheads of buffaloes, sheep, and other domestic animals, none of them will suffer illness, and no tiger or leopard will harm them. If one of the pills is coated with tiger gall or snake fat and thrown into the enemy's camp on a day marked by the month's cyclical number, it will cause mutiny for no apparent reason, and the enemy soldiers will scatter, wounding and slaying one *10b* another. One pill smeared with buffalo blood and thrown into a well will make its water spout; if thrown into a running stream, it will reverse the current for a hundred paces. Smeared with the blood of a white dog and thrown into the local deity's shrine, it will make its ghosts and gods visible immediately, so that they may be employed. If it is coated with hare's blood and placed in a spot belonging to the Six Yin, the Traveling Canteen and the fairies will appear immediately and place themselves at your disposal, to a total of sixty or seventy individuals.

When coated with carp's gall and held when you enter a stream, it will open a way for you for ten feet, and you will be able to continue breathing and traveling through the water without getting wet. If you go out in the rain your clothes will not get wet. If one pill is cooked with purple amaranth and some of the juice held in the mouth or throat, it is possible to go a hundred days without hunger. If it is cooked with magnetite and placed in your topknot, you will go unscathed even when struck at by the bare blades of bandits or by flying arrows; in fact, arrows shot at you will turn against the archers. One pill, mixed with superior Six-Ting or Six-Jen earth and used to cover the raphe below the nose will make you invisible. If, while holding one pill in the mouth, you face north and spit upon a fire, it will go out; if, between three and seven in the afternoon on the seventh or eighth day of each ten, you face west and throw one pill at a tree, that tree will wither on the selfsame day. If, while walking Yü's Pace (11.16a), you throw one pill at a tiger, wolf, or snake, that animal will die immediately.

Grind one pill and write with it on stone, and the writing will be engraved thereon. Likewise if you write on metal or on wood. What you write will enter the very sinews of the substance and become indelible, even when the substance is melted.   *11a*

Before a night has passed after the death of a person, drop a pill into water obtained on the first day marked by the cyclical number of the month, place some of it in the throat of the corpse and take some of it in your own mouth and spit it into the face of the corpse. It will return to life immediately. Coat one of these pills with fox's or crane's blood, place it under a finger nail, and point it at any object, and the thing will be transformed as you command. You can even make everyone see mountains moving and trees transporting themselves, although no actual motion takes place.

When yellow and white are being created, altars are erected to T'ai-i, Heaven-fairy, and Lao Tan, and libations and offerings are made there just as in the case of the preparation of the Nine-crucible cinnabars. The five sorts of fragrance are kept burning continuously. Further, once the gold has been made, three pounds of it are thrown into a deep stream and one pound into the market place. Only after that may you use it as you wish.

17

Into Mountains:
Over Streams

ALL THOSE CULTIVATING the divine process or preparing medicines, as well as all those fleeing political disorders or living as hermits, go to the mountains. Many, however, meet with harm or even death because they do not know the right method for entering mountains. Hence the saying, "At the foot of T'ai-hua bleached bones lie scattered." Everyone knows that a man may have a special knowledge of one thing but he cannot know everything about all things. Some persons bent upon the search for life, drove themselves to their own deaths.

All mountains, whether large or small, contain gods and powers, and the strength of these divinities is directly proportional to the size of the mountain. To enter the mountains without the proper recipe is to be certain of anxiety or harm. In some cases people fall ill, are wounded, or become stricken with fear. In other cases, lights and shadows are seen, strange sounds are heard. Lack of the proper recipe can make a large tree fall when there is no wind; or a high rock fall for no apparent reason, striking and killing people. It can confuse such travelers or drive them madly on so that they fall into ravines. Lack of preparation may cause you to meet with tigers, wolves, or poisonous insects that will harm you. Mountains are not to be entered lightly.

1b

In the first place one enters mountains only during the third or ninth moons (11.7*b*11), these being the times when mountains are open. Then you must choose a propitious day and a good hour in one of those moons. If your business is of long standing and cannot permit long waiting for one of these two moons, you will merely pick a good day and hour. Before entering the mountain ordinary folk must first fast and purify themselves for seven days, not allowing themselves to become soiled in any way. Let them leave their homes wearing a Mount-mountain amulet from their belts. Let the Whole-body-three-five method(?) be set into operation.

There are years when the five revered mountains suffer calamities, just as places in the nine divisions of the world have their successive times of prosperity and decline; when a place is suffering from Express-death miasma, no sovereign can arise in it. According to *Chou kung ch'eng ming lu* any division of the world affected by disaster may be fled, but the disaster cannot be conjured away. And the same holds true for dwellings and also for mountains, ordinary as well as revered.

Here are some important taboos: In the first and second moons of years marked by *chia, i, yin,* or *mao* [from the sexagenary cycle] the eastern revered mountain is not to be entered. In the fourth and fifth moons of years marked by *ping, ting, ssu,* or *wu* the southern revered mountain is not to be entered. In the seventh and eighth moons of years marked by *keng, hsin, shen,* or *yu* the western revered mountain is not to be entered. In the last moons of the four seasons of years marked by *wu* or *chi* the central revered mountain is not to be entered. In the tenth and eleventh moons of years marked by *jen, kuei, hai,* or *tzu* the northern revered mountain is not to be entered. Unless obliged to enter Mount T'ai-hua (W), Mount Huo (S), Mount Heng (N), Mount T'ai (E), or Mount Sung-kao (C) observe these forbidden periods; this taboo applies to all faces of these mountains.

2a

The spirits in old objects (3.2*b*2) are capable of assuming human shape for the purpose of confusing human vision and constantly putting human beings to a test. It is only when reflected in a mirror that they are unable to alter their true forms. Therefore, in the old days, all processors entering the mountains suspended on their backs a mirror measuring nine inches or more in diameter, so that aged demons would not dare approach them. If any did come to test them, they were to turn and look at them in the mirror. If they were genii or good mountain gods, they would look like human beings when viewed in the mirror. If they were birds, animals, or evil demons, their true forms would appear in the mirror. If such a demon comes toward you, you must walk backward, turning your mirror toward it, in order to drive it away. Then observe it. If it is an aged demon, it is sure to have no heels. If it has heels, it is a mountain god.

Long ago, Chang Kai-t'a and Ou Kao-ch'eng were both giving earnest thought to the divine process in a cave on Mount Yün-t'ai in Shu [Szechuan], when a man approached them wearing a single garment of coarse yellow silk and a kerchief of Kudzu. "Rest yourselves, processors," he said, "for you are suffering from your life as hermits." When the two of them looked into their mirrors, they saw that it was a tiger. Immediately they greeted it with: "You are an old tiger belonging to this mountain. How dare you pretend to be a human being!" Before they had finished speaking, the 2b man changed into a tiger and left.

At the foot of Mount Lin-lü there was a shelter inhabited by ghosts. Whenever someone spent the night there he either died or fell ill. Every night several dozen individuals were there clad in yellow, white, or black — some of them men

and others women. Po-i once spent a night there. Lighting
a lamp or torch, he was sitting, intoning a Classic, when at
midnight about a dozen characters, entering and sitting
down opposite him, proceeded to play dice and backgammon with one another. Po-i secretly looked at them in
his mirror, and they proved to be a pack of dogs. He then
seized his torch and stood up as though he were going to
extinguish it, but as it singed the clothing of one of the
visitors there was an odor of scorched hair. Then when he
stabbed another one of them with the dagger that had been
concealed in his breast, there was at first a human cry, but at
death the creature became a dog. Thereupon, all the other
dogs left. With that, the haunting of the shelter ended. Such
is the power of a mirror.

When superior processors enter the mountains they carry
★San huang nei wen and *Wu yüeh chen hsing t'u* (TT 884.5.2b).
Wherever they may be they summon the gods of the
mountains and, according to *Kuei lu*, they summon the
earth-god of the state, the ministers of the mountain, and
the guardians of the homes in order to pay their respects to
them. In this way the monstrosities among trees and rocks
and the powers of the mountains and streams dare not come
and test them. They then erect Seventy-two-powers-defense
amulets. With seals against all evils, red official seals and the
twelve *pao-yüan* seals, they close the four sides of their
abode, and thus no evils dare approach them. After that, with
an Eight-prestige baton grasped in the hand and a Lao Tan
jade badge hanging from their belts, they can command the
mountain gods. What would have the courage to harm them.

Such are the facts I learned from my teacher, Cheng Yin,
but I do not claim to know everything about such matters.
My teacher always told his candidates, "If any man would
seek for the divine process in the way he worries about his
household becoming poor or in the way he is concerned
about his position becoming lower, would he fail in the
search? My only fear is that your will is not sincere; that you

3a

will concern yourself with the patent but forget the implicit. You will be glad for the instruction, but before you have been giving undivided attention very long, you will suddenly feel all alone. Before the slightest benefit has become assured, there will be mountains of losses without cease (*via purgativa*). How, indeed, can one ever exhaust the subtleties of speech in its highest form, or achieve the towering glories that never culminate?"

Highly tabooed for entrance into mountains are the following: *wu* days of the first moon; *hai* of the second; *shen* of the third; *ch'ou* of the fourth; *hsü* of the fifth; *mao* of the sixth; *tzu* of the seventh; *ssu* of the eighth; *yin* of the ninth; *wei* of the tenth; *ch'en* of the eleventh; and *yu* of the twelfth. The best days for entering mountains are: *chia-tzu,* *chia-yin, i-hai, i-ssu, i-mao, ping-hsü, ping-wu,* and *ping-ch'en.* These days are the most propitious.

3b

Chiu t'ien pi chi and *T'ai i tun chia* read: "In a long month [=30 days] the following days are tabooed for entering mountains: third, eleventh, fifteenth, eighteenth, twenty-fourth, twenty-sixth, and thirtieth. In a short month [=29 days]: first, fifth, thirteenth, sixteenth, twenty-sixth, and twenty-eighth. If you enter the mountains on these days you are sure to be put to the test by mountain gods. You will not get what you seek, and your work will be unsuccessful. This holds not only for processors, but anyone entering mountains on those days will suffer harm and meet with tigers, wolves, and poisonous insects."

Conditions relative to heaven and earth and the good and bad luck associated with yin and yang are so various that it would indeed be most difficult to give all the details. For my own part, I am certainly not going to state that these things are so, nor am I going to guarantee that they are not so. It is to be remembered, however, that Yellow Emperor and T'ai-kung both placed their reliance in such a system, and in a more recent period intelligent persons like Yen Tsun and Ssu-ma Ch'ien employed it. The Classics and the Accounts

4a mention "giving orders to the calendar to clarify the seasons" and "hard and soft days." *The Poems* (180) read: "The lucky day was *wu*." There is, therefore, a good tradition for this system. Our kings established the office of Grand Astrologer. For appointments, establishings, worship in the ancestral temples, and sacrifices to heaven and earth, they always chose the best times. People knowing nothing of the past, however, permit themselves to undertake work without following this old custom, for they are ashamed to choose a good day. Isn't it really stupid? I invariably notice that when people enter mountains without having secured a conjunction of the best season and day, there is later evidence that mountains are not to be entered lightheartedly.

Yü ch'ien ching reads, "To enter the famous mountains one must know the secret art found in *Tun chia* writings," but it does not undertake to expound the system for us in all details. *Ling pao ching* reads, "Entrance into the mountains should be on protective days (17.5*a*11—) and proper days. If it is a specially designated day you will enjoy great good fortune. If you go on a constraining day (17.5*b*5—) or an attacking day, you will certainly die." It too does not expound the matter item by item. When I was young, wishing to enter the mountains, I traveled about studying these *Tun chia*, and there proved to be more than sixty scrolls of them. Since the whole question could not be gone into completely and in all detail, I composed a summary of it as something ready at hand in my bag, but it is not suitable to be transmitted in writing. I discuss it summarily today with the thought that amateurs wishing to travel into the mountains will be obliged to discover experts in these questions, for there is no dearth of them in our world.

4b *Tun chia chung ching* reads, "If you wish to seek the divine process, exorcize the ghosts and demons and distribute the amulets and documents on a day and at an hour when heaven is receptive. Enter the famous mountains on a day and at an hour that heaven holds in its grasp. If you wish evils, tigers, wolves, poisonous insects, and bandits to fear approaching you, leave home when heaven is storing and enter [seven days later] the mountain when earth is serving as a door." As a general rule, times marked by the six cyclical combinations containing *kuei* are the times when heaven is storing; the six containing *chi* are the times when earth is serving as a door. It continues, "To free oneself from all anxieties when fleeing from political troubles or living as a hermit in the famous mountains, choose a fifteenth day of the first moon that is a day *ting-mao* (No. 4) and an hour called Yin Excellence, or Heart of Heaven, at which time one may conceal oneself, for it is said that 'when the bright sun has sunk into the earth and the sun and moon lack brilliance, neither men nor ghosts are able to see.'"

Again, "When entering a famous mountain in search of the divine process leading to geniehood, choose one of the *six kuei* days and hours, also known as Heaven-public Days, and you will be sure to become a genie." Again, "On the way to the mountains or forests you must take some superior *ch'ing-lung* (see below) grass in your left hand, break it and place half under *feng-hsing*. Pass through the *ming-t'ang* and enter *yin-chung*. Walking with Yü's Pace, pray three times as follows: 'May Generals No-kao and T'ai-yin open the way solely for me, their great-grandson, so-and-so by name. Let it not be opened for others. If anyone sees me, he is to be considered a bundle of grass; those that do not see me, non-men.' Then break the grass that you are holding and place it on the ground. With the left hand take some earth and apply it to the first man in your group. Let the right hand take some grass with which to cover itself, and let the left hand extend forward. Walk with Yü's Pace, and on attaining the Six-Kuei site, hold your breaths and stay where you are. Neither men nor ghosts will be able to see you." As a general rule, the Six Chia constitute the *ch'ing-lung*; the Six I, the *feng-hsing*; the Six Ping, the *ming-t'ang*; and the Six Ting, the *yin-chung*.

5a

"As you proceed with the prescribed Yü's Pace you will keep forming hexagram No. 63.

> *Initial one foot forward,*
> *Initial two side by side,*
> *Prints not enough.*
> *Nine prints are the count,*
> *Successively up to snuff.*

One pace (or three prints) equals seven feet; total, twenty-one feet; and on looking back you will see nine prints."

Method for walking Yü's Pace. Stand straight (11.16a). Advance the right foot while the left remains behind. Then advance in turn the left foot and the right foot, so that they are both side by side. This constitutes pace No. 1. Advance the right foot, then the left, then bring the right side by side with the left. This constitutes pace No. 2. Advance the left foot, then the right, then bring the left side by side with the right. This constitutes pace No. 3, with which a Yü's Pace is completed. It should be known by all who are practicing the various recipes in our world; it is not enough to know only the recipes.

When *Ling pao ching* speaks of *protective* days (17.4a6), it means the Twelve Branches and the Ten Trunks where a first element in a binary begets the second one. This is true in the case of the days *chia-wu* (No. 31 in the 60-cycle) and *i-ssu* (No. 42). *Chia* is wood, and *wu* is fire; *i* too is wood, and *ssu* fire, fire being born of wood. When it speaks of *proper* days, it means those cases where the second element begets the first. Examples of this are *jen-shen* (No. 9) and *kuei-yu* (No. 10). *Jen* is water, and *shen* is metal; *kuei* is water, and *yu* is metal, water being born of metal. By *constraining* days it means those where the first element conquers the second; for example *wu-tzu* (No. 25) and *chi-hai* (36). *Wu* is earth, and *tzu* is water; *chi* too is earth, and *hai* water, and according to the theory of the Five Agents earth conquers water. By *attacking* days it means those where

5b

the second element conquers the first; for example *chia-shen* (21) and *i-yu* (22). *Chia* is wood, and *shen* is metal; *i* too is wood, and *yu* metal, metal conquering wood. From these examples you can deduce the rest.

To enter a famous mountain, choose an opening day, which can be determined by its cyclical binary. Hang silk of the five colors, each piece five inches wide, from a large rock, so that you may be sure to succeed in your goal. Further, while entering the mountain you should know the Six-Chia secret prayer. It goes like this: "May the presiders over warriors all be my vanguard!" This nine-word prayer must be constantly recited in secret. It means, "May all evils flee me and the essential procedures present no trouble."

6a

The mountain power in the form of a little boy hopping backward on one foot likes to come and harm people. If you hear a human voice at night in the mountains talking loud, its name is Ch'i. By knowing this name and shouting it, you will prevent it from harming you. Another name for it is Jo-nei; you may use both these names together.

There is another mountain power, this one in the shape of a drum, colored red, and also with only one foot. Its name is Hui. Still another power has the shape of a human being nine feet tall, dressed in fur-lined clothes and wearing a large straw hat. Its name is Chin-lei. Another is like a dragon, variegated in color and with red horns, the name being Fei-fei. Whenever one of these appears, shout its name, and it will not dare harm you.

There are huge trees in the mountains and some of them can speak. However, it is not the tree that speaks, but the power in it named Yün-yang. Shout that name, and all will be well. If you happen to see light from a fire at night in the mountains, it will always be caused by some tree that has long been dead. Don't let it surprise you.

6b

If you should see there at night an alien (*hu*), it will be the power in copper and iron; if it looks like a man from Ch'in, it will be the power from a hundred-year-old tree. Don't let them surprise you, for neither of them can do you any harm.

If you should see an official in a mountain stream, his name will be Ssu-chiao. Shout that name, and everything will be well. Proceed likewise, should you meet in the mountains with a large snake wearing a turban, its name being Sheng-ch'ing.

If you encounter an official, but only hear his voice without seeing any shape as it keeps shouting to you, throw a white stone at it, and it will stop. Another way is to make a reed spear and prick the creature with it, then everything will be all right. If you meet a ghost coming and shouting continuously to you for food, throw a white reed at it and it will die instantly. In the mountains, ghosts are constantly creating confusion to make people lose their way, but if you throw a reed staff at them they will die immediately.

If on a day numbered *yin* there is someone in the mountains calling himself an inspector, it is really a tiger; if he calls himself Lord of the Road, it is a wolf; Commander-in-Chief, an old fox. If it is a day *mao* and he calls himself an elder, it is a hare; East-king father, an elk; West-king mother, a deer. If it is a day *ch'en* and he calls himself a rainmaker, it is a dragon; Lord of the River, a fish; Lord Intestineless, a crab. If it is a day *ssu* and he calls himself Poor Me, it is an earth-altar snake; Lord of Seasons, a tortoise. If it is a day *wu* and he calls himself a *san-kung*, it is a horse; a genie, it is an aged tree. If it is a day *wei* and he calls himself master, it is a ram; official, it is a fallow deer. On a day *shen*, a man calling himself a lord is a monkey; a *chiu-ch'ing*, an ape. On a day *yu*, one calling himself general (18.3*a*10) is an aged fowl; bandit-catcher, a pheasant. On a day *hsü*, anyone giving himself a man's name is a dog; Ch'eng-yang kung, a fox. On a day *hai*, anyone calling himself lord of the gods is a boar; a lady, gold or jade. On a day *tzu*, anyone calling himself Lord of the Earth-altar is a rat; a god, a bat. On a day *ch'ou*, anyone calling himself a student is an ox. Only if you know the names of these creatures will they be unable to harm you.

How to avoid snakes while on retreat in the mountains and swamps. In antiquity Round Hill abounded in large snakes, but it also produced good medicines. When Yellow Emperor was about to mount there, Kuang-ch'eng tzu instructed him to carry some realgar at his belt, and all the snakes fled the place. Today, therefore, if five or more ounces of Wu-tu realgar, red as a chicken's comb, is carried from the belt when entering mountains, forests, or bush, there will be nothing to fear from snakes. If you should happen to be bitten, rub a small quantity of the realgar into the wound and it will immediately get better. There are many sorts of snakes, but only the bites of the viper and the "blue-gold" snake are very critical. If a bite from one of these is not treated, it will kill a man within twenty-four hours. When bitten by one of these two snakes, anyone who does not know a recipe for treatment should immediately cut out the affected flesh with a knife and throw it to the ground. Cauterize the wound as in moxa and in a minute the burning will cease and the patient continue to live. The poison in these snakes is at its peak during the seventh and eighth moons. If they do not bite a human being, their poison does not get out, and they then bite large bamboos and small trees, causing them in every case to dry and wither. It can prove to be of no little consequence today if you enter the mountains as a processor knowing only some important recipe but no prophylactic procedures.

Before entering the mountains you should spend a preparatory period at home and first study the art of charming things, and give thought to the sun and moon, as well as to the four cardinal points, to protect yourself. [The cardinal points are here designated as Vermilion Sparrow, Hsüan-wu (=black), Blue Dragon, and White Tiger, respectively.] Only then will you undertake the trip into the mountains, forests, and bush. Take three mouthfuls of breath from your

7b

left and confine them for blowing against plants in the mountains. In your thought, make this breath become red in color and like a cloud or mist spreading out fully in an area of several dozen miles. If any are accompanying you, no matter what number, have them all take up regular positions and then blow on them with your breath. After that, even though they were to tread upon a snake, it would not dare move, and indeed no snakes will normally be met after taking these precautions. If you do happen to see one, face the sun and, taking three mouthfuls of breath from the left, confine it. Press your tongue against the roof of your mouth, and place a hand upon your principal barrier (?). Close your mouth, plug your nose, and then press something against the snake's head while making a circle about it with your hand, drawing a prison on the ground to confine it. You may also take it up and play with it. Even if you place it around your head and neck it will not dare bite you. As an automatically unremovable charm, blow upon the snake with your exhalations, and it will never again leave the prison you made.

When others have been bitten by a snake, take three mouthfuls of breath from the left and blow upon the wound; it will immediately get better and cause no more pain. If you and the patient are separated by a dozen or so miles, you may do the breath procedure from a distance and shout the name of the patient; for a male the prayer is to be made over your left hand, and for a female, over the right, and that patient will get better.

Master Chieh's Method. Before going to the mountains to stay, create imaginatively one snake in each of the five colors. Holding your breath, twist and stab them with slats of green bamboo and young trees. Use Yü's Pace as you make a turn about them to the left. Imagine that there are several thousand scolopendrids (see below) to clothe the persons of your party; then you may leave for the mountains. You will never meet a snake.

Some people carry dried ginger and aconite at their elbows; some smoke their persons in burned buffalo's, ram's, or deer's horn. Others carry at their belts Wang Yüan's *8b* realgar pills; still others place boar's cerumen and musk pills under their toenails. All of these things are effective. Since musk deer and wild boars both eat snakes, they may be used to keep them in check.

Secretary birds and *ying* tortoises also eat snakes; therefore people from the south all take *ying* tortoise tails and secretary-bird beaks with them when they go into the forests, in order to put snakes to flight. If anyone is bitten, they scrape these two things as a salve for the wound, and the patient gets better immediately. When such people go into the mountains, they all take a tube of bamboo filled with live scolopendrids, for these spiders sense where the snakes are and will immediately become active in the tube. Then you can look carefully in the grass and be sure to find a snake. If it is more than ten feet long and comes out of the complete encirclement you made about it, the scolopendrids will see it and be able to charm it with their breaths, and the snake will immediately die. When a snake on the bank of a stream or on a cliff espies scolopendrids, even if large, it will flee to the very depths of the stream or valley. Nobody can see the scolopendrids merely floating on the water, for they are perfectly blue in color and no larger than the quadrangular plaque atop a ceremonial hat. They then go straight into the water where the snake is, and shortly later the snake will float on the surface, dead. People from the south there- *9a* fore make a powder of scolopendrids to treat snake bite; this is immediately effective.

To avoid the many poisonous and bad things in the valleys south of the Yangtze. On the high plateaus of our central provinces the climate is pure and moderate, but the famous mountains in southern China (*shang kuo*) are quite different. Today the fields of Wu and Ch'u are hot, damp, odorous, and humid, so that even the standard revered mountains

Heng (N) and Huo (S) abound in poisons. There you will
find the *tuan-hu* (also called *yü*, *she-kung*, or *she-ying*), which
is in fact a water insect. It resembles the cicada and is the size
of a three-gill cup. It has wings and can fly; no eyes, but
sharp hearing. In its mouth there is something horizontal,
like a horn or a crossbow. If it hears a human voice, it makes
an arrow of its breath by means of this object in its mouth
and shoots at the person through the water. An injury is
produced wherever it hits a person. A hurt results even
though only the person's shadow was hit, but this does not
produce a sore spot. This injury will kill you, however,
unless you know how to treat it, for it causes an illness
resembling a mortal fever and will produce death in less than
ten days.

You will also find chiggers in these regions, both in the
water and on the land. After showers and before dawn or
after sunset they are sure to attack you while going through
grass or across streams. It is only in bright sunlight or in
burning grass that they are somewhat less abundant. They
9b   are the size of the tip of a hair. When they first attack a man,
they promptly enter his skin, leaving a mark like the prick
of a barb, small but very painful. They can be removed with
a needle and will prove to be bright red as cinnabar, and
when you place one on your finger nail it will move. If you
fail to remove them, they will bore their way to the bone
and travel throughout the body. Like the *she-kung* (9a5),
they can kill you. On returning from a trip through places
where the chigger abounds, one should go over the whole
body with a flame to make the chiggers drop to the ground.
Chiggers and *tuan-hu* can be kept away by carrying on the
person the pellets known as "Eight-things musk," *tu-shih*,
"life-preserver," "jade-pot," rhinoceros horn, "Big-bear
constellation," and Adenophora. If you are utterly unable
to procure all these medicaments, and can carry only
"Fond-of-life musk," it would be adequate, and it would
also be good to carry a pellet, the size of a chicken's egg,

made of realgar and shallot pestled either separately or together. If you have already been bitten, you can bring improvement by smearing the wound with these medicines. It is also beneficial to drink or apply juice pressed from Amaranthus. The three items *wu-ch'ieh* root, Rubus, and vetch may be used separately, or they may be ground together and one or two quarts of the juice taken as a remedy against these bites. Further, the *she-kung* hibernates in the valleys, and if you search for it during Big Snows (December), the snow will not accumulate high where it is and its breath will be rising like steam. You can dig it out, not going more than one foot into the ground to get it. If you will dry it in the shade, pulverize it, and carry it with you, it will keep *she-kung* away from you in the summer. If a processor knows the recipe for Unity charm, as well as the hundred *Tung* charms and *Ch'ang-ts'un* charm, and constantly maintains Truth-Unity (18.2*b*3, 10), none of the poisons will dare approach him. He will have no need for the various medicines.

10a

A processor living in the mountains in a hut or cave perched high on a cliff must have no fondness for cushions and ornament, but he must know how to protect himself against winds and dampness. If certain medicines are taken for no more than fifty days and then stopped, it may still be possible to go for ten years without any fear of winds and dampness. These medicines are *chin-ping* powder, *san-yang* exudate, *ch'ang-hsin* pills, extract of shallot and Trachelospermum, Amelanchier paste, Skimmia and *hsüan-hua* powders, and *ch'iu-ti-huang-hsüeh* pills. If you take the great medicines gold or cinnabar, your body will not suffer from illness, even though you may have not yet risen into space or practiced levitation. You cannot be harmed even though you are exposed to winds or lie in damp places. Those taking these seven medicines are known merely as neophytes in the study of the divine process. Master Yao took only *san-yang* exudate and was immediately able to lie bare on ice without

10b shivering. These are all secret methods tried by Chieh Hsiang and Liang Yu-tao and found effective for lying on rocks and facing wind and cold during fall and winter.

To rout snakes and dragons while crossing rivers and seas. Processors finding themselves obliged to travel on or across large rivers against their own better judgment should break one egg and mix it in a water-drawing vessel with a certain amount of rice powder and assorted perfume powders and wash themselves with it before venturing upon the stream. Then they will know no fear of winds, waves, crocodiles, or dragons. They will also wear from their belts the Eastern-ocean-small-boy amulet, Command-water amulet, and a P'eng-lai plaque, all of which will dispel anything that is harmful in waters. There are also the *Liu-chia-san-chih* amulet and the five-tree charms.

Another method is to start by shouting this prayer over the stream:

> *Bong! Bong! May River Count lead the way*
> > *and banish crocodiles and dragons!*
> *May all disasters melt away,*
> > *and heaven be pure and bright.*

Chin chien chi reads; "At noon on the *ping-wu* day of a fifth moon pestle the Five Minerals to a mixture. (The Five Minerals are realgar, cinnabar, orpiment, alum, and laminar malachite [cf. 4.9*b*9].) When they have all been reduced to a powder, wash it in 'Gold Flower' solvent and place in a Six-One divine crucible, heat over cinnamon wood using a bellows. When this mixture has been completed, refine it with hardwood charcoal, having young girls and boys approach the fire. With a male mixture (see below), make a *11a* male dagger; with a female one, make a female dagger, each of them 5.5 inches long. (Earth's number, 5, is used in order to suppress the stream's powers.) Wear these daggers when traveling on water, and no crocodiles, dragons, large fish, or water gods will dare approach you."

In order to determine whether a mixture is male or

female, have boys and girls sprinkle it with water at a time when it is on the fire and turning red. The mixture will then automatically divide into two parts. The part that rises and protrudes is the male mixture; the part that forms a hole and sinks is the female mixture. Carve the correct designations of the daggers directly on them, and when you wish to enter water, wear the male on your left side and the female on your right. However, when you board a boat and do not personally ford the stream, wear the male dagger on a yang day, and the female one on a yin day. If you write the words "Emperor of the North" in large heaven characters on a piece of silk and wear it, it too will protect you against all ill winds, waves, crocodiles, dragons, and water insects.

To rout the various ghosts haunting the shrines in the mountains and at rivers. If the processors will always wear from their belts *t'ien-shui* amulets, *shang-huang-chu-shih* amulets, Lao Tan contracts, and at the same time preserve Truth-Unity (10a3) and reflect upon the *san-pu* generals, ghosts will not dare approach them. In addition, let them study the lists of ghosts to learn their names, and also the *Pai-tse-t'u* and the *Chiu-ting-chi*, then the whole mass of ghosts will depart of themselves. Then let them take quail-egg-hematite pills, malachite-torch powders, onion-seed-crow-eye pills, and swallow some white-quartz-praying-mother powders, all of which will enable a man to see the ghosts, so that they will straightway stand in awe of him.

There are forty-nine true and secret Lao-chün, Huang-t'ing, and Chung-t'ai (fetus) amulets. When you are going to the mountains and forests, choose a *chia-yin* day on which to write them in red on plain silk, place them at night on a table, and as you face the Northern Dipper offer them sacrifices of wine and salted meat. To each of them introduce yourself briefly by name, bow twice, and then place them in the neck of your garment. This will drive from you the many ghosts and powers, the tigers, wolves, insects, and poisons of the mountains and rivers. These requirements do

11b

not apply solely to processors. Any persons entering mountains and forests to avoid a time of turmoil may also

12a–14b   properly know these methods.

[*On the five preceding pages of the Chinese text five enter-mountain amulets are illustrated. They have been so distorted by repeated copying over the centuries that there is no point in reproducing them here.*] These five are Lao-chün enter-mountain amulets. They are to be written in large, red letters on peach-wood plaques in such a way that they fill the whole plaque. Then they are placed above the door, at the four sides of the house, at the four corners, and at strategic points at the side of the paths leading to your house, about fifty paces from your dwelling; this will keep away the mountain powers, ghosts, and demons. They may also be placed on all the beams and pillars within the house. They are to be used by all in the mountains and forests or on the point of entering them, so that no creatures will dare harm

15a–16a   them. Three amulets may be written in series on one plaque.

[*This is followed by 2 more pages illustrating amulets.*] Here are two more Lao-chün enter-mountain amulets. These may be distributed over the beams and pillars within the house. They are to be used by all who are in the mountains and

16b–17b   forests or on the point of entering them.

[*Two more illustrations here.*] The two preceding amulets for putting tigers and wolves to flight when one is in the mountains were taught by the genie Ch'en An-shih. They are to be written on silk with red ink and kept separate. Wear them constantly, place four of each in your dwelling, and take them with you wherever you move about. They are secrets furnished by important gods. Mountain-opening amulets are to be made of *Vitis flexuosa*, but those for use on the famous mountains are particularly precious, being written in old-style writing on gold or jade; and they must be kept secret.

18b   [*One illustration here.*] This amulet is the seal carried by Lao Tan against ghosts, snakes, tigers, wolves, and gods. It is to be carved on a plaque two inches square, made from the pith of the jujube. Bow twice and then wear it. It will prove very effective. It was also the amulet of the genie Ch'en An-shih.

Amulets to be worn from the belt during entrance into the mountains. [*Three illustrations.*] These three amulets are to be placed jointly to the left, right, front, and back of the buffalo and horse stables and above the pigsty to drive away tigers and wolves. *19a–20b*

Method to be pursued in order to walk on water or stay long under water. Three times daily for three years, take seven pills the size of a Cola nut, made of onion juice mixed with cinnamon, and you will be able to walk on water.

My teacher, Cheng Yin, said that by merely practicing to hold one's breath for a thousand respirations, one would ultimately be able to stay under water for one whole day or more. If you get a three-inch piece of genuine T'ung-t'ien rhinoceros horn, carve a fish on it and carry it in your teeth, any stream will open up for you three feet square as you enter it, and you will be able to breathe under water.

If a T'ung-t'ien rhinoceros horn with a red streak in it like a thread running from base to tip is filled with rice and placed in the midst of a flock of chickens, the chickens will wish to pick at it, but before they get within a few inches of it they will become frightened and run away. People from the south, therefore, sometimes call this horn a chicken-frightening rhinoceros horn. If it is placed on a pile of grain no birds will dare gather there. If it is placed in a courtyard on a very foggy or dewy night the place will not become soaked. This is due to the fact that when the rhinoceros is deep in the mountains the horn shines brightly like a torch at night. *21a*

A potion of poison stirred with this horn will always produce a white froth and completely lose its efficacy. This also serves as a sign, because when a nonpoisonous substance is stirred with it there is no foam. When traveling in foreign countries, in districts where there are poisons, always first stir with this horn anything offered to you by others as food and drink. Whenever anyone is about to die from being hit with a poison arrow, open the wound with this horn. Froth will rise from it and it will heal.

T'ung-t'ien rhinoceros is an antiseptic because this animal is especially given to the eating of all the poisonous herbs and bushes which are prickly, but it does not carelessly eat plants and bushes that are soft and unctuous. Once a year it sheds its horn among rocks in the mountains. Whoever finds it must carve a wooden one of the same color, striation, and shape to replace it, so that the rhinoceros does not notice the disappearance. Then the following year it will again drop its horn in the same place. Other rhinoceroses also rout evils and dissipate poisons, but not as marvelously as the T'ung-t'ien.

21b Some people eat *liu-wu-fu* for one thousand days. Others combine red-spotted spiders, primula, and water starworts into Feng-I-water-genie pills and take them in order to be able to stay under water. By merely smearing the soles of the feet with this mixture it becomes possible to walk on water. Still more marvelous than this, however, is the fact that dandruff can make gold and iron float on water.

The divine process is normally carried out in mountains and forests which tend to abound in harmful tigers and wolves that one must know how to scatter. For this purpose the Ancients all wore from their belts *Huang-shen* and *Yüeh-chang* seals consisting of 120 characters on a four-inch-square plaque, of which impressions were made in soft substances and placed at a distance of one hundred paces in each of the four directions from their abode, so that the tigers and wolves dared not approach within these confines.

When fresh footprints of a tiger are seen in your travels, the tiger will leave immediately if you apply this seal to them and its impression faces in the direction the animal is traveling; however, it will return immediately if you stamp them in the wrong direction. If you wear these seals when traveling in the mountains and forests, you will have nothing to fear from tigers and wolves. But they will do more than merely put tigers and wolves to flight; when there is a vampire in any of the mountain or river shrines capable of causing either good fortune or bad, you can cut its route with impressions of this seal and it will lose its powers.

Long ago, there was a large tortoise inhabiting a deep pool in Stony River, so that the pool was known as Tortoise Pool. This creature could produce ghosts and demons that caused illness among the people. A Wu processor named Tai Ping, happening to notice this, made several hundred impressions of the *Yüeh-chang* seal and threw them throughout the pool from a boat. After quite some time a tortoise more than ten feet in diameter floated to the surface and dared not move. Then Tai Ping killed it with a pole, and immediately all the sick people got well. Further, a large number of small tortoises came out of the pool in series and died on the sand banks.

22a

If you suddenly encounter a tiger in the mountains, perform the *san-wu* charm and it will leave immediately. The method for performing this charm must be given orally, for it would be impossible to go into all its details in writing. Another method is simply to imagine that your own person is a vermilion bird thirty feet tall standing on the head of the approaching tiger and then to hold your breath; the tiger will then leave immediately. During the night in the mountains, secretly take the hairpin from your head, hold your breath, and stab toward the west. In this way you will have nothing to fear.

Another method is to seize a knife with your left hand, hold your breath, and draw a square on the ground, as you say this prayer:

> *On Mount Heng's north,*
> *On Mount T'ai's south,*
> *No bandits move,*
> *No tigers or wolves about.*
> *If the ramparts are not tight,*
> *Closed let them be with metal bright.*

Then lay a knife horizontal for ten days to the west, and you will have nothing to fear.

Some people use a very potent charm. After swallowing 360 breaths, they shout angrily from left to right at the tigers, so that they do not dare appear. If you will use this method when entering the mountains, you will have nothing to fear from tigers. Others use the Seven-star-tiger pace along with Jade-god amulets, *pa-wei-wu-sheng* amulets, Li Tan's *t'ai-p'ing* amulets, *chung-huang* and *hua-kai* inscribed seals, sulphur powder, and burned buffalo or ram's horn, while still others institute Hsi-yüeh kung's amulet for charming mountains. All prove effective.

22b

23a–25b

[*At this point there are five more illustrations of amulets.*] Here are five more of Lao Tan's amulets for entering the mountains; the explanation for them can be found above. They may also be placed on the pillars and crossbeams in the house, and they are for the use of those already in the mountains and forests as well as for those about to enter.

18

Truth on Earth

I ONCE HEARD my teacher say,

*If men Unity [God] could know,
Then they'd know all here below.*

For there is nothing that such men would not know, but those ignorant of Unity can really know nothing.

God arises from Unity and is honored without peer. Everything dwelling in Unity thereby becomes the image of heaven, earth, and man; whence our expression "triune." Heaven gets its purity from Unity; earth, its tranquillity; man, his existence; and the gods, their powers. Metal sinks, feathers float, mountains loom, and the rivers flow: but our eyes cannot see, nor can our ears hear how this is. Yet these things remain so long as they preserve Unity; they perish when It is neglected. While facing It they know good fortune, but when they turn their backs, misfortune. While It is the fortress, there is long prosperity that knows no end. Let It be neglected, and life declines; breath is exhausted. Lao Tan (T 21) exclaimed with reference to Unity, "All disorder! All confusion! Yet within there are images. All confusion! All disorder! Yet within there is all creation."

Therefore we read in the Genii Classics,

Wish to enjoy Fullness of Life,
Preservation of Unity must be rife.
Reflect on Unity till famine,
Unity will provide to dine.
Reflect on Unity till drought,
Unity will provide the draught.

1b   Unity possesses names, uniforms, and colors. In the male It is 0.9 inch long; in the female, 0.6. Sometimes It is 2.4 inches below the navel: Lower Cinnabar Field; at other times, It is Golden Gate or Purple Palace below the heart: Central Cinnabar Field. Then again, It is one inch behind the space between man's eyebrows forming Hall of Enlightenment; two inches in It constitutes Innermost Chamber; three inches in It forms Upper Cinnabar Field. Such are things stressed by Taoists, who for generations have merely been smearing their lips with blood as a seal of secrecy as they transmitted Its names orally.

Unity can form yin and beget yang; bring on the cold and the heat. Through Unity there is sprouting in spring, growing in summer, harvesting in autumn, and storing in winter. All space is no analogy for Its magnitude; nor is a hair or sprout an analogy for Its minuteness.

Of old, when passing Mount Feng on the road east to Mount Ch'ing, Yellow Emperor met the Master of Purple House and received from him *San huang nei wen*, which enabled him to control all divinities. On going south to Chien Tree on the northern slope of Yüan-lung, he surveyed the place mounted by the commanders, he gathered flowers from the trees Jo and Ch'ien, and he drank the waters of the Tan and the P'ei. In the west he met Chung-huang tzu and received from him the *Chiu-chia* prescription. When passing through Tung-t'ing he received *Tzu-ch'eng-chih-ching* (on self-perfection) from Kuang-ch'eng tzu. On the way north to Hung-t'i he mounted Chü-tz'u and met Ta-wei (13.3a5) and the youth Huang Kai, from whom he received draw-

ings of divine excrescences. While returning to his duties as
emperor, he obtained the *Shen tan chin chüeh chi*. 2a

On Mount O-mei he met T'ien-chen Huang-jen in the
Jade Chamber and inquired of him concerning the process
for retaining Truth-Unity. The reply came, "Since you are
already sovereign over the whole world, isn't it avarice on
your part to seek for Fullness of Life?" Since it is impossible
to give their conversation in full, I will provide one aspect
of it only: As prescriptions leading to Fullness of Life and to
geniehood there are only gold and cinnabar; for the preservation of physical form and driving evils afar there is only
Truth-Unity. For this reason the Ancients valued these
things highly.

The Genii Classics say that the *Chiu chuan tan*, the *Chin i
ching*, and the oral directions for preserving Unity were
stored in a jade envelope on Mount K'un-lun (the head), at
Wu-ch'eng (the five vital organs); that they were engraved
on gold plaques sealed with purple, and that they bear the
imprint of the seal of state. I learned the directions from my
teacher Cheng Yin in this form:

Unity's at Extreme North, in the Grand Abyss.
Up front, in Chamber of Enlightenment [in head]; to rear, in Purple
  Palace [heart].
Imposing, Its Flowered Canopy [heart region]; Its Gold Pavilion [flesh]
  all loftiness.
To left and right in the four stars of the Great Dipper; It is like a
  dashing wave in the void.
It is the dark excrescence on steep ledges, the vermilion grass in the
  thickets;
The white jade high in the mountains, sun and moon shedding their light.
Unity passes through fire and water; traverses heaven and fords earth.
Its walls and gateways intertwine; Its canopies and hangings, studded
  with gems.
Lines of dragons and tigers guard Unity; gods stand at Its side.
No dispensing and no giving, Unity is secure anywhere.
Not dilatory, not rushing, Unity is secure in Its abode.
Able to take ease and precautions, Unity never quits.
Preserve Unity and guard Truth, and you can communicate with the gods. 2b

Lessen desire, restrain eating, and Unity will abide quietly.
Bare blade at the neck, and realize that through Unity we live.
Unity is not hard to know; persistence is the difficulty.
Guard It without loss, and you will never know exhaustion.
On land, It routs evil animals; on water, dispels crocodiles and dragons.
No fear of demons, nor of poisonous insects.
Ghosts will not dare approach, nor blades strike.

This is a rough outline of Truth-Unity.

I once heard my teacher, Cheng Yin, say that Taoist Classics evoked or recalled several thousand methods and procedures for dispelling evils and defending our persons. For example, there were methods without number for making shadow and body invisible; for suspending one's personal animation; for undergoing nine mutations, twelve transformations, and twenty-four births, etc.; for feeling that one is seeing the gods within the body, looking inward, and causing them to become visible. All of them were effective. Nevertheless, at times the thought of bringing into existence several thousand creatures to protect oneself could be so cumbersome that it confused the mind. He felt that if a single process for preserving Unity were known, all these other methods could be rejected. This is why he said (18.1*a*3),

> *Unity if can know, know all below.*

There are clear outward requisites for receiving the secret oral directions concerning Truth-Unity. The lips are smeared with the blood of a white victim. The directions are received on a propitious, lucky day. An agreement is entered into by means of white gauze and white silver. A tally of gold is notched and split. If one expounds these oral directions lightheartedly or transmits them heedlessly, their
3a gods will not operate.

If a man can preserve Unity, Unity will also preserve him. In this way the bare blade finds no place in his body to inserts its edge; harmful things find no place in him that will admit entrance to their evil. Therefore, in defeat it is possible to be victorious; in positions of peril, to feel only security. Whether in the shrine of a ghost, in the mountains or forests, in a place suffering the plague, within a tomb, in bush inhabited by tigers and wolves, or in the habitation of snakes, all evils will go far away as long as one remains diligent in the preservation of Unity.

If, on the other hand, you forget to preserve Unity for but a single moment, the ghosts will harm you. If you are lying down and having a nightmare, leave the room quickly, look at the star Fu (in the Great Dipper), devote yourself firmly to preserving Unity, and the evil ghosts will depart immediately. If the weather is rainy, remain in your room, face north, and merely imagine that you are seeing the star Fu. If you are surrounded by armed bandits and have no refuge, enter immediately into the shadow of the Six Chia gods, prostrate yourself and preserve your Unity, and no weapon will be able to harm you. Anyone who can preserve Unity will travel thousands of miles, enter among armed hosts, and ford large rivers without any need to divine the right day and hour. When beginning a task or moving to a new home, he will never again depend upon the geomancer's star calendar, nor will he need to observe the taboos of Jupiter, the moon, the General [a star], the cyclical number of the moon, and the gods of death. The life taboos will never again be considered fatal. This is an efficacious procedure that has been successively used by our competent predecessors.

The Mystery-Unity procedure is indeed an important method. Since there is nothing that it will not put to flight, it is as effective as the Truth-Unity method. This is the reason I called the first chapter of my book "God (Mystery) Defined." Preserving Mystery-Unity is much easier than preserving Truth-Unity. The latter has names, size, uniforms, and color. Mystery-Unity is seen only in the sun (?Manichaeism). The search for It begins in the sun, and is

3b

described as "knowing white and preserving black" or "unsuccessful in the desire for death."

To begin with, you must purify yourself and fast for a hundred days. Only then may you go to a teacher and seek It, but then It can be obtained in not more than three or four days; once you possess It you will never lose It provided you take steps to preserve It. The preservation of Mystery-Unity consists in imagining yourself as being divided into three persons. Once these three have become visible, you can continue to increase the number to several dozen, all like yourself, who may be concealed or revealed, and all of whom are automatically in possession of secret oral directions. This may be termed a process for multiplying the body.

Through this method Tso Tz'u, Chi Liao, and my uncle Ko Hsüan could be in several dozen places at one time. When guests were present they could be one host speaking with the guests in the house, another host greeting guests beside the stream, and still another host making casts with his fishing line, but the guests were unable to distinguish which was the true one. My teacher used to say that to preserve Unity was to practice jointly Bright Mirror, and that on becoming successful in the mirror procedure a man would be able to multiply his body to several dozen all with the same dress and facial expression.

4a

My teacher also used to say that you should take the great medicines diligently if you wished to enjoy Fullness of Life, and that you should use metal solutions and a multiplication of your person if you wished to communicate with the gods. By multiplying the body, the three *Hun* and the seven *Po* are automatically seen within the body, and in addition it becomes possible to meet and visit with the powers of heaven and the deities of earth and to have all the gods of the mountains and rivers in one's service.

One may regret being alive, and one may fear death, but the Fullness of Life, nurturing of existence, and the avoidance of death never fail to begin with diligence and end with everlasting vision. After the process has been completed, there remains practically nothing to do; before it is completed, all sorts of things need be done. All one's strength goes into the gathering of herbal medicines, working in the mountains and swamps, extracting, nibbling, regulating, and producing. Mounting to dangerous heights and crossing precipitous ledges, there is no relaxation either day or night, and unless one is very strong-willed it is impossible to persist.

You may wish to mount to heaven by preparing gold or elixir, but you discover that the important ingredients all require so much money that you cannot afford them all. It is necessary to go back and seek resources through farming, herding, business, and trading for years, and years, expending much effort. Only after that can the concocting be undertaken. Then, on the day the process begins it becomes necessary to fast again and to purify oneself, foregoing all normal human activities. To all these things, which are not easy, must be added concentrated thought of the gods, preservation of Unity, dispelling of evils, and protecting one's own person. By constantly acting like a sovereign ruling a state or a commander awaiting the enemy, it becomes possible to do the work that will achieve Fullness of Life. Only through intelligence and great wisdom and through the use of world-regulating and people-saving capacity can one be sure of success when working at this matter. Even with the best will and love, ordinary people of shallow experience cannot carry it through to the end.

The body of an individual can be pictured as a state. The diaphragm may be compared with the palace, the arms and legs, with the suburbs and frontiers. The bones and joints are like the officials; the inner gods like the sovereign; the blood like the ministers of state; the breath like the population. Therefore, anyone able to regulate his own body can regulate a state. To take good care of the population is the best way to make your state secure; by the same token, to

4b

nurture the breaths is the way to keep the body whole, for
when the population scatters, a state goes to ruin; when the
breaths are exhausted, the body dies. Anything that is dying
cannot be living, and anything that is perishing cannot be in
a state of preservation. Therefore, man in his highest form
dissipates fears before they arise; he controls illness before it
occurs. He does his doctoring before anything happens; he
does not pursue what has already gone. Just as a population
is hard to nurture but easy to endanger, so is it difficult to
purify the breaths, but easy to soil them. Therefore, as a
5a careful control of power is the way to protect a state, the
way to strengthen the blood and breaths is to whittle down
covetousness. After that, Truth-Unity survives, the three
Hun and seven *Po* are preserved, all harm is dispelled, and
life is extended.

Another frequent statement by my teacher was that by
taking the great medicines, gold or cinnabar, all evils would
be kept at bay even before one had quit this world. On the
other hand, if only herbal medicines were taken and bits of
the Eight Minerals, only illness might be dispelled and one's
longevity increased, but they would not be sufficient to avert
disasters arising from outside the body. At times one might
still be harmed by ghosts, and at other times disdained by the
gods of the great mountains or plundered by evil powers and
demons. Only by preserving Truth-Unity can one be completely without fear of this type of thing. Secondary to this
was the wearing of divine amulets. If one was completely
ignorant of these two things while seeking full enjoyment of
life, it could be very dangerous. When only three of four
gates have been closed, the robbers can still gain entrance.
But suppose all of them are left wide open!

19

Looking Farther Afield

Interlocutor: Face to a wall and bound to Confucianism, I have hitherto recognized only the existence of the Five Classics, the Three Histories, and the philosophers of antiquity, plus, of course, light, flowery poetry and short, profitless compositions. For years now I have thought only of preserving such things as these. From birth, however, I have been involved in the political troubles of our times; these disorders are still unresolved. For the use of shields, spears, and axes, literary pursuits have no value; they only waste time. No emolument whatever can be drawn from painful concepts, exhausting thought, studies of subtleties, and the search for hidden meanings. Further, my removal from these endeavors has been inimical to undistracted thought and of no benefit to my continued existence. Two gray hairs of my beard announce the arrival of my twilight; normal willpower is declining. My only desire now is to resolve the present confusion and seek the road to life.

I am completely in a whirl and have nowhere to turn. There is a big river to cross but I cannot recognize the ford. You, however, have exhaustively studied the writings of the

Augusti and the Emperors. To these studies you have also added the miraculous and the hermetic. Personally, I do not know how many volumes of Taoist writings there are. I wish you would give me their list.

Ko: I have at first shared the same urgency as yourself. Later, however, I was fortunate enough to meet with my intelligent teacher, Cheng Yin, whose only regret was that he had no pupils bright enough to penetrate the most difficult and the loftiest portion of his teaching. Although I was then an aspirant doing the sprinkling and sweeping about his place, I deplore deeply that my talents and knowledge were small; that I was still young and my thought unconcentrated; and that I was still a child of the world and unable to grasp much of what was being taught.

At that time Cheng Yin was leaving his eighties, but his hair remained black for several years longer before becoming streaked with white. He had a full and cheerful face, and could draw a sturdy crossbow and shoot for a hundred paces. He walked several hundred miles daily, and could drink two demijohns of wine without becoming drunk. Whenever he climbed the mountains he showed himself to be strong and agile. He mounted to dangerous heights and crossed at precipitous drops where many younger men shrank back. He ate and drank the same things as everyone else; I never noticed that he did not take starches.

In answer to my questions, an older student by the name of Huang Chang told me that once, when Cheng Yin was returning from Yü-chang where a canal had been dug, strong winds were constantly being encountered. It was also rumored that there was trouble with many bandits along the road ahead. Cheng Yin's companions made him halt and join a later group of travelers. Since everyone thought there was too little food, Cheng Yin yielded his ration, out of compassion for the others, and personally did no more eating for fifty days without suffering from hunger.

Unless you have seen him in action, you cannot under-

stand why I studied under him. He could write a finer hand
by firelight than many a younger man. He had a natural ear
for music and could play the lute. While many experts and
attendants were present, he would reply to their questions
without interrupting the tune, and at the same time his ear
heard with discrimination the other players about him,
pointing out their good and bad points with undeviating
precision. I was late in becoming one of his aspirants, and
when I asked for prescriptions he told me there was no need
for a large number of them; that a foot of silk could hold
the essential divine process, the best could make me a genie,
yet a wide experience with prescriptions would be far better
than being ignorant of them. Once a man's mind had been
enlightened, it would be appropriate to start with some less
profound arts in order to block the fears of beginners before
they are well formed. Then he began to instruct me little by
little about some less significant Taoist teachings and com-
mandments, almost a hundred scrolls of them, most of
which I had previously met. When I asked him about some
doubts they had raised in my mind, his reply was that I was
teachable, had a talent for clear thinking, and knew much
but had not yet gotten to the core of matters; that my
thoughts were on externals, so that I could not yet concentrate upon Unity. He continued that it was merely that
I had not yet reached the point of dealing with the subtleties
and the abstruse, so it was now fitting that we enlighten one
another from some better writings. He also allowed me
gradually to accumulate some short writings on silk. Over
the years I collected whatever I saw; they must amount to
something over two hundred scrolls, but I could not possibly
acquire everything. The other pupils assumed the labor of
gathering firewood and tilling the fields, but I, being thin
and weak, could not stand these labors. Being unfit for hard
work, I always did the sweeping, dusted the beds and tables,
ground the ink, and cared for the lamps.

After giving him some copies of old books I had made, I

2a

2b

noticed that Cheng Yin treated me like one of the older
students. He said to me, "A large number of volumes of the
various Taoist writings are bound to contain something
valuable, but you must compare the varying quality of the
contents and select what is practical. Don't just waste your
time and overwork your mind by learning all of them completely. Once the gold or elixir has been achieved, all these
other writings will become useless. At the same time, I
suppose we must have something to teach, and it is fitting
and proper to cover the whole subject by beginning with
the elementary in order to encourage neophytes, but this
procedure does not meet with my full approval.

Cheng Yin was unwilling to have his students begin by
copying his own writings. Everybody was obliged to reconcile himself to that. The students might spend a long time
disliking this approach, but none dared copy a single word
on the sly. Fundamentally, Cheng Yin was a great Confucian who turned to Taoism late. Since he continued to
teach *The Rites* and *The Writings of Old*, his presence was
imposing and his behavior correct. All who met him were
impressed. If you had a question to put to him, you waited
until he looked affable; you did not dare act precipitately.

I kept under cover the books that were with me and most
of which I could have copied in one month. If I did not dare
do it on my own initiative, it is because Cheng Yin was
keen; if he had learned of it, I should have fallen from his
good graces and lost something great in exchange for something paltry. This was a risk I dared not incur when I was
first seeking his instruction. It was only by carefully weigh-
ing the right moment that I made my requests. The result
is that I only learned to taste of the river, but I never
succeeded in drinking to utter satiation. Nevertheless, of his
more than fifty pupils I was the only one to receive the
classics concerning gold and cinnabar as well as *San huang
nei wen* and *Chen chung wu hsing chi*. Some of the others
never even saw the titles of these books. Although I did not

3a

get all his others, I did acquire their titles, and I am now going to list them for you in the hope that future book-lovers will search widely for them: [*The list which follows in the text has been given an alphabetical arrangement and is here printed on page 379 under the heading "A Taoist Library." The list of amulets from 5a10–5b10 is given on page 384.*] This is merely a catalog of the more important amulets. Others are of too little importance for me to list them.

3a–5b

Cheng Yin used to say that the amulets stemming from Lao Tan were all in heaven writing because he could com-municate with the gods and it was from them that he got them. If present-day people find them little efficacious, it is because their transmission goes so far back that many errors have crept into the later copies. Further, they work only for those who sincerely believe in them. In addition, they are like all other writing in that, as soon as there are errors in them, they are not only of no benefit but they will even be able to work harm. People may recognize ordinary writing, but they still make many errors in copying. That is why the following saying is applicable to them: "In the course of making three copies of a document, a *yü* [fish] becomes a *Lu*; a *hsü*, a *hu* [tiger]." The symbols for "seven" and "scholar" (No. 33) become changed by a mere difference in the curve or the length of a stroke. In the case of the amulets current today, however, we are unable to read them; therefore we cannot detect the errors. The result is that nobody knows when they are incorrect. There are some in our day endowed with the capacity for operating recipes and using amulets with unique success, just as some people be-come expert parfumeurs by handling musk. This is some-thing natural and not transmissible. Nevertheless, although we may obtain flawless amulets and use them sincerely, we can never enjoy the prompt efficacy of those truly endowed for such things; they have the benefit automatically.

6a

Let processors seeking Fullness of Life have their wills concentrated entirely to achieving the medicine. Amulets

6b and swords can merely dispel ghosts and drive away evils.
It is claimed by some that all the important amulets can be
used for achieving geniehood, but sole reliance is not to be
placed in them. In the time of the Wu dynasty [A.D. 222–280]
Chieh Hsiang could read what was written on the amulets
and know whether there were any errors or not. Someone
once tried removing the name tags from various amulets for
curing illnesses and exorcizing spirits and showing them to
Chieh Hsiang. The latter identified every last one of them
and corrected their errors. But since that time nobody has
been able to understand them.

Interlocutor: You have already told us that none of the
great genii medicines is superior to gold and cinnabar. But I
should like to inquire about the amulets and books, for it is
not clear to me which are the most potent.

Ko: I heard Cheng Yin say that no Taoist book surpasses
★San huang nei wen and *Wu yüeh chen hsing t'u* in importance. They were the honored secrets of the genii and superior
men of antiquity and could be taught only by those bearing
the title of genie. Those receiving them transmitted them
once after forty years, and in doing so oaths were taken by
smearing the lips with the blood of a victim, and agreements
were entered into by the giving of a present. Writings of
this type are to be found in all the famous mountains and
the five revered mountains, but they are stored in hidden
spots in caves. In response to those who have secured the
divine process and entered a mountain to give sincere
thought to it, the god of the mountain will automatically
open the mountain and let such persons see the texts, just as
Po Ho got his in a mountain, and immediately set up an
7a   altar, made a present of silk, drew one ordinary copy, and
then left with them. A purified place is always prepared for
such texts, and whenever anything is done about them one
must first announce it to them, as though one were serving
a sovereign or a father.

The classic itself states that if *★San huang nei wen* is in a household, it will banish evil and hateful ghosts, soften the effects of epidemics, block calamities, and rout misfortunes. If anyone is suffering from illness or on the point of death, let someone believing in the process with all his heart give this text to the patient to hold, and he will be sure not to die. If a wife is having trouble in childbirth to the point of possible death, let her hold this text, and her son will be born immediately. If processors wishing to seek Fullness of Life will hold this text when entering the mountains, it will rout tigers and wolves, and none of the mountain powers, poisons, or evils will dare approach. When crossing rivers and seas, the processors will be able to dispel crocodiles and dragons, and halt the wind and waves with this book.

With the method taught in this text it is possible to initiate undertakings positively or negatively without inquiring about the correct site or choosing the right day, and one's household will be free from calamities. If you wish to build a new house or tomb, write several dozen copies of the Earth Augustus text and spread them on the site. Look at them on the following day, and if a yellow color is seen adhering to them, one may begin the work there and the household will be sure to become rich and prosperous. When others are being interred, copy the Man Augustus text and include your own full name written on a folded sheet of paper. Insert this in that person's grave without letting others know what you are doing, and you will be free from sudden misfortune and robbers. Anyone plotting against *7b* you will be sure to have his harm turned against himself.

According to this text, after a period of purification and fast lasting a hundred days one may command the gods of heaven and the Director of Fates. When you wander on any of the five revered mountains or four big streams on a Jupiter day (Thursday), the gods of the local altars and shrines will all reveal themselves in human form, and you will be able to ask them about good and bad fortune, about the things that are safe or dangerous, and about what is bad or good for the sick. There are also eighteen characters to be placed within your clothing, which will enable you to travel far over rivers and seas completely free from all concern for winds and waves.

If a household has a copy of *Wu yüeh chen hsing t'u* it will be able to dispel harm from the soldiery. All wishing to harm its members will have their harm turned against themselves. Processors may possess this text wherever they go, but if they cannot practice the human ideal, propriety, and compassion, or if they are not wholehearted and orthodox in their pursuit of the divine process, they must not treat lightly the possibility of incurring disaster or the destruction of their homes.

For the art of metamorphosis the only work of significance is ★*Mo tzu wu hsing chi*, which was originally in five scrolls. Long ago, however, before becoming a genie, Liu An reduced its essence to one scroll. Its methods use medicines and amulets to make people fly up and down or conceal themselves anywhere. By a mere smile, a man knowing this art can become a woman. By distorting his face, he can become an old man. On kneeling upon the ground he becomes a little boy. By grasping a pole he becomes a tree. He plants something, and it immediately produces edible melons or fruit. He draws a line on the ground, and it becomes a river; *8a* he piles up dirt and it becomes a hill. He sits down and causes the Traveling Canteen to arrive. He produces clouds and fire. There is nothing that such a person cannot produce.

Next in importance is *Yü nü yin wei*, in one scroll. By its methods people can change into flying birds or stalking animals. Clouds are raised and rain brought for an area a hundred miles square by means of metal, wood, jade, or rock. Snow can be produced in the same fashion. By its method people cross large streams without a boat or weir. They split themselves into thousands of persons. They fly high on the winds; pass in and out of barriers; exhale breath of seven colors. While sitting still, they can see into all eight points of the compass and even to things under ground. They emit light shining for thousands of feet; in a dark room, they are their own light. The book does indeed teach a great art. I can hardly list, however, the several dozen sections on horoscopes, which are hard to understand with all their variations. Even *Huai-nan tzu*, *Hung lieh*, and *Wan pi shu* are not to be compared with *Yü nü yin wei*.

There is also the method taught by *★Pai hu ch'i pien ching*. Take the head and skin of a white tiger killed on the third day of the third moon, blood from a live camel, tiger's blood, some floating algae known as Scarlet Ribbon and Shoe Thong, and plant them together on the third day of the third moon. Take the seeds from the first herbs to spring up at this spot resembling sesame, and plant them. Whatever comes up will be able to work wonders. Plant seven of these and use the resulting seeds in a mixture, and you will be able to change your shape, alter your appearance, fly in the air, or go down into streams at will, just about the same as with the methods taught by *★Mo tzu chen chung wu hsing chi* and *Yü nü yin wei*.

Let me say nothing further. You who are looking farther afield wished to learn the titles of writings dealing with marvels from a man conversant with the divine process. Cheng Yin not only knew the Five Classics and understood the divine process leading to geniehood; in addition he also embraced a thorough knowledge of the Nine Palaces [astrological divisions of the sky], the Three Marvels [sperm, breath, and gods], astrological calculation, and divination by *Ho t'u* and *Lo shu*. In January of A.D. 303, aware of the political disorders characteristic of an age of perdition and of the troubles lying ahead for China south of the Yangtze — his postulants carrying the ingredients for making geniehood medicines — he led the pupils who had been admitted to the presence east and took asylum in Mount Huo; nobody knows where.

8b

20

Allay Your Doubts

NOBODY WILL GET a pearl like *li-lung*, which shone in the dark, unless he searches in the depths at Ho-p'u. Nobody will get a circular jade a foot in diameter and worth a string of cities unless he does his collecting in the Ching mountain caves. Similarly, when you inquire of a teacher about the divine process and fail to find the right man — if you quit him, you may entertain from time to time the hope of finding the right teacher. If you stay, however, you will finally accomplish nothing; you will waste your substance fruitlessly, and bring all your efforts to naught. You may later have regrets, but you will never attain the goal sought.

None of the ordinary, everyday affairs of the world can be learned sitting down; so, how much the more does this apply to learning about the gods and the genii! Even the sages and the enlightened would not have succeeded by a long train of thought, nor by their five senses, if they had not had the wellspring of self-enlightenment. It is truly necessary that your teacher be so deeply and broadly learned that you will seem to be drawing water while crossing the great ocean or going to a mighty forest to cut trees. The only uncertainty should be that your own strength might fail; there should be no concern about a lack of water or wood. Foxes and rats fight for what tigers and leopards leave behind. The millionaire Fan Li threw away things which Yüan Hsien and Yen Hui — those Confucian paragons — never had.

If the man under whom you study is not a teacher of   *1b*
broad and profound understanding, but a man of low and paltry learning, his knowledge will be restricted and his resources short and of brief duration. When emptying his bag for others, he will niggardly let nothing go. As he transmits fragments, his teaching will be superficial and thin, provoking no wonder. The next morning, what he has stressed will be no longer important. If you undertake in turn to teach his poor material, how will you accomplish anything? It is like borrowing grain from those poor fellows Po-i and Shu-ch'i, or complaining of the cold to a Ch'ien Lou (who did not have enough to cover himself). In such places you would get only acorns and horse chestnuts along with hemp clothing; there would certainly be no pork, mutton, beef, silks, or furs.

Some continue studying under a poor teacher without realizing it. Others are fortunate enough to have a learned one but are unable to pursue their studies diligently. Loss due to unawareness is not recoverable. It is indeed never easy to determine whether a teacher is shallow or profound, and it is certainly with reason that the Ancients complained on this score. Any white stone may resemble jade, and a pernicious flatterer can resemble a man of the highest caliber. The true man of high caliber, however, will continue trying to conceal himself; his possession will resemble lack. The flatterer will huckster himself more and more; his void will resemble plenitude. Only the keenest insight can distinguish between them. Those continuing to work with a poor teacher are not acting deliberately in full consciousness of his ignorance; they sincerely believe that it is possible to study under him. Those meeting a wise teacher but finding it impossible to study under him are not acting deliberately in   *2a* full knowledge of his genuine profundity, but because they sincerely think him no different from others.

Those competent to understand the essentials of the divine process desire nothing of anything in creation; they are not looking for praise from their generation. Why should they, indeed, flaunt themselves before the crowd? On the other hand, the shallow and superficial are all given to boasting and self-praise. They adorn their empty claims with bright colors and rare sounds to dazzle those who become students late in life, and they dare make great claims for themselves. They pretend that they have been to famous mountains to visit with genii. Those rushing to listen to them but unable to make clear comparisons seldom realize their deceit. In my time I have frequently seen such a group of miscellaneous processors wending its way to the homes of honored citizens only so that their followers might make unfounded claims for them by saying, for example, that they were already four or five hundred years old. If, however, someone happened to ask their age specifically, they pretended not to hear. Or, smiling and bowing, they replied, eighty or ninety. Then suddenly they would claim to have gone without starches on the northern slope of Mount Hua for fifty years, and then again on the Shao-shih of Mount Sung for forty years, and again on Mount T'ai for sixty years. Or they further claim to have been associated with so-and-so for fifty years on Mount Chi. If they gave this detailed account of the places where they had been, it was to get their followers to reckon them up as being several centuries old. Then people who fall for this sort of thing never fail to park their vehicles at their schools in great masses of cloud or mist, as it were.

Tricksters sometimes happen to be naturally endowed with the ability to see ghosts and gods, and are able to divine from within themselves about the future or past affairs of others, but it is really impossible to influence the good or bad fortune which they foresee. They are merely like old tortoises. On observing some slight evidence of this ability,

2b

the crowd straightway calls them gods and claims that there
is certainly nothing they do not know or do not treat
familiarly. Sometimes their forte is the preparation of holy
water and the casting of spells that are effective against evils,
but it is not certain that they know the divine process leading
to immortality. Others are adept in various arts and can
reveal ghosts and miracles, but these are of no benefit to our
longevity. When asked about the gold or cinnabar process,
they prove totally ignorant. This is the reason they show
slight evidence of truth. They practice many deceptions to
beguile the people of their day and amass wealth; they will
do anything. Such people as these may follow a path different from that of the thieves who burrow through our walls
(Ana. 17.10), but in the end they are identical. Rather than
trust them for their empty claims, it would be better to
bring their deeds into the open or compare them with others
for the benefit of late-starters. This would then prove them
frauds.

Formerly a certain Ku Ch'iang followed recipes of herbal
medicines and was much given to the sexual procedures of
Jung-ch'eng. At the age of more than eighty he was still
mentally active and showed none of the ravages of old age. *3a*
Consequently, his contemporaries called him either Genie or
the Millenary. The Imperial Commissioner of Kuang-chou,
Chi Han, heard about him and tried to go and meet him at
I-tu. Upon his arrival, Ku Ch'iang's pronouncements were
terse and he assumed the air of one acquainted with truly
distant things about which he had not yet told all. Thereupon, the curious took up the cry of the hearsay which had
reached them. Like the shadow that always goes with an
object, people in droves vied with one another to chant his
praises. Presents of food came to him in profusion, and he
was never without money. The honors showered upon
Luan Ta and Li Shao-chün under the First Han were in no
way superior.

Since Ku Ch'iang constantly took asparagus, we know

that his body never contained the great medicines, gold or cinnabar. However, he had some acquaintance with books and a good knowledge of ancient history. He dared claim for himself four thousand years, and told fables without ever a blush: "I personally met Yao, Shun, Yü, and T'ang the Victorious." Then he went on to describe them in full detail:

The tradition that Yao's eyebrows were of eight different colors is wrong; the inner ends of the eyebrows merely stood very straight like the symbol for eight. Yao was a tall man with a fine moustache and sideburns. Since in one day he drank more than two kegs of wine, *3b* the people of his day called him Thousand-kegs, which of course was not really justified. I frequently saw him quite intoxicated. Though he was a sage, he was not as good a governor in his old age as he had been in his youth. After he had chased the Four Scoundrels and elevated the Eight Eminent Persons, he trusted everything to Shun, who was merely the motherless son of a humble family.

Shun had, however, extraordinary natural talent. He farmed in private and traversed mountains. He fished in Thunder Pool, and made pottery on the seacoast. Before any of his contemporaries could appreciate his unusual gifts, I noticed that wherever he was his excellence affected the people. He had two pupils in each eye, which I recognized as a sign of his great nobility. I constantly encouraged and comforted him: "Keep your mind on the higher things, and don't worry about your present lack of wealth and honors. The cyclical agent Fire has reached its term and the essence of Yellow is about to rise. Since you were born under a good star, no one can be meant for higher things than yourself!"

His father, however, out of utter stupidity, and his younger brother, out of extreme hate, were ever plotting to murder him. I constantly admonished them, "This boy is fated to bring prosperity to your clan, and the whole world is going to benefit from him. It is not just your own family that should not deprive him of this cosmic destiny." Then, suddenly, he received the succession from Yao, and I felt that my prediction had been justified.

When the mother of Confucius was but sixteen or seventeen, I predicted from her general appearance that she would have a son worthy to be honored, and after she had given birth to him he turned out to be a truly remarkable man. He was 9.6 feet tall. His forehead *4a* was like Yao's; his neck, like Kao-yao's, Shun's minister; his shoulders were like Kung-sun Ch'iao's. From the waist down he was

three inches shorter than Yü. Despite all these qualities, he was poor
and orphaned. Yet because as a boy he was fond of anything having
to do with sacrificial vessels, I knew that he would certainly amount
to something, and when he grew up his exalted conversation did
astonish people. They came from far and near to study under him,
several thousand, as the records show. I liked to listen to him and
frequently attended his lessons. His only regret was that I was untutored and could not study under him. He constantly urged me to
study *The Changes*, saying, "This is a very good book. I am so fond
of it that the leather thongs holding my copy together have broken
three times, as has also my iron head scratcher, but the result is my
present full enlightenment."

In the fourteenth year of the reign of Duke Ai of Lu [481 B.C.],
hunters caught a unicorn to the west, and when it died Confucius
asked me what it meant. When I told him that it was not a good sign,
he wept with disappointment. Later, having had a bad dream, he
wanted to see me, but I could not go to him because we were in the
middle of the fourth moon and the weather was too hot. I learned
afterwards that he had fallen sick and died seven days later. I feel that
I can still see him exactly as he was.

When First Emperor of the Ch'in took me to P'eng-ch'eng to
retrieve a Chou dynasty tripod from the river, I told him that the
tripod was something divine. "In the presence of excellence it will
come forth automatically, but if God is not present, it will sink. Let
Your Majesty merely see to his own personal state, and this thing will
certainly rise of itself; it cannot be had by force." At the time, the
emperor had only utter disdain for my attitude, and undertook to
have the tripod dragged from the river. Of course he failed. Then he
apologized to me in these words, "You are certainly a thinking man
who sees far ahead."

4b

He also spoke in full detail of Kao-tsu of the Han and
Hsiang Chi, and of other things of this same ilk, which I
cannot record here in full. Those of us who knew the stories
he told treated them as laughing matters. The crowd, however, believed everything it heard from him. Then the
ravages of old age set in for Ku Ch'iang, and he became
forgetful. When Commissioner Chi gave him a jade cup, he
told him, "Master An-ch'i left me this a long time ago."
Later Ku Ch'iang fell sick at the home of Huang Cheng of
Shou-ch'un, where he died. Huang Cheng suspected that he

had been transformed, and a little over a year later he tried boring into the coffin to have a look, but the corpse was resting right there. Things like this are all without foundation and are responsible for the common belief that there are no genii. I charge all such impostors with using the false to confound the true.

The Governor of Ch'eng-tu, Wu Wen, tells the story of a certain Ts'ai Tan of Wu-yüan. He was interested in the divine process but did not succeed in getting the essentials from a good teacher. Completely neglecting the livelihood of his family, he spent days and nights reciting such classics as *Huang-t'ing*, *T'ai-ch'ing*, and *Chung-huang*, and looking for lucky signs in the stars. He devoted himself to the quite nonessential writings of various authors, and claimed that the divine process was there in all fullness. But he was totally ignorant of anything practical; he merely deluded others by lauding the vague, flowery language of these texts and teaching that one's heart's desire could be had merely by reciting them a thousand times. He continued this so long that his household was greatly troubled. With work suspended, the supplies of clothing and food were diminishing, but nothing extraordinary was occurring. Ts'ai Tan himself became so embarrassed that he could not free himself from his depression. Finally, he quit the household, saying that he had completed the process leading to geniehood. He went off elsewhere, deep into the mountains, but he knew nothing about gathering herbal medicines that would permit him to give up starches. All he could do was to sell firewood in exchange for clothing and food. By the end of three years he was suffering from hunger and cold. When an acquaintance met him, he pretended not to know him. When he could stand it no longer, he returned home black and emaciated, a standing skeleton, not at all like a human being.

When the family inquired where he was coming from, and whether he had not become a genie after all, his deceiving reply was, "I cannot yet mount to heaven; I can only be an

5a

earth genie. My initial position is a lowly one in which I am obliged to serve those who have already become genii. The full change will take effect only gradually. I have been shepherding several head of dragons for Lao Tan. A dappled, variegated one was the best and the one which Lao Tan normally rides. They had me guard and look after it, but I became careless and merely played backgammon with genii who had been promoted after me, and suddenly I lost sight of this dragon. Nobody knew where it was. For this mistake I was reprimanded and escorted to the foot of Mount K'un-lun to weed thirty or forty acres of herbs growing there very close together and including many bad weeds. It took an incalculable amount of hard work to keep the place in order. After ten years of this punishment I was pardoned.

"At that point, the genii Wo-ch'üan tzu and Wang Ch'iao came to inspect my conduct. Since I turned to them with a plea to exert themselves in my behalf, I have been released for return here. Now I must retrain myself and seek to depart once more." Whereupon he died of old age.

When Ts'ai Tan first returned and said that he had come from Mount K'un-lun, all his relations vied with one another in questioning him about it. He replied:

Nobody asks how high heaven is; one just looks up at it. Well, Mount K'un-lun is only a little more than two rods lower. Tree-like grain forty-nine feet tall grows there, a single spike filling a cart. There are trees of pearls and jade; pear, precious-stone, and jasper trees. Jade plums, jade squashes, and jade peaches, where the fruit resembles what we have here in the world, only the sheen is more penetrating, and they are harder. They are eaten only after being softened by washing in jade well water. Whenever the wind begins to blow, the branches, flowers, and leaves of the pearl-jade trees produce impressive music by knocking against one another.

On first learning of my punishment I lost all initiative, but when I heard the music from these trees I knew there was nobody who would not have been deeply affected. I further noticed that to one side on top of Mount K'un-lun there are 440 gateways, each four miles broad. Within them is Wu-ch'eng with twelve towers, at the foot of which are blue dragons, white tigers, serpents more than a

hundred miles long in whose mouths the teeth are like boats of many
tons displacement, and hornets ten feet long whose poison would kill
an elephant. There are also divine beasts called lions to keep evil influences at bay, heavenly stags, flaming sheep with copper heads and
foreheads of iron, and thirty-six sorts of creatures with long tusks and
chisel-like teeth. If we knew the names of all these animals, the bad
ghosts and animals of our world would not dare harm us. The gods
there are Wu-t'ou tzu (Headless), Tao-ching chün (Lord of Highest
Heaven where Light comes from Below), Hsi-lu kung (Unite-stags
Lord), Master Chung-huang, and Grand Officer of Six Gates, Chang
Yang, whose sobriquet is Tzu-yüan. These gods defend the jade gateways, and if I had not worn both the left and right parts of the *Lao-
chün-chu-shih* amulet, I should not have been able to gain entrance.

Five rivers flow from this mountain's ramparts. Weak River sur-
rounds it, where goose feathers will not float, and which flying birds
do not cross. Only genii can cross it. On this mountain the divine
birds and horses Yu-ch'ang, Chiao-ming, T'eng-huang, and Chi-
kuang all talk like human beings and are immortal. It is really a
beautiful place to delight genii. I only regret that I could not get
approval to make a complete circuit of it all. When people heard
6b   Ts'ai Tan's clear account they tended to believe him.

In P'u-pan, a subdivision of Ho-tung, there was a certain
Hsiang Wan-tu who entered the mountains with one son to
study geniehood. After ten years they returned home, and
the people of the household asked why. "After we had been
giving serious thought to our task for three years a genie
came to meet us, and we all mounted to heaven on a dragon.
After a while I lowered my head to look at the earth which
was far, far away and invisible. We were not yet reaching
anywhere above, and we were very far from earth. The
dragon traveled very quickly, head raised and tail dragging,
causing us on its back to be frightened and feel the danger.
On reaching heaven we first passed through a building where
the beds were of gold and the tables of jade, gleaming and
shining, a truly luxurious place. The genie merely gave us a
cup of flowing red vapor to drink, and straightway we were
free from hunger and thirst. Then suddenly we thought of
home, with the result that in going before the Emperor of

Heaven we bowed but made some error in ceremonial. Having been denounced for this, we had to return in order to resume our self-improvement, so that after a time we may again return to heaven.

"Formerly, Liu An, Prince of Huai-nan, went to heaven to visit Emperor-up-there, but he was chided when he sat down with his legs apart and loudly called himself by the term Orphan. He was obliged to guard Heaven's Kitchen [a constellation] for three years. So, who am I not to be punished?" The people of Ho-tung, accordingly, gave Hsiang Wan-tu the sobriquet "Denounced Genie."

There are many liars of this class in the world, and they come in various types. I cannot list them all. This is exactly how their mad talk goes, and yet some people still do not *7a* feel that it is all imagination. What can they do, therefore, about subtle lies where there is a grain of verisimilitude with facts? Without being very intelligent, how can they make a distinction on the spur of the moment?

There are also instances of creating wholly out of imagination famous processors of an earlier age, such as Pai Ho. We are told that he was 8700 years old when he appeared among the people and then suddenly disappeared again. While he was in Lo, processors already experienced and learned in arts and tricks took their difficulties to Pai Ho for consultation. He would make full inquiry and then give them explanations removing all their previous doubts. Consequently he became widely known. Nobody, however, knew how old he really was; it was merely believed that it could be close to a thousand years. Later, he precipitately left for nobody knows where.

Then there was an individual in Ho-pei claiming to be Pai Ho, and there was a rush from far and near to study under him, with the result that he attracted presents and became very rich. When his former pupils heard that he had reappeared, they were very happy and went to visit him, but he proved to be an impostor. Then the man vanished.

It has already been shown how the Five Classics and the whole mass of our older books are "straw dogs," effigies of the past. What we call footprints were of course produced by feet, but they are not actually the feet (*Chuang* 14.30, 75). In the same way, books were written by sages, but they are not the sages. If the Confucianists carry their books for thousands of miles in search of a teacher, shouldn't the divine process, conferring Fullness of Life, so valued by God's Men, be earnestly sought where our inquiries may be addressed? It is indispensable, however, that you most carefully distinguish true teachers from the false, for I fear that there will never fail to be Ku Ch'iangs, Ts'ai Tans, Hsiang Wan-tus, and Pai Hos in our world. An examination of this book of mine by curiosity-seekers may help them somewhat to sort the good from the bad. The Genii Classics tell us that the eyes of all genii are square, and Po Ho, whom I met at Lo-yang, explained to me that his eyes were square, so, naturally he was an extraordinary man.

Index

(Page references to Sun Hsing-yen's Edition)

329

A Taoist Library

(19.3*a*6—)

An hun chi 安魂記 4*b*7
An mo ching 按摩經 3*b*1
Chang hsü ching 張虛經 3*b*3
Chao ming ching 召命經 4*b*5
Chao pai li ch'ung she chi 召百里蟲蛇記 5*a*3
Chao t'ai pai nang chung yao, 5★ 趙太白囊中要 4*b*11
Chen chung ch'ing chi 枕中清記 4*b*4 (? = TT 836)
Chen chung huang pai ching, 5 枕中黃白經 4*a*5
Chen chung wu hsing chi, 5 枕中五行記 3*a*9
Chen jen yü t'ai ching 真人玉胎經 4*b*3
Ch'en she ching 陳赦經 3*b*2
Cheng chi ching 正機經 3*b*5
Ch'i kung tao yao 郗公道要 5*a*6
Chi shan ching, 10 箕山經 4*b*1
Chia i ching, 170 甲乙經 3*a*11
Chieh chieh ching 節解經 4*a*11
Chien kuei chi 見鬼記 4*b*3
Ch'ien niu chung ching 牽牛中經 3*b*8
Chin hua shan ching 金(今)華山經 4*b*4
Chin pan ching 金板經 4*b*8
Chin yen ching 金鷹經 4*a*3
Ch'ing lung ching 青龍經 3*b*1
Ching shan chi 荊山記 5*a*8
Chiu ching ching 九敬經 3*a*11
Chiu hsien ching 九仙經 3*a*8

★ Numerals following names indicate number of scrolls.

Nei shih ching 內視經 4a10

Pa kung huang pai ching 八公黃白經 4a5

Pa shih t'u 八史圖 3b10

Pai hu ch'i pien ching 白虎七變經 4a4

Pai shou she t'i ching 百守攝提經 4a1

Pai (?Po) tzu pien hua ching 白帛子變化經 4a6

Pao shen chi 保神記 4b5

Pao yüan ching 包元經 4a8

P'eng tsu ching 彭祖經 3b2

P'ing heng ching 平衡經 3b5

P'ing tu chi 平都記 3b9

Pu san kang liu chi ching 步三罡六紀經 4a2

San huang nei wen (t'ien wen), 3 三皇內文天文 3a6

San huang nei wen (yüan wen), 3 三皇內文元文 3a7

San shih chi 三尸集 4b9

San shih liu shui ching 三十六水經 4a4

San wu chung ching 三五中經 4a11

Shan lin chi 山林記 5a3

Shan yang chi 山陽記 3b9

Shao chün tao i, 10 少君道意 5a6

Shen kuang (?hsien) chan fang lai ching 神光仙占方來經 4a7

Sheng chung ching, 10 勝中經 4a1

Sheng t'ien i chiu ch'i ching 昇天儀九奇經 3b10

Shih chieh ching 尸解經 4a8

Shih chih t'u 石芝圖 3b7

Shih erh hua ching 十二化經 3a8

Shih jih yüeh ching ching 食日月精經 3b11

Shih liu ch'i ching 食六氣經 3b11

Shou chih pai kuei chao wu yüeh ch'eng t'ai shan chu che chi, 3 收治百鬼召五岳丞太山
主者記 5a2

Shou hsing t'u 守形圖 3b6

Shou shan kuei lao mei chih hsieh ching ching, 3 收山鬼老魅治邪精經 4b9

Shui hsien ching 水仙經 4a8

Ssu chin ching, 10 四衿經 3b11

Ssu chün yao yung ching 四君要用經 4a3

Ssu kuei ching 四規經 3b4

Ssu ling ching, 3 思靈經 5a7

Su nü ching 素女經 3b2

Ta po tsa chih t'u 大魄雜芝圖 3b7

T'ai ch'ing ching 太清經 3b1

T'ai hsi ching 胎息經 4a1

T'ai p'ing ching, 50 太平經 3a11

T'ai su ching 太素經 4a9

Tan hu ching 丹壺經 4a1

Tan i ching 丹一經 3b11

Tao chi ching, 5 道機經 4b3

Tao chia ti hsing hsien ching 道家地行仙經 4a4

Tao hsing chi 蹈形記 3b6

Tao ken ching 道根經 4b3

Tao shih to suan lü, 3 道士奪算律 5a5

Tao yin ching, 10 道引經 3b1

Teng ming shan tu chiang hai ch'ih ti shen fa, 3 登名山渡江海勅地神法 4b11

T'ien men tzu ching 天門子經 3b3

T'ien shih shen ch'i ching 天師神器氣經 4a5

Ting hsin chi 定心記 3b9

Tsa chi shu lu 雜集書錄 4b7

Ts'ai shen yao chih tso pi fa, 3 採神藥治作祕法 4b10

Tso wang t'u 坐亡圖 3b6

Tso yu ch'i yü li ching 左右契玉曆經 3b10

Tsou sheng yen ming ching 鄒生延命經 4b7

Tsou yang tzu ching 鄒陽子經 4a11

Ts'ui wen tzu chou hou ching 崔文子肘後經 4a7

Tuan hu lang chin 斷虎狼禁 5a3

Tung ching t'u 東井圖 3b8

Tung chün ti hsien ch'üeh lao yao chi 董君地仙卻老要記 5a8

T'ung ming ching 通明經 3b1

Tzu jan ching 自然經 3a10

Tzu tu ching 子都經 3b2

Wan pi kao ch'iu hsien sheng fa, 3 萬畢高丘先生法 5a3

Wang Ch'iao yang hsing chih shen ching, 3 王喬養性治身經 5a4

Wang (?Yü) mi chi 王玉彌記 3b8

Wang (?Yü) tzu wu hsing yao chen ching 王玉子五行要真經 4b6

Wei po yang nei ching 魏伯陽內經 4a2

Wei yen, 3 微言 4a9

Wen jen ching 文人經 4a6

Wen pao ching 溫寶經 3a10

Wen shih hsien sheng ching 文始先生經 4a10

Wu chi ching 無極經 4b3

Wu yen ching 五言經 3b4

Wu yüeh ching, 5 五嶽經 (?= TT 441) 3b7

Yang sheng shu, 105 養生書 3a10

Yen huo ching 厭禍經 4a6

Yin han yü k'uei chi 銀函玉匱記 4b8

Yin shou chi 隱守記 3b8

Yin yang ching 陰陽記 3a10

Yü ts'e chi 玉策記 3b10

Yüan t'i ching 淵體經 4a9

Yüan tu ching 原都經 4b8

Yüan yang tzu ching 元陽子經 3b2

Amulets

(19.5a10–5b10)

Chen chung fu 枕中符 5a11, 5b7
Ch'i chi fu 七機符 5b3
Ch'i fu 七符 5b4
Chien ch'ien fu 監乾符 5b5
Chih pai ping fu, 10 治百病符 5b7
Chin kuang fu 金光符 5a10
Ch'ing lung fu 青龍符 5b2
Chiu ling fu 九靈符 5a11
Chiu t'ai fu, 9 九臺符 5b8
Chiu t'ien fa ping fu 九天發兵符 5b3
Chiu t'ien fu 九天符 5b3
Chu ch'üeh fu 朱雀符 5b3
Chü sheng fu 巨勝符 5b6
Chu t'ai fu 朱胎符 5b3
Chün huo chao chih fu 軍火召治符 5b10
Hsiao tsai fu 消災符 5b5
Hsiao t'ung fu 小童符 5a11
Hsing ch'u fu, NN★ 行廚符 5b9
Hsüan ching fu 玄精符 5b7
Hsüan tu fu 玄都符 5b1
Hsüan tzu fu 玄子符 5b4
Hu kung fu 壺公符 5b8, 20
Huang ti fu 黃帝符 5b1
Lao ching fu 老經符 5b4
Lei tien fu 雷電符 5b6
Liu chia t'ung ling fu, 10 六甲通靈符 5b9
Liu chün fu 六君符 5b1
Liu yin fu, NN★ 六陰符 5b9
Lung t'ai fu, NN★ 龍胎符 5b9
Pa kua fu 八卦符 5b5
Pa wei wu sheng fu 八威五勝符 5b6
Pao yüan fu 包元符 5b5
Pai hu fu 白虎符 5b2
Pei t'ai fu 北臺符 5b7
San chin wu mu fang chung fu, NN★ 三金五木防終符 5b9
Shao ch'ien san shih liu chiang chün fu 少千三十六將軍符 5b1
Shen Hsi fu 沈羲符 5b5
Shih shih fu 石室符 5a11, NN★5b9
Ssu shih chiu chen fu 四十九真符 5b2

★ The NN's together total 500 scrolls.

Ta han o fu 大捍厄符   5*b*4

T'ai hsüan fu, 3 太玄符   5*a*10

T'ien shui fu 天水符   5*b*2

T'ien shui shen fu 天水神符   5*b*2

Ts'ai nü fu 採女符   5*b*6

T'ung t'ien fu 通天符   5*a*11

Tzu lai fu 自來符   5*a*10

Wan pi fu 萬畢符   5*b*6

Wei hsi fu 威喜符   5*b*6

Wu ching fu 五精符   5*a*11

Wu hsiao ching yen chün lung hu san nang pi ping fu 武孝經燕君龍虎三囊辟兵符
  5*b*4

Yen kuai fu, 10 厭怪符   5*b*8

Yen ming shen fu 延命神符   5*b*1

Yin yang ta chen fu 陰陽大鎮符   5*b*7

Yü ch'iao fu 禹蹻符   5*b*5

Yü fu fu, 10 玉斧符   5*b*10

Yü li fu 玉歷符   5*b*7

Yü ts'e fu 玉策符   5*a*11

Yüan wu fu 元武符   5*b*3

The Chinese Dynasties

Chinese prehistory is a mythology of euhemeristic heroes gradually developing Three Augusti, Five Emperors, Yao, Shun, and Yü the Great, the last being founder of the first dynasty.

Hsia — prehistoric North China

Shang (or Yin) ends about 1100 B.C.

Chou: *The Annals* (*Ch'un-ch'iu*) 722–481 B.C.

    Warring States 403–250 B.C.

Ch'in (or Ts'in) 221–207 B.C. — Founding of the empire

First Han 202 B.C.–A.D. 8 — Buddhism arrives

    Wang Mang 9–23

Second Han 23–220

Three Kingdoms:

    Wei 220–265 — North China

    Shu 221–263 — West China

    Wu 222–280 — South China

Chin (or Tsin) 265–316 — All China

             317–420 — South China (16 Kingdoms in North)

Southern and Northern Dynasties:
 Five successive dynasties in South 420–589
 Northern Wei (Turks) and its four successors in North
  399–581
Sui 581–618 — China reunited
T'ang 618–907
Five Dynasties and Ten Kingdoms (contemporaneous or
 successive) 907–979
Sung 960–1126 — All China
  1127–1279 — South China
   Liao (Kitan) 916–1125 — Manchuria
   Hsi Hsia (Tangut) 1032–1227 — Kansu
   Chin or Kin (Juchen) 1115–1234 — North China
Yüan (Mongols) 1279–1368 — All China
Ming (Chinese) 1368–1644
Ch'ing or Ts'ing (Manchus) 1644–1912
Chinese Republic (Chinese) 1912–
  Chiang to Formosa 1949–
  The Chinese People's Republic 1949–